Anatomy

PreTest®
Self-Assessment
and Review

Anatomy

PreTest®
Self-Assessment
and Review

Sixth Edition

Edited by

Ernest W. April, Ph.D.
Associate Professor of Anatomy and Cell Biology
College of Physicians & Surgeons
of Columbia University
New York, New York

McGraw-Hill, Inc.
Health Professions Division/PreTest Series

New York   St. Louis   San Francisco   Colorado Springs
Auckland   Bogotá   Hamburg   Lisbon   London   Madrid
Mexico   Milan   Montreal   New Delhi   Panama   Paris
San Juan   São Paulo   Singapore   Sydney   Tokyo   Toronto

Anatomy: PreTest Self-Assessment and Review

1 2 3 4 5 6 7 8 9 0   DOCDOC   9 8 7 6 5 4 3 2 1 0

ISBN 0-07-051976-5

This book was set in Times Roman by Waldman Graphics, Inc.
The editors were Gail Gavert and Bruce MacGregor.
The production supervisor was Clara B. Stanley.
R.R. Donnelley & Sons was printer and binder.

Library of Congress Cataloging-in-Publication Data

Anatomy: PreTest self-assessment and review/edited by Ernest
W. April. — 6th ed.
     p.   cm.
Includes bibliographical references.
ISBN 0-07-051976-5
    1. Human anatomy—Examinations, questions, etc.
I. April, Ernest W.
    [DNLM: 1. Anatomy—examination questions. QS 18 A537]
QM32.A65   1991
611'.0076—dc20
DNLM/DLC
for Library of Congress   90-5556
                                        CIP

Contents

Introduction

Anatomy: PreTest® Self-Assessment and Review provides medical students, as well as physicians, with a comprehensive and convenient instrument for self-assessment and review within the field of anatomy. The 500 questions parallel the format and degree of difficulty of the questions contained in Part I of the National Board of Medical Examiners examinations, the Federation Licensing Examination (FLEX), and the Foreign Medical Graduate Examination in the Medical Sciences (FMGEMS).

Questions with multiple-answer combinations (K-types) are being phased-out of these examinations and have been deleted from this edition.

Each question in the book is accompanied by an answer, an explanation, and specific page references to current textbooks. A bibliography, listing all the sources used, follows the last chapter.

Perhaps the most effective way to use this book is to allow yourself one minute to answer each question in a given chapter; as you proceed, indicate your answer beside each question. By following this suggestion, you will be approximating the time limits imposed by the board examinations previously mentioned.

When you finish answering the questions in a chapter, you should then spend as much time as you need verifying your answers and carefully reading the explanations. Although you should pay special attention to the explanations for the questions you answered incorrectly, you should read *every* explanation. The author of this book has designed the explanations to reinforce and supplement the information tested by the questions. If, after reading the explanations for a given chapter, you feel you need still more information about the material covered, you should consult and study the references indicated.

Embryology

DIRECTIONS: Each question below contains five suggested responses. Select the **one best** response to each question.

1. Oogonia reach their maximum number at which of the following stages of human development?

(A) Five months of fetal life
(B) Birth
(C) Puberty (12 to 14 years of age)
(D) Adolescence (16 to 20 years of age)
(E) Early adulthood (21 to 26 years of age)

2. At the time of ovulation in the human female, all the following are true EXCEPT that

(A) the first meiotic division has just occurred
(B) expulsion of the first polar body has just occurred
(C) the secondary oocyte is arrested in the second maturation division
(D) the zona pellucida has broken down
(E) fertilization is possible

3. A 26-year-old man contracted viral influenza with an unremitting fever of 39.5°C (103°F) for 3 days. Since spermatogenesis cannot occur above a scrotal temperature of 35.5°C (96°F), he was left with no viable sperm on his recovery. The time required for spermatogenesis, spermiogenesis, and passage of viable sperm to the epididymis is approximately

(A) 3 days
(B) 1 week
(C) 5 weeks
(D) 2 months
(E) 4 months

4. All the following statements concerning the acrosome reaction are correct EXCEPT

(A) it injects the contents of the acrosomal envelope into the cytoplasm of the egg
(B) it involves the formation of the acrosomal process
(C) it releases acid hydrolases onto the zona pellucida
(D) it terminates upon fusion of the plasma membrane of the sperm with that of the egg
(E) it triggers fusion of the outer acrosomal membrane with the plasma membrane of the sperm

5. To prevent polyspermy, fertilization initiates the cortical reaction, which involves all the following processes EXCEPT

(A) alteration of the binding affinity of sperm receptors on the surface
(B) development of a gap between the zona pellucida and the plasma membrane
(C) inhibition of the acrosomal reaction in subsequent sperm
(D) rapid membrane depolarization
(E) release of the contents of the cortical granules by fusion with the plasma membrane

6. A pleuripotential cell that passes the checkpoint in G_1, i.e., the presence of cytoplasmic S-phase activator, and enters the S phase of the cell cycle will undergo all the following EXCEPT

(A) completion of the cell cycle by undergoing mitosis and cytokinesis
(B) continued cycling through mitoses until the microenvironment signals the cell to enter the prolonged interphase G_0
(C) production of enzymes necessary for DNA replication
(D) production of secretory products
(E) replication of the complete genome

7. One example of cellular differentiation is offered by myoblasts, which cease mitosis before they form myotubes and produce contractile proteins. Correct statements concerning differentiation include all the following EXCEPT

(A) cells must move out of the cell cycle into the G_0 phase before they are able to express specific, genetically determined properties
(B) gene transcription is a characteristic of the G_0 state
(C) growth factors are most effective on highly differentiated cells in the G_0 state
(D) the probability of entering G_0 is a direct function of the number of times that a cell has divided
(E) cell memory of differentiated cells is minimally affected by the microenvironment

8. All the following appear to be functions of cell-cell interaction EXCEPT

(A) determining the plane of the next cleavage
(B) influencing gene expression
(C) limiting cell proliferation
(D) promoting cell differentiation
(E) maintaining cells in a differentiated state

9. By the fourth day of development, fluid accumulation by the morula results in a separation of the cells into trophoblast and embryoblast, or inner cell mass. From the eighth to the twelfth day of development, the role of the trophoblast includes all the following EXCEPT

(A) enclosure of the inner cell mass and blastocyst cavity
(B) formation of the embryo proper
(C) invasion of the endometrial epithelium
(D) production of hormones
(E) production of two distinct cell populations by differentiation

10. The primitive streak, which develops during the second week, provides orientation to a developing embryo. All the following statements are true of the primitive streak EXCEPT

(A) it extends to the cranial end of the embryonic disk
(B) it gives rise to cells that migrate cranially to form the notochord
(C) it gives rise to cells that migrate laterally to form intraembryonic mesoderm
(D) it gives rise to the neural crest cells
(E) it terminates as the primitive node (of Hensen)

11. Nerve growth factor (NGF) may be responsible for the normal development of neural crest derivatives. An embryo deficient in NGF could generate developmental anomalies that may be associated with all the following EXCEPT the

(A) adenohypophysis
(B) autonomic ganglia
(C) chromaffin cells of the adrenal medulla
(D) melanocytes
(E) neurilemma (Schwann cells)

12. By the process of induction, certain embryonic tissues alter the microenvironment of adjacent cells and tissues. Examples of induction during embryogenesis include development of all the following structures EXCEPT the

(A) adenohypophysis by neural ectoderm
(B) lens by the optic vesicle
(C) mammary gland by the underlying mesoderm
(D) mesenchyme of a limb by the apical ectodermal ridge
(E) neural plate by brain and notochord

13. Derivatives of the mesodermal cell layer of the embryo include all the following structures EXCEPT the

(A) adrenal cortex
(B) gonads
(C) peritoneal serosa
(D) spleen
(E) tonsillar parenchyma

14. In the developing human embryo, most of the internal organs begin to form in the

(A) first month
(B) second month
(C) fourth month
(D) sixth month
(E) ninth month

15. In the diagram below of a human fetus in its second month of development, all the structures have been correctly labeled EXCEPT the

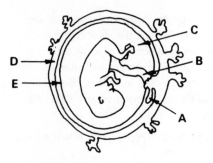

(A) yolk sac
(B) umbilical cord
(C) extraembryonic coelom
(D) chorion
(E) amnion

16. Which of the following statements is true of cardiac development?

(A) During formation of the heart loop, a single-tube heart remains suspended by a complete dorsal mesocardium (mesentery)
(B) The atria are represented by cranial portions of the endocardial tubes
(C) The heart bends into an S-shape because the caudal regions of the endocardial tubes grow faster than the cranial regions
(D) The left and right sides of the heart result directly from the side-by-side apposition of the left and right endocardial tubes
(E) The sinus venosus becomes incorporated into the atrium prior to the formation of the heart loop

17. During development of the heart, the sinus venosus becomes incorporated into other structures. Derivatives of the embryonic sinus venosus include all the following EXCEPT the

(A) coronary sinus
(B) smooth-walled portion of the right atrium
(C) trabeculated portion of the right atrium
(D) valve of the coronary sinus
(E) valve of the inferior vena cava

18. Normally, the endocardial cushions of the atrioventricular canal participate in all the following EXCEPT

(A) closure of the ostium primum between the left and right atria
(B) division of the atrium into right and left chambers
(C) formation of the atrioventricular valves
(D) formation of the membranous interventricular septum
(E) formation of the semilunar valves

19. The truncus and conus of the developing heart are separated by the fusion of the two spiral ridges. The truncoconal septum takes a spiral, descending course in the normally developing heart. If the course were straight downward without the spiral, which of the following would occur?

(A) The aorta would originate from the right ventricle
(B) The pulmonary veins would enter the right atrium
(C) The pulmonary artery would originate from the aorta
(D) The vena cava would enter the left atrium
(E) None of the above

20. All the following statements concerning circulation through the primitive heart are true EXCEPT

(A) blood leaving the heart via the truncus arteriosus passes directly into the single dorsal aorta
(B) blood rich in nutrients enters the sinus venosus via the vitelline veins
(C) blood rich in oxygen enters the sinus venosus via the umbilical veins
(D) contraction of the single-tube heart begins during the third week
(E) unidirectional circulation of blood through the heart begins during the fourth week

21. Blood from the placenta is about 80 percent oxygenated. However, mixture with unoxygenated blood at various points reduces the oxygen content. Which of the following vessels contains blood with the highest oxygen content?

(A) Abdominal aorta
(B) Common carotid arteries
(C) Ductus arteriosus
(D) Pulmonary artery
(E) Pulmonary vein

22. Because the collapsed lungs have a high vascular resistance, the ductus arteriosus is an important shunt in the fetal circulation. Correct statements concerning the ductus arteriosus include all the following EXCEPT

(A) anatomic obliteration of the ductus usually takes several weeks
(B) functional closure of the ductus occurs soon after the lungs first expand
(C) functional closure of the ductus is mediated by bradykinin
(D) the ductus forms the ligamentum venosum in the adult
(E) there may be a slight reversal of blood flow through the ductus during the postnatal period

23. Which of the following statements concerning the ductus venosus is true?

(A) It develops from the subcardinal venous system
(B) It forms a direct channel through the liver from the umbilical vein to the inferior vena cava
(C) It lies adjacent to the ductus arteriosus
(D) It persists in the adult as the hepatic portal vein
(E) None of the above

24. During the third to sixth month of gestation, the structure *primarily* responsible for erythropoiesis is the

(A) bone marrow
(B) liver
(C) spleen
(D) thymus
(E) yolk sac

25. In the fifth week of development, the pancreas develops from a dorsal bud immediately cranial to the hepatic diverticulum and from a ventral bud caudal to, and opposite, the hepatic diverticulum. The *dorsal* bud contributes all the following pancreatic structures EXCEPT the

(A) body of the pancreas
(B) distal portion of the main pancreatic duct
(C) secondary pancreatic duct (of Santorini)
(D) uncinate process
(E) upper half of the head of the pancreas

26. The last segment of the gastrointestinal tract to become fully closed into a tube and separated from the yolk sac is

(A) the anal canal
(B) the appendix
(C) the cecum
(D) the ileum
(E) none of the above

27. Structures derived from the hindgut in the male include all the following EXCEPT the

(A) allantois
(B) descending colon
(C) inferior portion of the anal canal
(D) prostatic urethra
(E) urinary bladder

28. The metanephric kidney begins to develop during the fifth week. All the following statements concerning the ureteric bud are true EXCEPT that it

(A) forms as an outgrowth of the mesonephric (wolffian) duct
(B) forms the renal pelvis and calyces
(C) forms the penile urethra
(D) induces the metanephric blastema to form the metanephric kidney
(E) is of mesodermal origin

29. The skeletal and connective tissue structures of the lower portion of the face and anterior neck are derived from neural crest cells in the branchial arches. All the following structures derive from the second branchial arch EXCEPT the

(A) lesser horn of the hyoid bone
(B) malleus
(C) stapes
(D) styloid process of the temporal bone
(E) stylohyoid ligament

30. A common developmental pattern shared by sebaceous glands, sweat glands, mammary glands, hair follicles, and nails includes

(A) development from neural crest cells
(B) derivation from mesenchyme
(C) differentiation under the influence of steroids
(D) invagination of epidermal cells into the dermis
(E) none of the above

31. Efferent cranial nerves develop from

(A) the alar plate
(B) the basal plate
(C) the floor plate
(D) the roof plate
(E) none of the above

DIRECTIONS: Each group of questions below consists of four lettered headings followed by a set of numbered items. For each numbered item select

A	if the item is associated with	(A) **only**
B	if the item is associated with	(B) **only**
C	if the item is associated with	**both** (A) and (B)
D	if the item is associated with	**neither** (A) nor (B)

Each lettered heading may be used **once, more than once, or not at all.**

Questions 32-34

(A) Testicular androgens
(B) Placental estrogen
(C) Both
(D) Neither

32. Will influence development of gonad into a testis

33. Will influence virilization of meso-nephric ducts

34. Will influence phenotypic differentiation of the urogenital sinus

Questions 35-38

(A) Third pharyngeal pouch
(B) Fourth pharyngeal pouch
(C) Both
(D) Neither

35. Parafollicular cells of the thyroid gland

36. Thymus gland

37. Parathyroid glands

38. Pharyngeal tonsil

DIRECTIONS: Each group of questions below consists of lettered headings followed by a set of numbered items. For each numbered item select the **one** lettered heading with which it is **most** closely associated. Each lettered heading may be used **once, more than once, or not at all.**

Questions 39-42

For each anatomic description that follows, select from the diagram below the labeled structure that is most appropriate.

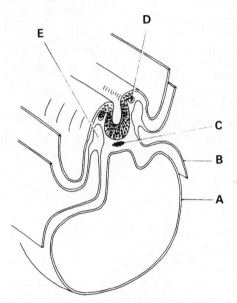

Embryo—Third Week of Development

39. Gives rise to dorsal root ganglia
40. Contributes to the neural arch of the vertebral column
41. Represents a unique characteristic of vertebrates
42. Forms the muscle layers of the gastrointestinal tract

Questions 43-46

For each developmental remnant in the questions below, select the most appropriate precursor from the list of embryologic structures.

(A) Ductus venosus
(B) Umbilical artery
(C) Umbilical vein
(D) Urachus
(E) Vitelline duct

43. Ileal diverticulum

44. Round ligament of the liver

45. Lateral umbilical ligament

46. Median umbilical ligament

Questions 47-50

Adult structures arise from embryologic anlages. For each adult structure below, select the most appropriate anlage.

(A) Paramesonephric (müllerian) duct
(B) Mesonephric (wolffian) duct
(C) Genital tubercle
(D) Urogenital sinus
(E) Mesonephric tubules

47. Penile urethra

48. Ampulla of the oviducts

49. Seminal vesicles

50. Ureters in the female

Embryology
Answers

1. **The answer is A.** *(Langman, ed 6. pp 8-10. Moore, ed 4. p 15.)* Differentiation into oogonia begins once the primordial germ cells have arrived in the gonad of a genetic female. After undergoing a number of mitotic divisions, these fetal cells form a cluster in the cortical part of the ovary. Some of these oogonia differentiate into the larger primary oocytes, which by the third month of development are found in the deeper layers of the gonad. The primary oocytes begin meiosis to produce secondary oocytes. At the same time, the number of oogonia continues to increase to about 6,000,000 in the fifth month. At this time most of the surviving oogonia and some of the oocytes become atretic. However, the surviving secondary oocytes (400,000 to 1,000,000) become surrounded by epithelial cells, forming the primordial follicles by the seventh month. During childhood there is continued atresia so that by puberty only about 40,000 secondary oocytes remain.

2. **The answer is D.** *(Langman, ed 6. pp 11-13, 21-24. Moore, ed 4. pp 22, 35.)* At the time of ovulation, the zona pellucida is intact, and it is maintained around the viable secondary oocyte for approximately 5 days. Prior to ovulation, the first meiotic division occurs, with reduction of the chromosomal number to the haploid condition and expulsion of the first polar body. The resulting secondary oocyte immediately proceeds as far as the spindle stage of the second maturation division. At this time ovulation occurs, and the secondary oocyte may be fertilized. Once a spermatozoon penetrates the corona radiata and comes into contact with the zona pellucida, it becomes firmly attached and begins to penetrate this layer with the aid of enzymes located in the acrosomal cap. The penetration of the zona pellucida by the initial spermatozoon alters the properties of this layer such that multiple sperm penetration is precluded. Once the zona pellucida is breached, the plasma membranes of the spermatozoon and secondary oocyte fuse and the haploid sperm nucleus moves into the oocyte cytoplasm. The secondary oocyte then finishes its second maturation division and gives off the second polar body before the nuclear materials combine. The zona pellucida is maintained until implantation is imminent, about 5 to 6 days.

3. **The answer is D.** *(Langman, ed 6. pp 14-18. Moore, ed 4. pp 14-15.)* Spermatogenesis, the process by which spermatogonia undergo mitotic division to produce primary spermatocytes, occurs at 1°C (2°F) below normal body temperature. Subsequent meiotic divisions produce secondary spermatocytes with a bivalent haploid chromosome number and then spermatids with a monovalent haploid chromosome number. The maturation of the spermatid, spermiogenesis, results in sperma-

tozoa. Morphologically adult spermatozoa are moved to the epididymis where they become fully motile. In man the time period required for the progression from spermatogonium to motile spermatozoon is 61 to 64 days.

4. The answer is A. *(Alberts, ed 2. pp 868-870. Moore, ed 4. p 28.)* The acrosome reaction occurs when the sperm encounters the zona pellucida of the ovum. This contact triggers fusion of the outer acrosomal membrane with the plasma membrane of the sperm, thereby releasing acid hydrolases onto the zona pellucida to digest its constituent glycoproteins. This discharge is accompanied by the formation of the acrosomal process, which bores through the softened zona pellucida to reach the plasma membrane of the egg—to which it adheres. This process terminates with the fusion of the plasma membrane of the sperm to that of the egg. The genetic material of the sperm then enters the egg and produces a zygote.

5. The answer is C. *(Alberts, ed 2. pp 871-872. Langman, ed 6. pp 27-28. Moore, ed 4. p 28.)* Nearly every sperm that encounters the zona pellucida initiates an acrosome reaction. However, only one sperm will complete the process because the cortical reaction is initiated immediately upon penetration of the ovum. This involves a rapid membrane depolarization, which transiently inhibits subsequent plasma membrane fusions between the egg and sperm. A calcium influx associated with this depolarization causes the cortical granules to fuse with the plasma membrane and release their contents beneath the zona pellucida, resulting in a physical separation of the zona pellucida from the plasma membrane, a decrease in the binding affinity of surface receptors for sperm, and a cross-linking of proteins—all of which contribute to the concept of a fertilization membrane which is impenetrable to subsequent sperm.

6. The answer is D. *(Alberts, ed 2. pp 728-729.)* The cell cycle consists of four distinct phases. The brief mitotic (M) phase is subdivided into prophase, metaphase, anaphase, and telophase. Telophase is followed by the so-called gap 1 (G_1) phase, which is characterized by growth of the cell accompanied by active ribonucleic acid (RNA) and protein synthesis. The synthesis (S) phase is one of DNA synthesis and assembly. During the subsequent gap 2 (G_2) phase, preparations occur for the impending mitotic, or divisional, phase. As long as cells are induced to cycle, they will produce only products needed for this function. When cells fail to pass the checkpoint in the G_1 phase, most probably owing to signals in the microenvironment, they enter a prolonged interphase (G_0). At this point, the cells may differentiate and become specifically functional. The more highly differentiated a cell becomes with respect to morphology (such as nerve cells), or specific protein content (such as muscle), the less likely it is to revert to the cell cycle.

7. The answer is C. *(Alberts, ed 2. pp 746-748, 951-954.)* Cellular differentiation commences when a cell moves out of the cell cycle into a prolonged interphase (G_0).

The mechanisms for this move appear to be a combination of the absence of specific growth factors and the number of times that a cell has divided. It is during this state that gene transcription occurs with production of mRNA specific for the protein synthesis associated with the differentiated cell. Some mature cells, such as hepatocytes and connective tissue cells, that do not undergo highly complex differentiation may, under the influence of growth factors, move back into the cell cycle. However, "cell memory" is strong and there are no known signals that may move a mature, highly differentiated cell, such as muscle or nerve, back into the S-phase. Growth factors are most effective on cells in the G_1 state, apparently opening the checkpoint for DNA synthesis.

8.　The answer is E. *(Alberts, ed 2. pp 896-899.)* Cell-cell interactions start in the morula stage where cell surfaces not in contact with other cells develop microvilli, while those surface areas lying adjacent to other cells develop gap and tight junctions. This establishes cell polarity, which determines the plane of the next cleavage. The surface layer of daughter cells is subject to a different microenvironment and extent of cell-cell interaction than the deeper daughter cells. There is strong evidence that cell-cell interaction influences gene expression and promotes cell differentiation. In addition, cell-cell interaction limits cell proliferation. However, there is no evidence that cell-cell interaction is a factor in maintaining cells in a differentiated state. Once a cell is determined, i.e., a prehepatocyte will produce daughter prehepatocytes, its distinctive character is not subject to external influence.

9.　The answer is B. *(Langman, ed 6. p 31. Moore, ed 4. p 35.)* The trophoblast encloses the inner cell mass and blastocyst cavity. Implantation occurs through invasion of the endometrial epithelium and stroma by the trophoblastic villi. The trophoblast also differentiates into two layers. The inner layer of the trophoblast—the cytotrophoblast—is composed of mononuclear cells that rapidly divide and subsequently migrate into the syncytiotrophoblast, where their plasma membranes fuse with the other cells of that layer. It is the syncytiotrophoblast that produces human chorionic gonadotropin (hCG); the cytotrophoblast produces estrogenic hormones until just before the termination of pregnancy. Cessation of this estrogenic production is considered to initiate parturition. The inner cell mass forms the embryo proper as well as the yolk sac.

10.　The answer is A. *(Langman, ed 6. pp 50-52, 61-65, 334. Moore, ed 4. pp 50-53.)* The primitive streak, which develops in the embryonic disk of the epiblast, consists of a central primitive groove and flanking primitive ridges. At the cephalic end of the primitive groove, a cranially directed invagination—the primitive node (of Hensen)—forms the notochord. Concomitantly, lateral delamination and lateral migration of cells form the intraembryonic mesodermal germ layer. Subsequently, the primitive ridges develop into neural folds that migrate dorsally and fuse in the midline to form the neural tube. Specialized groups of cells along the primitive ridges form the neural crest cells.

11. The answer is A. *(Langman, ed 6. pp 359-360. Moore, ed 4. p 372.)* Neural crest cells from the dorsolateral aspect of the neural tube form a number of structures, including the sensory neurons of both the dorsal root ganglia of the spinal nerves and those cranial nerves having sensory components. The neural crest cells also form the postganglionic autonomic neurons of the autonomic nervous system, the adrenal medulla, and other related chromaffin tissue such as the aortic and carotid bodies and the parafollicular cells of the thyroid. Schwann cells of the neurilemma sheaths, melanocytes of the epithelium, and odontoblasts of the teeth all are neural crest derivatives; neural crest tissue also has been implicated in the formation of the leptomeninges (pia and arachnoid). Lack of nerve growth factor may result in agenesis or abnormal development in any of these structures. The adenohypophysis is a derivative of entoderm of the oral cavity (Rathke's pouch).

12. The answer is C. *(Alberts, ed 2. pp 941-942. Moore, ed 4. pp 69-72, 426.)* Induction is the process by which one embryonic tissue markedly influences the development of adjacent tissues. The basic organization of an embryo is established by primary inductors, such as the primitive streak, notochord, and preaxial mesoderm. Primary induction of the forebrain by the notochord is followed by secondary induction of the optic vesicle, which then induces formation of the lens from ectoderm. The lens subsequently induces formation of the corneal epithelium. The limb buds arise as masses of mesenchyme derived from the somatic layer of lateral plate mesoderm. Each is covered by the apical ectodermal ridge, which exerts influential inductive control over the mesenchyme. This promotes secondary induction in a subjacent progress zone wherein mesenchyme condenses to hyaline cartilage, which then promotes development of muscle. Other examples of primary ectodermal induction include development of nasal and otic placodes by cranial mesothelium and the development of the adenohypophysis from the oral cavity by neural ectodermal influence. The mammary gland develops by a permissive process whereby its development is influenced minimally, if at all, by adjacent tissues.

13. The answer is E. *(Langman, ed 6. pp 66-68. Moore, ed 4. p 69.)* Mesoderm forms a wide variety of adult tissues. Serous membranes, the spleen, and the gonads are derived from mesoderm. Other tissues of mesodermal origin are blood vessels, heart, bone, cartilage, skeletal and smooth muscle, skin, excretory units of the urinary system, adrenal cortex, and vas deferens. The endodermal germ layer initially forms the epithelial lining of the primitive gut, but later in development it gives rise to the following: the epithelial lining of the respiratory tract; the parenchyma of the tonsil, thyroid, parathyroid, thymus, liver, and pancreas; the lining of the tympanic cavity and eustachian tube; and the epithelial lining of the urinary bladder and urethra.

14. The answer is B. *(Langman, ed 6. p 61. Moore, ed 4. pp 65, 87.)* The first month of embryonic development generally is concerned with cleavage, formation of the germ layers, and establishment of the embryonic body. Formation of most internal organs occurs during the second month, the period of organogenesis. The period from the ninth week to the end of intrauterine life, known as the fetal period, is characterized by maturation of tissues and rapid growth of the fetal body.

15. The answer is C. *(Langman, ed 6. pp 96, 106, 107. Moore, ed 4. pp 119-121.)* The extraembryonic coelom contains the yolk sac and is synonymous with the chorionic cavity, or the space between the amnion and the chorionic plate. The structure labeled C in the diagram accompanying the question is the amniotic cavity, which enlarges rapidly at the expense of the chorionic cavity. The amnion envelops the yolk stalk and the connecting stalk to form the umbilical cord. By the ninth week of gestation, the connection between the intraembryonic and extraembryonic coeloms has been obliterated by the compression of the amnioectodermal juncture (umbilical ring). By the end of the third month of gestation, the amnion and chorion have fused.

16. The answer is C. *(Langman, ed 6. pp 179-185. Moore, ed 4. pp 292-294.)* The heart forms during the third week by the apposition of left and right endocardial tubes as the head fold progresses caudally. The endocardial tubes fuse to form a single-tube heart. This fusion begins cranially in the region of the bulbus cordis (outflow trunks) and proceeds caudally through the ventricles and the atria to the sinus venosus, which is incorporated into the atrium after loop formation. Rapid proliferation of the ventricular region results in the single-tube heart taking an S-shaped loop. During this process, the dorsal mesocardium partially breaks down, leaving the heart suspended only at the cranial and caudal ends; the discontinuity in the mesocardium is the transverse sinus. The left and right sides of the heart are established by the subsequent division of the single-tube heart, not by the apposition of left and right endocardial tubes.

17. The answer is C. *(Langman, ed 6. pp 185-186. Moore, ed 4. pp 294, 300.)* By the end of the first month of development the sinus venosus receives the vitelline veins, umbilical veins, and the common cardinal veins, thereby returning blood to the heart from the intraembryonic and extraembryonic portions of the embryo. Early in the second month of development, the left horn of the sinus venosus becomes the coronary sinus and also contributes the valve of the coronary sinus. The right horn becomes incorporated into the right atrium as the smooth-walled (sinus venarum) portion. This is separated from the original trabeculated common atrium by the crista terminalis. The right horn also gives rise to the valve of the inferior vena cava.

18. The answer is E. *(Langman, ed 6. pp 187-189, 191-192. Moore, ed 4. pp 294-295, 303-304.)* Although the atrioventricular valves are formed chiefly from localized proliferations of mesenchymal tissue surrounding the right and left atrial orifices, portions of the anterior leaflet of the mitral valve and the septal leaflet of the tricuspid valve are derived from the endocardial cushions. During the fourth week of development, endocardial cushions develop in the atrioventricular canal and fuse to divide the canal. These cushions then grow cranially to contribute to the closure of the septum primum and caudally to contribute to the membranous portion of the interventricular septum. When the endocardial cushions *fail* to fuse, the results may include a persistent atrioventricular canal, an ostium primum defect in the interatrial septum, and a partial interventricular defect. An ostium primum defect frequently is associated with a cleft in the anterior leaflet of the mitral valve and in the septal leaflet of the tricuspid valve. The semilunar valves develop from tubercles on the truncus swellings.

19. The answer is A. *(Langman, ed 6. pp 196-197, 199-203. Moore, ed 4. pp 303, 313.)* Failure of the truncoconal septum to rotate results in a cardiac anomaly known as transposition of the great vessels, wherein the aorta arises from the right ventricle and the pulmonary trunk from the left. It usually is associated with a patent ductus arteriosus and sometimes with a defect in the membranous portion of the interventricular septum. This particular anomaly is not immediately fatal inasmuch as blood may pass through the interventricular septum to reach the lungs and then pass into the aorta through the ductus arteriosus. The pulmonary trunk would arise from the aorta when the truncoconal septum fails to form.

20. The answer is A. *(Langman, ed 6. pp 207-209. Moore, ed 4. pp 294, 321-323.)* Blood leaving the heart via the truncus arteriosus passes through the aortic arches of the branchial arches before entering the paired dorsal aortae. Although five or six pairs of aortic arches develop, not all are functional at the same time. A single dorsal aorta forms by the eighth week by persistence of the left fourth aortic arch, degeneration of the left dorsal aorta in the branchial region, and fusion of the left and right dorsal aortae caudally.

21. The answer is B. *(Langman, ed 6. pp 221-225. Moore, ed 4. pp 321-325.)* Blood from the placenta in the umbilical vein is about 80 percent oxygenated. Mixture with unoxygenated blood from the vitelline veins and the inferior vena reduces the oxygen content somewhat. However, this stream with a relatively high oxygen content is directed by the valve of the inferior vena cava directly through the foramen ovale into the left atrium. This prevents admixture with oxygen-depleted blood entering the right atrium from the superior vena cava. Thus, the oxygen-saturated blood entering the left ventricle and pumped into the aortic arch, subclavian arteries, and common carotid arteries has the highest oxygen content. The oxygen-depleted blood from the superior vena cava is directed into the right ventricle and thence to the pulmonary trunk. While a small portion of this flow passes through the lungs (where any residual oxygen is extracted by the tissue of the nonrespiring lung), most is shunted into the thoracic aorta via the ductus arteriosus, thereby lowering the oxygen content of that vessel. This occurs distal to the origins of the carotid arteries and ensures that the rapidly developing brain has the best oxygen supply.

22. The answer is D. *(Langman, ed 6. pp 212-213. Moore, ed 4. p 323.)* The ductus arteriosus is the persistent sixth aortic arch on the left side. Owing to the high vascular resistance of the collapsed lungs, the ductus arteriosus functions as a shunt, directing blood away from the nonfunctional fetal lungs into the descending aorta. Initial inflation of the lungs results in a release of bradykinin, which causes contraction of the muscular wall of the ductus arteriosus, thereby effecting a functional closure. However, since anatomic obliteration of the lumen of the ductus arteriosus is not complete until several weeks after birth, there may be slight or occasional reversal of blood flow. The obliterated ductus arteriosus persists in the adult as the ligamentum arteriosum between the left pulmonary artery and the aortic arch.

23. The answer is B. *(Langman, ed 6. pp 221-224. Moore, ed 4. p 325.)* The umbilical vein returns oxygenated blood from the placenta to the fetus. While supplying the sinusoids of the liver, the umbilical vein also forms a direct channel through the liver to the inferior vena cava—the ductus venosus. A sphincteric mechanism in the muscular walls of the ductus determines whether the returning blood flow is through the hepatic sinusoids or through the ductus to bypass the liver. Functionally, the umbilical vein closes shortly after birth. The extrahepatic portion of the umbilical vein becomes the ligamentum teres hepatis (round ligament of the liver) and the ductus venosus becomes the ligamentum venosum on complete obliteration of the venous channel.

24. The answer is B. *(Langman, ed 6. pp 244-245. Moore, ed 4. p 223.)* The yolk sac produces hematocytoblasts and primitive erythroblasts from the third week through the second month of gestation. Hepatic erythropoiesis begins during the sixth week, reaches its maximum in the third month, and then ceases about the seventh month. The spleen enters an erythropoietic period early in the third month and remains active in erythrocyte production until shortly after birth. Although erythropoiesis ceases in the spleen, this organ continues to produce monocytes and lymphocytes throughout life. In addition, from the second month the lymph nodes and the thymus produce lymphocytes. The major hematopoietic organ is the bone marrow, which first becomes functional during the third month of fetal development and continues its major role in erythrocyte production throughout life.

25. The answer is D. *(Langman, ed 6. pp 245-246. Moore, ed 4. pp 224-225.)* The dorsal pancreatic bud is the source of the body, tail, and isthmus of the pancreas, as well as of the upper half of the head. It also gives rise to the accessory pancreatic duct (of Santorini). The ventral pancreatic bud, which migrates to the right with the lower end of the common bile duct and fuses with the dorsal primordium, forms the uncinate process and the lower half of the head of the pancreas. The *proximal* portion of the *ventral* pancreatic duct anastomoses with the *distal* portion of the *dorsal* pancreatic duct to form the primary pancreatic duct (of Wirsung). The primary duct, in conjunction with the bile duct, most commonly opens into the duodenal papilla (of Vater).

26. The answer is D. *(Langman, ed 6. pp 248-250. Moore, ed 4. pp 228-231.)* During the first month of development, the midgut communicates over its entirety with the yolk sac. This connection narrows during the next month to form the vitelline duct (yolk stalk, omphalomesenteric duct) as the midgut closes and usually disappears during the ninth week. Because the vitelline duct joins the ileum, this section of the gastrointestinal tract is the last to close. Failure of closure results in a persistent vitelline fistula, while partial obliteration results in an ileal diverticulum (of Meckel).

27. The answer is C. *(Langman, ed 6. pp 255, 257-258, 268-269. Moore, ed 4. pp 238-240, 257-258.)* The hindgut gives rise to the allantois, urinary bladder, and the prostatic and membranous urethrae in the male as well as most of the urethra in the female. It also gives rise to those portions of the large intestine supplied by the inferior mesenteric artery, i.e., the descending colon, sigmoid colon, rectum, and upper part of the anal canal. The inferior portion of the anal canal is derived from somatic ectoderm of the proctodeum.

28. The answer is C. *(Langman, ed 6. pp 263-264. Moore, ed 4. pp 246-248, 258-259.)* At the beginning of the second month, the mesonephros starts to regress. The ureteric bud arises from the lower end of the mesonephric (wolffian) duct and rapidly penetrates the metanephric blastema, inducing formation of the definitive kidney. The ureteric bud subsequently dilates, forming the primitive renal pelvis and simultaneously splitting to form the future major and minor calyces. The collecting tubules proliferate from the minor calyces. Failure of the nephrons to effect proper junction with the ureteric collecting system produces congenital polycystic kidney. The penile urethra arises from the urogenital sinus.

29. The answer is B. *(Langman, ed 6. pp 304-305. Moore, ed 4. pp 173, 176.)* The cartilage of the first pharyngeal arch consists of a maxillary process and a mandibular process. During development both cartilages regress, except for two portions at the dorsal ends that persist as the incus and the malleus. The cartilage of the second (hyoid) arch gives rise to the stapes, the styloid process of the temporal bone, the stylohyoid ligament, and the lesser horn of the hyoid bone. The body and greater horn of the hyoid bone are derivatives of the third branchial arch.

30. The answer is D. *(Langman, ed 6. pp 347-350. Moore, ed 4. pp 421-426.)* Sebaceous glands, sweat glands, mammary glands, hair follicles, and nails all develop as invaginations of the epidermal layer into the underlying dermis. Melanocytes of the epidermis are of neural crest origin. The dermis is derived from mesenchyme.

Mammary glands remain undeveloped until puberty, at which time ovarian steroids promote the growth of fat and the duct system. However, this is not a trait shared in common with other epidermal derivatives.

31. The answer is B. *(Langman, ed 6. p 356. Moore, ed 4. pp 370, 395-397.)* The basal plate of the neural tube gives rise to the motor nuclei of the cranial nerves, divided into three groups: general somatic efferent, special visceral efferent, and general visceral efferent. The alar plate contains three similarly divided groups of sensory nuclei and also gives rise to the cerebral hemispheres and the cerebellum. The roof plate consists of a single layer of ependymal cells, which later join with the pia mater to develop into the coroid plexuses of the lateral, third, and fourth ventricles. The floor plate is also devoid of neuroblasts.

32-34. The answers are: 32-D, 33-A, 34-C. *(Langman, ed 6. pp 272-274, 276-278, 283. Moore, ed 4. pp 262-265, 267-268, 271-273.)* The Y chromosome determines whether medullary cords will develop to form a testis, or whether cortical cords will fail to develop with a resultant ovary. The presence of the double X chromosome promotes the converse.

Testicular testosterone mediates virilization of the mesonephric duct system, which develops into epididymis, vas deferens, and seminal vesicles. Concomitantly, a nonsteroid product of Sertoli cells inhibits paramesonephric duct development.

Testicular or placental hormones act upon the undifferentiated external genitalia to produce phenotypic differentiation. Testosterone, produced by the differentiating testis, stimulates development of the mesonephric duct system as well as the external genitalia. In the absence of testicular androgens, placental estrogens stimulate the paramesonephric duct system as well as both inhibit development of the male external genitalia and promote development of the female external genitalia.

35-38. The answers are: 35-D, 36-A, 37-C, 38-D. *(Langman, ed 6. pp 305-308. Moore, ed 4. pp 176-179.)* The thyroid gland develops from the foramen caecum, an evagination of the floor of the pharynx dissociated from the pharyngeal pouches. However, as it descends into the neck it becomes associated with the ultimobranchial bodies of the fifth pharyngeal pouch. The ultimobranchial bodies disseminate into the thyroid tissue to form the parafollicular (C) cells, which secrete calcitonin.

The thymus gland develops from the ventral wing of the third pharyngeal pouch. The left and right thymic primordia migrate medially to the midline and fuse in the midline before descending into the superior mediastinum in association with the developing heart.

The superior parathyroid glands (parathyroid IV) develop from the fourth pharyngeal pouch, while the inferior parathyroid glands (parathyroid III) develop from the dorsal wing of the third pharyngeal pouch in association with the thymus primordia. The inferior parathyroids usually lose their association with the thymus, and both pairs of parathyroids become associated with the thyroid gland as it migrates caudally from the foramen caecum into the neck. However, persistence of the thymic connections may result in a mediastinal location of the inferior parathyroid glands.

The pharyngeal tonsillar cleft is a remnant of the second pharyngeal pouch. The endoderm of the pouch becomes infiltrated with lymphatic tissue about the tonsillar crypts to form the pharyngeal tonsil. Failure of the second pharyngeal pouches and the second pharyngeal groove to obliterate results in branchial cysts, sinuses, or fistulas.

39-42. The answers are: 39-D, 40-E, 41-C, 42-B. *(Langman, ed 6. pp 44, 52-53, 139, 151, 237, 359-360. Moore, ed 4. pp 53, 63, 338-339, 370-371.)* In a developing embryo, the neural crest tissue (D in the diagram accompanying the question) underlies the neural ridges dorsolateral to the developing neural tube. Some cells of the neural crest aggregate to form the dorsal root ganglia. The peripheral processes of these sensory neurons, which terminate in somatic or visceral receptors, form the sensory components of the spinal—and some cranial—nerves. The central processes synapse within the dorsal portion of the spinal cord. In addition, the neural crest tissue forms the postganglionic autonomic neurons and their associated paravertebral, prevertebral, and enteric ganglia. Other neural crest derivatives include the adrenal medulla and other chromaffin tissue, melanocytes, neurilemma, and myelin sheaths, as well as various structures of the head such as the odontoblasts of the teeth, cartilage cells of the branchial arches, and the leptomeninges.

During the fourth week of development, the neural arch of the vertebra is derived from the somites (E). The sclerotome portion of each somite migrates in three directions. One portion migrates ventrally around the notochord to form the centrum of the vertebra; a second migrates dorsally around the developing neural tube to form the neural arch; and a third section migrates ventrolaterally to form the ribs. Other divisions of the somites are dermatome and myotome; the somites also divide into somatopleure and splanchnopleure.

The notochord (C) represents a unique characteristic of the vertebrate phylum. This structure develops as a cellular rod during the first week of growth. Later, the notochord induces formation of the bodies of the vertebrae from the sclerotome. Remnants of the notochord persist in the adult human as the nucleus pulposus, which forms the center of the intervertebral disk.

Formation of the intraembryonic coelom divides the lateral mesoderm into somatopleure and splanchnopleure (B). The splanchnic mesoderm, overlying the primitive endoderm, contributes the walls and musculature of the gastrointestinal tract. This layer also is continuous with the extraembryonic mesoderm covering the yolk sac. The somatic mesoderm, underlying the ectoderm, differentiates into dermatome and myotome, both of which contribute to the soft tissue elements of the body wall.

The yolk sac (A) develops from the primitive blastocyst cavity subjacent to the embryonic disk. The infolding of the cephalic, caudal, and lateral parts of the developing embryo forms the primitive gut, into which a small portion of the yolk sac is incorporated. The remainder of the yolk sac remains extraembryonic and, by means of the vitelline (omphalomesenteric) duct, retains its connection to the midgut until the eighth week, when this connection is usually lost just prior to the withdrawal of the primary intestinal loop from the umbilical herniation. A Meckel's diverticulum results from persistence of a portion of the vitelline duct with the adult ileum.

43-46. The answers are: 43-E, 44-C, 45-B, 46-D. *(Langman, ed 6. pp 212, 223-224, 251-252, 268-270. Moore, ed 4. pp 235, 259, 325.)* An ileal diverticulum (of Meckel) occurs in 3 percent of the population. This abnormal structure represents a partial persistence of the vitelline (omphalomesenteric) duct, which connects the midgut and the yolk sac. The mucosal lining of Meckel's diverticulum may contain gastric mucosa rather than intestinal mucosa, and the acid secretions may produce adjacent intestinal ulceration resulting in hemorrhage. In addition, a persistent fibrous remnant between the vitelline duct or vitelline artery and the umbilicus creates an axis about which volvulus may occur, leading to intestinal obstruction and the possibility of intestinal infarct. A patent omphalomesenteric duct results in the oozing of chyme from the umbilicus.

The extrahepatic portion of the umbilical vein becomes occluded and forms the round ligament of the liver (ligamentum teres hepatis), which lies in the free edge of the falciform ligament. However, the lumen may be reestablished for the purpose of cannulating the hepatic portal system. The intrahepatic portion of the umbilical vein (ductus venosus) also becomes occluded and forms the ligamentum venosum.

The distal portions of the umbilical arteries become occluded and form the lateral umbilical ligaments over which the peritoneum forms the medial umbilical folds. The proximal portions of the umbilical arteries persist as the internal iliac arteries with the superior vesical arteries to the urinary bladder the most distal patent branches.

The embryonic connection between the hindgut and the allantois involutes and the basal portion becomes the urinary bladder. The portion between the fundus of the urinary bladder and the umbilicus becomes occluded to form the urachus, which persists as a fibrous cord—the median umbilical ligament. Portions of the urachus may remain patent and be the site of cysts, while a completely patent urachus results in leakage of urine from the umbilicus. The peritoneum lying over the urachus forms the median umbilical fold.

47-50. The answers are: 47-D, 48-A, 49-B, 50-B. *(Langman, ed 6. pp 260-262, 274-279, 283. Moore, ed 4. pp 246, 267-273.)* The external genitalia are derived from the genital swellings, which give rise to the labia majora in the female and fuse to form the scrotum in the male; from the genital tubercle, which gives rise to the clitoris in the female and the glans penis in the male; and from the folds of the urogenital sinus. In the female, the folds of the urogenital sinus remain open and become the labia minora. The underlying mesenchyme forms the vestibular bulbs, erectile bodies flanking the vaginal introitus. Under the influence of testicular androgenic hormones in the male, the folds of the urogenital sinus fuse in the midline to form the penile urethra. The underlying mesenchymal tissue fuses in the midline to form the corpus spongiosum (corpus cavernosus urethrae), one of the three erectile bodies that contribute to the penis.

In the female embryo, the paramesonephric (müllerian) ducts develop into the uterine (fallopian) tubes, uterus, and a portion of the vagina. There is nearly complete regression of the mesonephric (wolffian) ducts by the eleventh week. The paramesonephric (müllerian) ducts develop independently as epithelial buds along the mesonephric ducts, where they open into the coelomic cavity and progress caudally to the urogenital sinus. During the ninth week, fusion of the caudal portions of the paramesonephric ducts forms the upper vagina and uterus, whereas the cranial unfused portions develop into the oviducts. Concomitantly, there is degeneration of that portion of the mesonephric ducts cranial to the metanephric diverticulum. Some mesonephric tubules persist in the vicinity of the ovary as the epoophoron and paroophoron.

As the male urogenital excretory system develops, the mesonephric (wolffian) ducts differentiate under the influence of androgenic stimulation and develop into the epididymis, vas deferens, appendix testis, seminal vesicles, ejaculatory ducts, and ureters. The most cranial portion of the mesonephric ducts degenerates, except for a remnant—the appendix epididymis. Further caudally, the tubules of the mesonephros become the efferent ductules of the testes, which join the mesonephric duct and which, caudal to this point, in turn become the vas deferens. Some of the rudimentary mesonephric tubules persist as the paradidymis. The seminal vesicles, which are derived from the ductus deferens, join to form the ejaculatory duct that opens on the posterior side of the urogenital sinus at the level of the verumontanum (seminal colliculus) of the prostatic urethra. In the male, the paramesonephric (müllerian) ducts degenerate by the eleventh week except for the appendix testis situated on the superior pole of each testis. The utriculus prostaticus also may develop from the paramesonephric ducts, although some textbooks of embryology state that it is formed from the urogenital sinus.

The metanephric kidney begins to develop during the fifth week, and by the beginning of the second month, the mesonephros commences regression. In both male and female, the ureters, the renal pelvis, and the calyces develop from metanephric or ureteric buds as outgrowths from terminal portions of the mesonephric (wolffian) ducts. The ureteric bud rapidly penetrates the metanephric blastema and induces the formation of the metanephric, or definitive, kidney. The ureteric bud subsequently dilates, forming the primitive renal pelvis, which immediately splits to form the future major and minor calyces. The collecting tubules proliferate from the minor calyces and join with numerous nephrons to complete the excretory system. Failure of the nephrons to effect proper fusion with the ureteric collecting system results in congenital polycystic kidney disease.

The prostate gland in the male and the urethral glands (of Skene) in the female are derived from evaginations of the urogenital sinus. In the male, the prostate develops under androgenic stimulation. The urogenital sinus also gives rise to the urinary bladder and the portion of the urethra within, and deep to, the urogenital diaphragm of the pelvis. The apex of the bladder continues as the allantoic stalk, continuing to the allantois. At birth the allantoic stalk becomes obliterated and forms the urachus.

Histology

DIRECTIONS: Each question below contains four or five suggested responses. Select the **one best** response to each question.

51. The cell component responsible for packaging, and perhaps producing, glycosylated cellular products is the

(A) Golgi apparatus
(B) mitochondrion
(C) nucleolus
(D) rough endoplasmic reticulum
(E) smooth endoplasmic reticulum

52. All the following statements characterize the integral proteins of the plasma membrane EXCEPT

(A) they aggregate into lipid-filled channels through which lipid-soluble molecules may diffuse
(B) they can freely move laterally within the membrane
(C) they pass completely through the phospholipid bilayer
(D) they project from the external surface as receptors
(E) they project from the internal surface as anchors for cytoskeletal elements

53. When a cell needs cholesterol for membrane synthesis, it makes receptors for low-density lipoprotein (LDL) and incorporates them in its plasma membrane. All the following statements are correct concerning the LDL receptor EXCEPT

(A) atherosclerosis can result from inability of the cytoplasmic pole of the LDL receptor to bind to clathrin
(B) LDL receptors are degraded in the endosome after one round-trip
(C) LDL receptors are internalized at coated pits
(D) the exterior pole of the receptor has an affinity for the protein portion of LDL
(E) the LDL receptor is a single transmembrane glycoprotein

54. Protein translocation across the membrane of endoplasmic reticulum involves a signal peptide, a signal-recognition particle, and a signal-recognition particle receptor. All the following statements are correct regarding the signal peptide EXCEPT

(A) it bonds directly to the signal-recognition particle receptor
(B) it is associated only with peptides destined for export
(C) it is cleaved from the peptide before the peptide is fully synthesized
(D) it is found within the endoplasmic reticulum
(E) it is located at the N-terminal of the synthesized peptide

55. All the following are characteristic of gap junctions EXCEPT

(A) arrays of filaments (such as keratin, desmin, and actin) originate from the cytoplasmic surface
(B) connexons allow small molecules and ions to pass from cell to cell
(C) connexons form liquid-crystalline lattice arrays
(D) each connexon is composed of six transmembrane subunits
(E) they permit chemical and electrical coupling between cells

56. Regions of the cell nucleus that stain darkly with basic dyes used for light microscopy correlate closely with

(A) decreased synthetic activity
(B) euchromatin
(C) increased metabolic activity
(D) a higher RNA/DNA ratio
(E) a lower histone/DNA ratio

57. The centrosome (cytocentrum) is considered to be the locus of a number of cell functions. Centrosomes are distinguished by all the following characteristics EXCEPT

(A) they are surrounded by a microtubular aster during mitosis
(B) they display usual juxtaposition with a nuclear pole and Golgi organelles
(C) they have the ability of self-duplication
(D) the component centrioles contain a pair of central tubules
(E) they organize microtubule formation

Questions 58-60

A population of fibroblasts is grown in tissue culture. The durations of each phase of the cell cycle of the population of cells are $G_1 = 9$ hours, $S = 6$ hours, $G_2 = 4$ hours, $M = 1/2$ hour.

58. The culture is incubated (pulsed) in a medium containing ^{3}H-thymidine for exactly 2 hours. Subsequently, the culture is incubated (chased) in a medium containing nonradioactive thymidine for exactly 1 hour. The cells are then fixed and prepared for radioautography. On examination with a light microscope, silver grains exposed by incorporated radioactivity are observed over a small percentage of nuclei. Which of the following conclusions is correct?

(A) Labeled cells are daughter cells with a 2n chromosome number
(B) Labeled cells were fixed when they were in the S phase of the cell cycle
(C) Labeled cells were in the S phase of the cell cycle during the pulse of ^{3}H-thymidine
(D) Unlabeled cells are incapable of gene replication and are not part of the cycling population of cells
(E) None of the above

59. If the culture had been pulsed with ^{3}H-thymidine for the same 2-hour period and then chased with a medium containing nonradioactive thymidine for a period of 10 hours before fixation for radioautography, all the following would be expected EXCEPT

(A) each labeled cell would have only one labeled strand of DNA in each gene
(B) in each labeled cell the nucleolus would be strongly labeled
(C) labeled cells would have a 2n chromosome number
(D) the number of cells with labeled nuclei would be double the number observed after a 1-hour chase
(E) unlabeled cells could have replicated DNA and divided during the 10-hour chase period

60. If the culture had been pulsed with ^{3}H-uracil for exactly 30 minutes and then chased with a medium containing nonradioactive uracil and colchicine for a period of 4 hours before fixation for radioautography, the radioactive labeling would be expected to be associated with

(A) the cytoplasm of some cells
(B) the mitotic figures of cells arrested in mitosis
(C) the nuclei of some daughter cells
(D) the nuclei of some mother cells
(E) none of the above

(End of question set)

61. Ciliated cells, like those in the accompanying photomicrograph, are important functional components of the epithelium of the

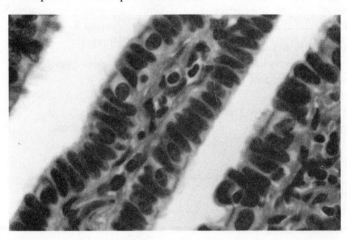

(A) duodenum
(B) epididymis
(C) proximal convoluted tubules
(D) respiratory alveolus
(E) uterine tube

62. The basal lamina can be observed by light microscopy when stained by the periodic acid-Schiff (PAS) reaction or with silver impregnation techniques. Characteristics of the basal lamina include all the following EXCEPT

(A) it consists in part of an amorphous carbohydrate matrix
(B) it consists in part of collagen fibrils (reticular fibers)
(C) it consists in part of dense collagen bundles
(D) it is a constant structural element beneath all epithelia
(E) it is secreted by both epithelial cells and fibroblasts

63. A tissue culture medium in which fibroblasts are growing and synthesizing collagen fibers is analyzed. The medium is likely to contain which of the following essential amino acid precursors for tropocollagen synthesis?

(A) Desmosine
(B) Proline
(C) Serine
(D) Tryptophan
(E) Tyrosine

64. All the following statements about tropocollagen (procollagen), the structural unit of collagen, are correct EXCEPT

(A) it aggregates with a 64-nm offset to form liquid-crystalline fibrils
(B) it is a double helix of two identical polypeptide chains
(C) it is about 300 nm long and 1.5 nm in diameter
(D) it is capable of inducing hydroxy-apatite crystal growth
(E) it is synthesized as a complete unit within the rough endoplasmic reticulum

65. Granules containing heparin, an anticoagulant, and histamine, a vasodilator, stain metachromatically. This can be demonstrated in which of the following cell types?

(A) Eosinophilic granulocytes
(B) Lymphocytes
(C) Neutrophilic granulocytes
(D) Plasma cells
(E) None of the above

---

66. In the accompanying photomicrograph, the several larger cells (containing eccentric nuclei, radially arranged coarse chromatin, and basophilic cytoplasm) normally function in

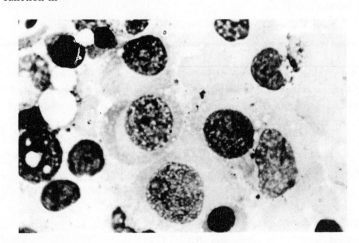

(A) antigen recognition
(B) cellular immunity
(C) histamine release
(D) immunoglobulin synthesis
(E) phagocytosis

67. The hypercellularity of the fat pads
typical of an obese middle-aged adult is
best explained by

(A) current treatment with norepineph-
     rine
(B) long-standing insulin deficiency
(C) obesity during early childhood
(D) substantial overeating over the past
     few years
(E) sympathectomy during the pre-
     vious 5 years

---

68. Two forms of bone can be distinguished by examination at low magnification.
The type shown in the accompanying photomicrograph could be found at all the
following locations EXCEPT the

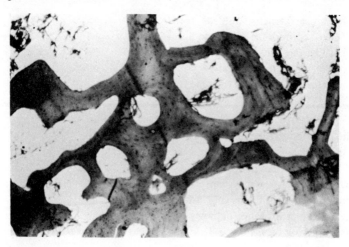

(A) metaphyses of long bones
(B) epiphyses of long bones
(C) medullary cavity of long bones
(D) central region (diploe) of flat bones
(E) outer plate of flat bones

69. In the accompanying photomicrograph of a bone section, all the following statements concerning the large multinucleate cell are correct EXCEPT

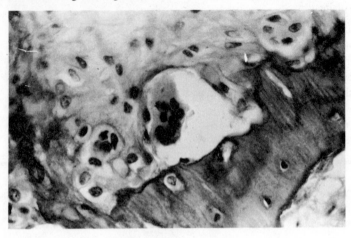

(A) it has a characteristic "ruffled" border
(B) it is derived from the monocyte lineage
(C) it is under the influence of parathyroid hormone
(D) it phagocytoses foreign bodies
(E) it secretes lysosomal enzymes, H^+, and collagenase

70. The majority of lamellae of compact bone is arranged concentrically around longitudinal vascular channels to form osteons (haversian systems). From the capillaries of the osteons, osteocytes receive or exchange nutrients and metabolites by means of

(A) canaliculi
(B) central canals
(C) diffusion through the bony matrix
(D) medullary vessels
(E) Volkmann's canals

71. The tissue shown in the accompanying photomicrograph is characterized by which of the following statements?

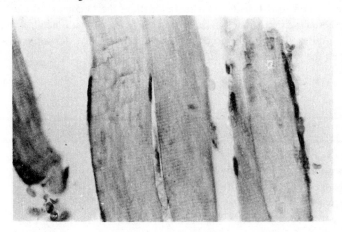

(A) Each cell possesses one or more neuromuscular junctions
(B) Impulses spread from cell to cell via nexuses or gap junctions
(C) The nuclei are located in the center of the cells
(D) The cells are modified to conduct electrical impulses and have very little contractile protein
(E) The cells are connected to each other by desmosomes

---

72. Filaments of actin and myosin compose the contractile apparatus in striated muscle. All the following statements about the myofilaments are correct EXCEPT

(A) the A-band lattice is a liquid-crystalline structure
(B) the actin filament is a triple helix of globular actin monomers
(C) the myosin heads undergo conformational changes when they bind to actin
(D) the parallel array of myosin filaments is strongly anisotropic in polarized light
(E) the thick filaments are composed of molecules having a structure similar to an antibody

73. The dimensions within the sarcomere are as follows: actin filaments = 1.00 μm, myosin filaments = 1.65 μm with a 0.20-μm bridge-free central zone, and Z line = 0.05 μm. Thus the maximum length of the sarcomere would be 3.6 μm. Shortening of a striated muscle fiber within its normal functional range from 2.25 μm (as shown in the accompanying illustration) to 2.05 μm is associated with all the following events EXCEPT

Z I   A   H   A   I Z

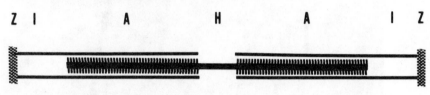

(A) an increase in the sarcomere diameter
(B) no change in the number of cross bridges
(C) an increase in the active force produced
(D) no change in the volume of the sarcomere
(E) obliteration of the H zone

74. The function of adenosine triphosphate (ATP) in striated muscle includes providing a direct energy source for which of the following mechanisms?

(A) Activation of the troponin/tropomyosin complex
(B) Formation of a high energy complex within light meromyosin
(C) Release of calcium by the smooth endoplasmic reticulum
(D) Separation of the actin/heavy meromyosin complex
(E) Sequestration of calcium by the T tubules

75. Cardiac muscle and skeletal muscle have which of the following characteristics in common?

(A) Arrangement of the contractile filaments
(B) Bifurcation of muscle fibers
(C) Number of mitochondria present
(D) Position of the nuclei in the cell
(E) Presence of intercalated disks

76. The cells illustrated in the accompanying photomicrograph most likely were obtained from the

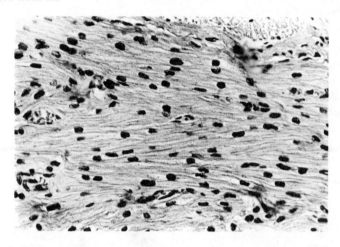

(A) deltoid muscle
(B) diaphragm
(C) heart
(D) tongue
(E) uterus

---

77. A factor applicable to *both* skeletal and smooth muscles is

(A) a system of T-tubules that conveys the membrane depolarization deep into the cell
(B) contraction regulated by controlling intracellular calcium concentration
(C) gap junctions that spread membrane depolarizations to adjacent fibers
(D) innervation that is generally by motor neurons that lie in the anterior horn of the spinal cord
(E) intercalated disks that serve as anchoring locations for thin filaments

78. Proteins synthesized by the neuron soma must be transported to the axon terminal. True statements concerning axonal transport include all the following EXCEPT

(A) axonal transport occurs in an anterograde direction only
(B) colchicine, which interrupts microtubule formation, blocks fast axonal transport
(C) membrane vesicles are transported at a fast rate of 100 to 400 mm per day
(D) mitochondria are transported at a fast rate of 100 to 400 mm per day
(E) soluble proteins and microtubules are transported at a slow rate of 1 to 3 mm per day

79. An axon within the spinal cord can be histologically distinguished from a dendrite because the axon

(A) contains a myelin or neurilemmal sheath
(B) contains Nissl bodies
(C) has numerous surface spines
(D) is wider than a dendrite
(E) reduces its diameter with each branching

Questions 80-81

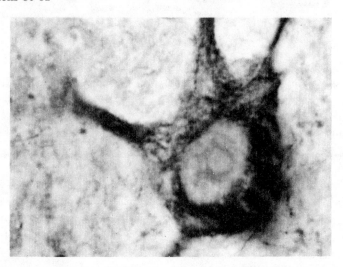

80. In the photomicrograph above of tissue taken from the cerebral cortex, the cell illustrated is a

(A) basket cell
(B) granule cell
(C) neuroglial cell
(D) pyramidal cell
(E) Purkinje cell

81. In the photomicrograph above, all the following structures are demonstrable EXCEPT the

(A) axon
(B) dendrites
(C) euchromatin
(D) Nissl bodies
(E) nucleolus

(End of question set)

82. The neurons shown in the accompanying photomicrograph of a peripheral ganglion have which of the following functions?

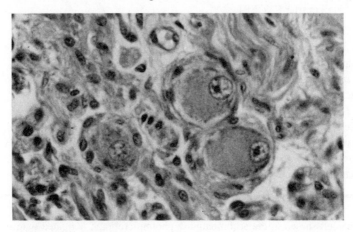

(A) Autonomic transmission
(B) Conduction of pain impulses
(C) Proprioception
(D) Innervation of striated muscle
(E) Transmission of visual stimuli

83. Oligodendroglia of the central nervous system

(A) are phagocytic
(B) compose the blood-brain barrier
(C) form the pial meningeal layer
(D) have processes associated with blood capillaries
(E) myelinate more than one axon per cell

84. The arachnoid villi allow cerebrospinal fluid to pass between which of the following two spaces?

(A) Choroid plexus and subdural space
(B) Subarachnoid space and subdural space
(C) Subarachnoid space and superior sagittal sinus
(D) Subdural space and cavernous sinus
(E) Superior sagittal sinus and jugular vein

85. All the following statements concerning the biconcave shape of the erythrocyte are true EXCEPT

(A) it facilitates exchange of gases
(B) it first appears in the polychromatophilic erythroblast
(C) it is a function in part of osmotic factors
(D) it is maintained in part by cytoskeletal elements
(E) it permits deformation to allow passage through spaces smaller than 7 μm

86. The cell shown in the accompanying photomicrograph is treated with fluorescein-labeled antihuman immunoglobulin. The positive cell-membrane fluorescence indicates that the cell is a

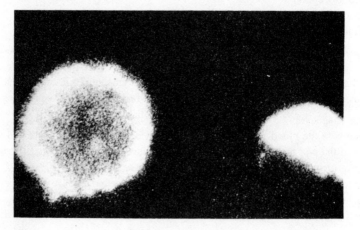

(A) B cell
(B) plasma cell
(C) T cell
(D) transformed T cell
(E) thymocyte

87. T lymphocytes *differ* from B lymphocytes in all the following ways
EXCEPT

(A) ability to further differentiate
(B) cell-mediated immunity vs.
humeral immunity
(C) cell surface antigens
(D) site of differentiation
(E) stem-cell precursor

88. The lymphoid tissue illustrated in the accompanying photomicrograph most probably is taken from

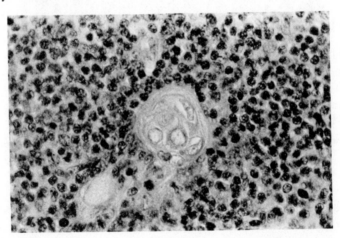

(A) a lymph node
(B) a Peyer's patch
(C) the spleen
(D) the thymus
(E) a tonsil

89. The vessel shown in the accompanying photomicrograph contains many black-staining elastic fibers. These are characteristic of the

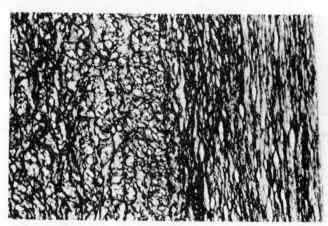

(A) aorta
(B) cavernous sinus
(C) inferior vena cava
(D) radial artery
(E) subclavian vein

---

90. The most prominent structural feature of large veins is

(A) a media with a large amount of circularly arranged muscle
(B) a media with a large amount of longitudinally arranged muscle
(C) a thick, muscular adventitia
(D) a well-defined internal elastic membrane
(E) no vasa vasorum in the adventitia

91. Tissue shown in the accompanying light micrograph produces

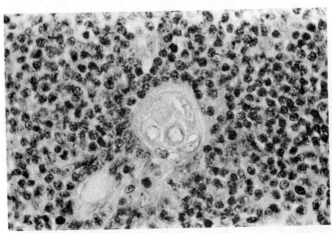

(A) acid phosphatase, citric acid, and amylase
(B) calcitonin
(C) glucagon
(D) melatonin and serotonin
(E) none of the above

92. The fully developed thymus resembles other members of the lymphoid organs in having a similar groundwork of relatively large branching cells infiltrated with small, deeply staining elements. Which of the following statements regarding the thymus and the lymph nodes is true?

(A) They are both divided into a cortex and a medulla
(B) They both contain germinal centers
(C) They both contain sinuses
(D) They both produce lymphocytes that mature into plasma cells
(E) They both produce new T lymphocytes

93. Blood-tissue barriers, whereby continuous tight junctions between contiguous cells prevent diffusion of large-molecular-weight substances, are characteristic of all the following organs EXCEPT the

(A) brain
(B) retina
(C) spleen
(D) testes
(E) thymus

94. The accompanying photomicrograph demonstrates normal tissue from the

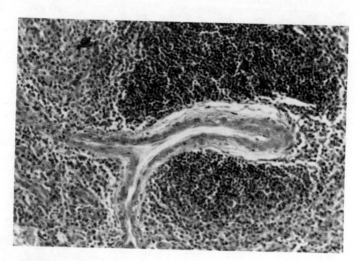

(A) circumvallate papilla
(B) lower esophagus
(C) palatine tonsil
(D) parotid gland
(E) spleen

---

95. True statements about splenic function include all the following EXCEPT

(A) splenic phagocytes destroy infective agents
(B) the spleen functions in antibody production
(C) the spleen is important in the metabolism and distribution of erythrocytes
(D) the spleen produces new erythrocytes during childhood
(E) worn-out erythrocytes are destroyed by lymphocytes in the white pulp

96. Each of the five layers of the epidermis is functionally distinct. The cells of the stratum spinosum are characterized by all the following EXCEPT

(A) desmosomes between adjacent cells
(B) extensive nets of tonofibrils within the cells
(C) keratohyalin granules
(D) membrane-coating granules (keratosomes)
(E) mitotic activity

97. Melanocytes are one of the factors that determine the color of skin. Characteristics of melanocytes include all the following EXCEPT that they

(A) are derived from the neural crest
(B) are far more numerous in persons of darker-skinned races than in those of lighter-skinned races
(C) are located in the basal stratum of the epidermis
(D) have long, irregular cytoplasmic processes that extend into the malpighian layer
(E) synthesize melanin in a granule that is subsequently transferred to keratinocytes by cytocrine secretion

98. The photomicrograph below is of the junction between the

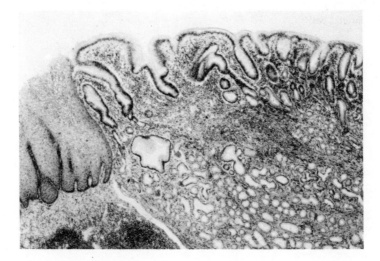

(A) anal canal and rectum
(B) esophagus and stomach
(C) skin of the face and mucous epithelium of the lip
(D) stomach and duodenum
(E) vagina and cervix

99. The mucosa shown in the accompanying photomicrograph characteristically contains all the following EXCEPT

(A) chief cells
(B) enteroendocrine cells
(C) mucous neck cells
(D) Paneth's cells
(E) parietal cells

100. A unique histologic feature helpful in identifying the tissue shown in the photomicrograph appearing below is the presence of

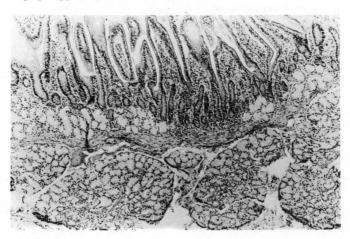

(A) Brunner's glands
(B) chief cells
(C) parietal cells
(D) Peyer's patches
(E) serous cells

---

101. The duodenum, jejunum, and ileum may be differentiated by subtle structural differences. The duodenum is characterized by all the following statements EXCEPT

(A) Brunner's glands are found in the submucosa
(B) duodenal villi are tall and leaf-shaped
(C) there are few, if any, Peyer's patches of lymphoid tissue
(D) goblet cells are the predominant cell type in the mucosa
(E) plicae circularis are absent in the first portion

102. The myenteric (Auerbach's) plexus is characterized by all the following statements EXCEPT

(A) it contains cell bodies of parasympathetic neurons
(B) it contains enteric neurons
(C) it innervates the glands of the mucosa
(D) it is located between the layers of the muscularis externa
(E) it is surrounded by satellite cells

103. Paneth's cells are absent in children with kwashiorkor, but reappear when nutrition is restored to normal. All the following are true of Paneth's cells EXCEPT

(A) their secretion is antibacterial
(B) they are found throughout the small intestine
(C) they are located at the base of the glands of Lieberkühn
(D) they are argyrophilic
(E) they store lysozyme

---

104. The tissue section shown in the accompanying photomicrograph demonstrates histologic features of normal

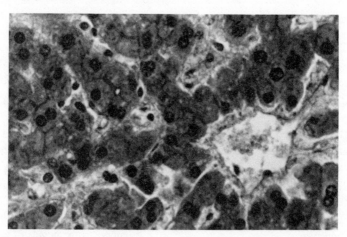

(A) adrenal gland
(B) apocrine gland
(C) liver
(D) salivary gland
(E) spleen

105. Liver parenchymal cells synthesize all the following plasma proteins EXCEPT

(A) albumin
(B) fibrinogen
(C) γ-globulin
(D) prothrombin

106. The wall of the bile canaliculi of the liver can best be described as

(A) a ciliated hepatic cell surface
(B) a locally modified hepatic cell surface
(C) stratified columnar epithelium
(D) stratified squamous epithelium
(E) a villiform surface

Questions 107-108

A somewhat obese, aged 42 mother of three children has experienced several episodes of severe pain in the upper right abdominal quadrant accompanied by pale-colored stools. Though she is not currently experiencing pain, the examiner notes that her skin and sclerae are somewhat yellow. A blood test indicates elevated bilirubin conjugated to glucuronic acid.

107. Bilirubin is produced primarily in which of the following organs?

(A) Gallbladder
(B) Kidney
(C) Pancreas
(D) Small intestine
(E) Spleen

108. Elevated bilirubin levels in the blood can result from all the following EXCEPT

(A) deficiency of an enzyme that makes bilirubin soluble
(B) hepatocellular damage
(C) increased destruction of red blood cells
(D) obstruction of the common bile duct
(E) obstruction of the cystic duct

(End of question set)

109. The structure indicated by the arrow in the accompanying photomicrograph is a branch of the

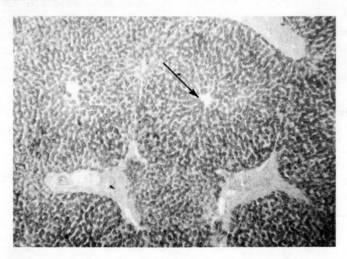

(A) hepatic artery
(B) hepatic vein
(C) portal lymph duct
(D) lobar bile duct
(E) portal vein

110. The cells of the pancreas that are responsible for the secretion of glucagon are the

(A) α cells
(B) β cells
(C) C cells
(D) δ cells
(E) G cells

111. The ciliated cells and mucus-secreting goblet cells of the respiratory airway function to remove particulate matter. Both cell types are found in which of the following structures?

(A) Alveolar duct
(B) Alveolus
(C) Respiratory bronchiole
(D) Terminal bronchiole

112. All the following are characteristic of the blood-air barrier of the lung EXCEPT

(A) it contains alveolar pores
(B) it is composed of both alveolar epithelium and capillary endothelium with a shared basal lamina
(C) it is maintained by tight junctions between contiguous endothelial cells
(D) it may thicken in pathological states
(E) it retards passage of plasma onto the alveolar surface

113. All the following are characteristic of the type II (great alveolar or septal) cells of the lung EXCEPT

(A) they are phagocytic
(B) they contain lamellar bodies
(C) they constitute less than 5 percent of the alveolar surface
(D) they contribute to the blood-air barrier
(E) they secrete surfactant

114. The renal cortex is the site of all the following subunits of the juxtamedullary nephron EXCEPT the

(A) descending limb of the loop of Henle
(B) distal convoluted tubule
(C) macula densa
(D) renal corpuscle
(E) proximal convoluted tubule

115. The cells of the nephron have distinctive structures that subserve different functions. Correct statements concerning the structure and function of the nephron include all the following EXCEPT

(A) the cells of the proximal convoluted tubule have a brush border (numerous microvilli) that provides an increased absorptive surface
(B) the cells of the visceral layer of Bowman's capsule (podocytes) act variably as a barrier to filtration
(C) the cuboidal cells of the collecting tubules are responsive to hormonal effects that determine their permeability to water
(D) the macula densa is a modification of the distal convoluted tubule
(E) the squamous cells of the descending limb of the loop of Henle are impermeable to water

116. The distal convoluted tubule of the kidney can be histologically differentiated from the proximal tubule by its

(A) cell nuclei being located further from the lumen
(B) cross section showing less densely packed cells
(C) lack of a brush border
(D) more convoluted course
(E) taller epithelium

117. The macula densa of the distal convoluted tubule is instrumental in the maintenance of hydration and blood pressure. These cells are located in a position that allows them to have direct contact with

(A) the afferent glomerular arteriole
(B) Bowman's capsule
(C) the efferent glomerular arteriole
(D) the loop of Henle
(E) the proximal convoluted tubule

118. Molecules secreted into the circulation by the renal cortex include

(A) aldosterone and antidiuretic hormone
(B) angiotensinogen and angiotensin II
(C) erythropoietin and renin
(D) glucocorticoids and mineralocorticoids
(E) none of the above

---

119. The type of epithelium shown in the accompanying photomicrograph characteristically lines all the following structures EXCEPT the

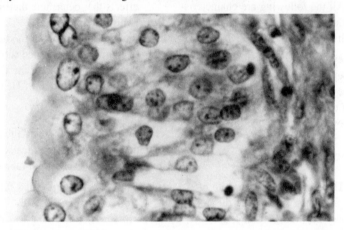

(A) medullary collecting ducts
(B) prostatic urethra
(C) renal pelvis
(D) ureters
(E) urinary bladder

120. A characteristic feature of transitional epithelium is which of the following?

(A) Impermeability to water
(B) Presence of pigment
(C) Production of lysozymes
(D) Production of mucin
(E) Rhythmic movement

121. The germinal epithelium of the seminiferous tubules is composed of a succession of different generations of cells arranged in concentric layers with the least mature form toward the periphery and the most mature toward the lumen. Which of the following are germinal cells located at the periphery?

(A) Sertoli cells
(B) Spermatids
(C) Spermatocytes
(D) Spermatogonia
(E) Spermatozoa

122. In gametogenesis, meiosis differs significantly from mitosis. All the following are characteristics of meiosis EXCEPT

(A) crossing-over occurs between sister chromatids during prophase I
(B) daughter cells enter a second M phase of the cell cycle after division I without passing through the G_1 phase and S phase
(C) independent assortment of maternal and paternal genetic material occurs in division I
(D) the result of division I is a chromosomal reduction to the haploid number
(E) there is pairing of homologous chromosomes

123. Under the influence of luteinizing hormone (LH), the production of androgenic hormones is a function of the

(A) interstitial (Leydig) cells
(B) myoepithelial cells
(C) spermatids
(D) spermatogonia
(E) sustentacular (Sertoli) cells

124. Spermiogenesis is the transformation from spermatid to spermatozoon. Which of the following is a correct statement about this maturation process?

(A) Mitochondria, which provide the energy for motility, become located in the tail piece of the spermatozoon
(B) The acrosomal cap, containing the hydrolytic enzymes necessary for fertilization, develops from rough endoplasmic reticulum
(C) The mature spermatozoa are motile and capable of fertilizing an ovum on leaving the seminiferous tubules
(D) The tail of the spermatozoon develops from one of two centrioles
(E) None of the above

125. Fructose, a source of energy for spermatozoa, is found primarily in secretions from the

(A) bulbourethral glands
(B) epididymis
(C) prostate
(D) seminal vesicles
(E) testis

126. The tissue section in the accompanying photomicrograph is taken from a structure that frequently contains concretions. The structure is which of the following?

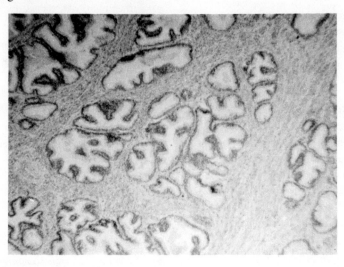

(A) Adrenal medulla
(B) Gallbladder
(C) Prostate
(D) Thyroid
(E) Uterine tube

127. Primary oocytes have developed by the time of birth. From puberty to menopause, these germ cells remain suspended in meiotic prophase. The oocyte of a mature follicle is induced to undergo the first meiotic division just prior to ovulation as a result of which of the following hormonal stimuli?

(A) The cessation of progesterone secretion
(B) The gradual elevation of follicle-stimulating hormone (FSH) titers
(C) The low estrogen titers associated with the maturing follicle
(D) The slow elevation of progesterone produced by luteal cells
(E) The surge of luteinizing hormone (LH) initiated by high estrogen titers

128. The secondary oocyte enters the second meiotic division and proceeds as far as metaphase. The stimulation for continuation of the second meiotic division to produce the haploid ovum is

(A) elevation of progesterone titers
(B) the environment of the oviduct and uterus
(C) expulsion from the mature follicle
(D) fertilization by a spermatozoon
(E) the presence of human chorionic gonadotropin (hCG)

129. The fully developed ovarian follicle, just prior to ovulation, with its multiple-cell layers, constitutes the graafian follicle. A graafian follicle consists of all the following structures EXCEPT

(A) antrum
(B) corona radiata
(C) germinal epithelium
(D) granulosa layer
(E) theca interna

130. The structure in the accompanying photomicrograph of an ovary develops from a ruptured ovarian follicle under the direct influence of

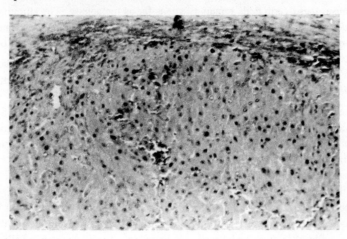

(A) estrogen
(B) FSH
(C) LH
(D) progesterone
(E) testosterone

131. The accompanying diagram shows a cross section of a developing human endometrium and myometrium. Hormonal ratios control the development of which of the labeled vessels?

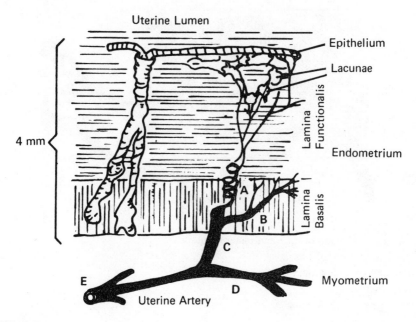

(A) A
(B) B
(C) C
(D) D
(E) E

132. The chorionic villi shown in the accompanying photomicrograph are derived from

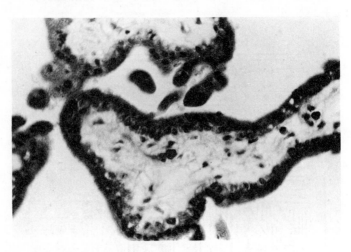

(A) a combination of fetal and maternal tissues
(B) endometrial glands
(C) endometrial stroma
(D) fetal tissues
(E) maternal blood vessels

---

133. Surgical removal of the pituitary gland (hypophysectomy) results in a *decrease* in all the following EXCEPT

(A) activity of the thyroid follicular cells
(B) growth of ovarian follicles
(C) size of the adrenal zona fasciculata cells
(D) size of the parathyroid chief cells
(E) spermatogenesis

134. The thyroid gland is of endodermal origin, but the parafollicular cells (C cells) derive from neural crest tissue. The secretory product of the parafollicular cells of the thyroid is

(A) calcitonin
(B) protease
(C) triiodothyronine
(D) thyroglobulin
(E) thyroxine

135. The gland shown in the accompanying photomicrograph produces which of the following hormones?

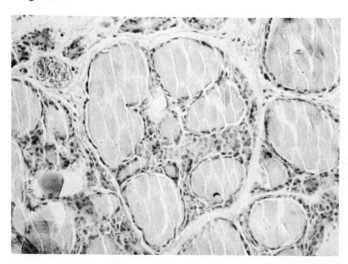

(A) Cortisone
(B) Growth hormone
(C) Parathormone
(D) Thyroxine
(E) Vasopressin

136. Regions of the retina that contain rod cells include

(A) the fovea centralis
(B) the macula lutea
(C) the optic disk
(D) the ora serrata
(E) none of the above

DIRECTIONS: Each group of questions below consists of four lettered headings followed by a set of numbered items. For each numbered item select

A	if the item is associated with	(A) **only**
B	if the item is associated with	(B) **only**
C	if the item is associated with	**both** (A) and (B)
D	if the item is associated with	**neither** (A) nor (B)

Each lettered heading may be used **once, more than once, or not at all.**

Questions 137-139

   (A) Electrical coupling
   (B) Permeability barrier
   (C) Both
   (D) Neither

137. Desmosomes

138. Gap junctions

139. Tight junctions

Questions 140-143

   (A) Actin
   (B) Keratin
   (C) Both
   (D) Neither

140. Spot desmosome (macula adherens)

141. Belt desmosome (zonula adherens)

142. Mitotic spindle

143. Microvilli

Questions 144-148

   (A) Continuous capillaries
   (B) Fenestrated capillaries
   (C) Both
   (D) Neither

144. Pancreas

145. Renal glomerulus

146. Brain

147. Liver

148. Cardiac muscle

Questions 149-154

   (A) Parietal cell
   (B) Chief cell
   (C) Both
   (D) Neither

149. Secretion of HCl

150. Found in the glands of the gastric corpus and gastric fundus

151. Located most frequently at the base of the gastric glands

152. Secretion of gastrin

153. Primarily absorptive

154. Secretion in response to vagal stimulation

DIRECTIONS: Each group of questions below consists of lettered headings followed by a set of numbered items. For each numbered item select the **one** lettered heading with which it is **most** closely associated. Each lettered heading may be used **once, more than once, or not at all.**

Questions 155-158

For each description that follows, select the lettered structure in the accompanying electron micrograph with which it is most closely associated.

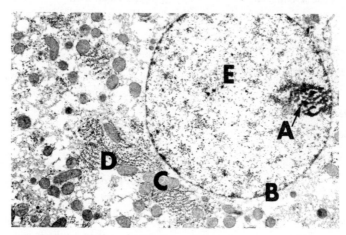

155. The most prominent site of oxidative phosphorylation

156. Site of mRNA synthesis

157. Correlation of size with cell growth and protein synthesis

158. Appearance in the microsomal fraction of a cell homogenate

Questions 159-163

For each structure below, select the principal collagen found there.

(A) Type I collagen
(B) Type II collagen
(C) Type III collagen
(D) Type IV collagen
(E) Type V collagen

159. Bone

160. Reticular fibers

161. Loose connective tissue and blood vessels

162. Hyaline cartilage

163. Basal lamina

Questions 164-167

For each description below, select the type of cell that is most appropriate.

(A) Monocyte
(B) Platelet
(C) Eosinophil
(D) Neutrophil
(E) Plasma cell

164. A cell that contains serotonin and thromboplastin

165. A cell that is highly phagocytic and has specific granules containing alkaline phosphatase and azurophil granules containing lysosomal enzymes and peroxidase

166. A cell that has granules containing both peroxidase and a large crystalloid inclusion

167. A cell that is extensively involved in protein synthesis and exocytosis

Questions 168-171

For each structure listed below, select from the diagram the labeled site that is most appropriate.

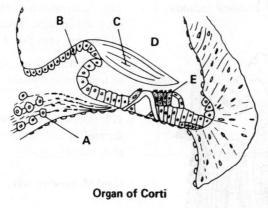

Organ of Corti

168. Tectorial membrane

169. Limbus spiralis

170. Cochlear duct

171. Spiral ganglion

Questions 172-175

Match each numbered description with the appropriate label on the diagram below of a coronal section of a human tooth.

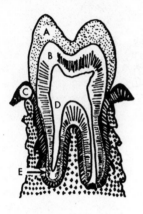

172. Has a composition similar to that of bone and is produced by cells similar in appearance to osteocytes

173. Is formed on a collagenous matrix that is resorbed upon mineralization by the same cells that secreted it

174. Contains abundant nerves, vessels, and loose connective tissue and odontoblasts

175. Consists of mineralized collagen secreted by cells derived from the neural crest

(End of question set)

Histology
Answers

51. The answer is A. *(Alberts, ed 2. p 458. Junqueira, ed 6. pp 37-38. Kelly, ed 18. pp 42-47.)* The Golgi apparatus is usually juxtanuclear and has a typical structure composed of small vesicles in close proximity to the endoplasmic reticulum, lamellar cisternae, and large vacuoles in which secretory material is concentrated. Studies have demonstrated that the Golgi complex is responsible for packaging the products of the endoplasmic reticulum and that it is perhaps also responsible for the posttranslational processing (e.g., glycosylation, sulfation, phosphorylation, amidation) of these products.

52. The answer is A. *(Cormack, ed 9. pp 76-77, 80-81. Junqueira, ed 6. pp 30-32.)* Unit membranes are composed of a phospholipid bilayer with incorporated integral proteins and attached peripheral proteins that are different on each membrane face. Arrays of integral proteins that pass completely through the membrane form fluid-filled channels through which ions may pass passively or be transported actively. Integral proteins that project from the external surface form receptors; those that project into the cytoplasm may form anchors for cytoskeletal elements. Because the membrane is a liquid-crystalline structure (fluid mosaic), the lipid components and the protein components (unless anchored internally or externally) can freely move laterally within the membrane.

53. The answer is B. *(Alberts, ed 2. pp 328-329, 461-462.)* When a cell needs cholesterol for membrane synthesis, it makes receptors for LDL and incorporates them in its plasma membrane. The LDL receptor is a single transmembrane glycoprotein. The exterior pole of the receptor has an affinity for the protein portion of LDL. The cytoplasmic pole of the LDL receptor binds to clathrin-coated pits. Atherosclerosis can result from an inability of the cytoplasmic pole of the LDL receptor to bind to submembrane clathrin. LDL receptors with bound LDL are internalized at these coated pits, forming endosomes. Transport vesicles bud from the endosomes, fuse with the plasma membrane, and thereby return LDL receptors and component membrane to the cell surface. Hundreds of 10-minute round-trips are likely to be made.

54. The answer is A. *(Alberts, ed 2. pp 436-440.)* Protein translocation across the membrane of the endoplasmic reticulum involves a signal peptide, a cytoplasmic signal-recognition particle, and a signal-recognition particle receptor in the ER membrane. The signal sequence is transcribed at the ribosome first, at the N-terminal of

61

the synthesized peptide. It bonds directly and immediately to the signal-recognition particle, which halts the peptide synthesis. When the signal-recognition particle locates a signal-recognition-particle receptor on the ER membrane, they bind. The signal sequence enters the pore in the ER membrane and the signal-recognition particle is released, allowing translation to proceed. Upon entering the ER cisterna, the signal sequence is cleaved from the peptide almost immediately to be found free within the endoplasmic reticulum as the signal peptide. The signal hypothesis is associated only with peptides destined for export.

55. The answer is A. *(Alberts, ed 2. pp 798-801.)* Unlike adhesion belts and adhesion plaques, which have arrays of transmembrane desmogleins that attach to filaments of keratin, desmin, or actin, gap junctions are instrumental in cell-cell communications. The basic unit of the gap junction is the connexon, a transmembrane protein composed of six subunits with a central canal. Connexons form liquid-crystalline lattice arrays. When those of one cell align end-to-end with those of an adjacent cell, they form intracellular channels that allow small molecules and ions to pass from cell to cell. Thus, gap junctions permit chemical and electrical coupling between cells.

56. The answer is A. *(Alberts, ed 2. pp 496, 500. Junqueira, ed 6. pp 53-57.)* The chromatin pattern is indicative of the metabolic activity of a cell. The DNA of heterochromatin is inaccessible for gene transcription. Therefore, the more heterochromatin in the nucleus, the lower the RNA/DNA ratio and the lower the rate of metabolic activity. Heterochromatin, a combination of DNA and histone as well as other structural proteins, stains intensely with basic dyes such as methylene blue or hematoxylin. A nucleus with considerable heterochromatin will have a high histone/DNA ratio. Euchromatin, a dispersed form of chromatin, is only slightly basophilic and is metabolically active in the formation of RNA used in cytoplasmic protein synthesis.

57. The answer is D. *(Alberts, ed 2. pp 654-656. Junqueira, ed 6. pp 45-48. Kelly, ed 18. pp 54-56.)* The centrosome is formed by a pair of self-replicating centrioles, called a diplosome. The centrosome (cytocentrum or centrosphere) usually is located at a nuclear pole near the Golgi complex. Each centriole is composed of nine parallel subunits, each consisting of three fused microtubules. In preparation for cytokinesis, each centriole replicates and the new diplosomes move to opposite poles of the nucleus, where they establish the centrospheres of the daughter cells. At this point, a microtubular aster or pericentriolar satellite develops. Only the axonemes of cilia and flagella contain two central tubules.

58. The answer is C. *(Alberts, ed 2. pp 728-730. Junqueira, ed 6. pp 60-62. Kelly, ed 18. pp 88-89.)* DNA synthesis occurs during the S phase of the cell cycle, and the DNA content goes from 2n to 4n as the genes replicate. If ^{3}H-thymidine is present at this time, it will be incorporated into the replica gene, but not into the template gene. Even though most of the population may be cycling, only those cells that were in the S phase at the time of the pulse are labeled. Inasmuch as the S phase is 6 hours and the G_2 phase is 4 hours, some of the cells that were labeled by incubation with ^{3}H-thymidine for 2 hours and then chased for 1 hour would still be in the S phase when fixed, while others would have passed into the G_2 phase when fixed. Within the short chase period, labeled cells would not have reached the M phase and divided into daughter cells with a 2n chromosome number.

59. The answer is B. *(Alberts, ed 2. pp 730-731. Junqueira, ed 6. pp 60-62. Kelly, ed 18. pp 88-89.)* During a 10-hour chase subsequent to a 2-hour ^{3}H-thymidine pulse, nearly all the labeled cells would have passed through the S, G_2, and M phases and would be in the G_1 phase. Because the cells had divided, there would be exactly twice the number of cells with labeled nuclei as there were before the M phase. Each daughter cell would have a 2n chromosome number, and only one strand of DNA in each gene would be labeled. During the 10-hour chase period, other cells would have entered the S, G_2, and M phases, but would not be labeled since the thymidine in the chase medium was not radioactive. The nucleolus produces ribosomal RNA that uses uracil, not thymidine, and would not be selectively labeled in this experiment.

60. The answer is A. *(Alberts, ed 2. pp 730-731. Junqueira, ed 6. pp 60-62. Kelly, ed 18. pp 88-89.)* Uracil is a nucleotide specific for RNA. Because RNA synthesis is relatively rapid, the label will be found within the nucleus if the cells are fixed within a few minutes of the pulse of ^{3}H-uracil, distributed equally between the nucleus and cytoplasm if fixed at 30 minutes after the pulse, and entirely within the cytoplasm if fixed after 1 hour following the pulse. RNA usually is transcribed in cells that have left the cell cycle. They have passed from the G_1 phase to the G_0 phase and will not undergo simultaneous DNA synthesis. Although colchicine arrests cell division in the metaphase of the M phase, it seems to have no effect on RNA synthesis.

61. The answer is E. *(Junqueira, ed 6. pp 446, 499. Kelly, ed 18. pp 135, 742-743, 751.)* Cilia are motile processes with a complex internal structure. An epithelial cell may have a single cilium or many hundred cilia. They are resolvable with light microscopy, as seen in the photomicrograph of endocervical epithelium that accompanies the question. In living cells, cilia beat in synchronous waves so that directionality is produced. Their principal function is to propel fluid or mucous films over the surface of the epithelium. Consequently, many structures, such as the respiratory tree above the respiratory bronchiole, the uterine tubes, and the endocervical canal, are ciliated. The convoluted tubules of the nephron and the duodenal mucosa have brush borders formed by microvilli.

62. The answer is C. *(Alberts, ed 2. pp 818-821. Junqueira, ed 6. p 66. Kelly, ed 18. pp 138, 161, 179.)* Between the epithelium and underlying connective tissue is an extracellular supporting layer that is called the *basal lamina*. Every epithelial layer, with the possible exception of the ependymal cells, has an associated basal lamina. Electron microscopy reveals two components to the basal lamina—an amorphous matrix immediately beneath the epithelial cells and a fine network of collagen fibrils. The carbohydrate component is responsible for the periodic acid-Schiff (PAS) staining reaction, whereas the collagen fibrils are argyrophilic and responsible for the silver impregnation. The carbohydrate matrix, composed of glycosaminoglycans, is secreted by the epithelial cells; the collagen fibrils (reticular fibers) are secreted by the subjacent fibroblasts. The collagen of the basal lamina has a high hydroxylysine and hydroxyproline content and does not form bundles.

63. The answer is B. *(Alberts, ed 2. pp 808-811. Junqueira, ed 6. pp 96-98. Kelly, ed 18. pp 173-174.)* Collagen molecules contain glycine, proline, hydroxyproline, lysine, and hydroxylysine, among other amino acids; however, fibroblasts active in the synthesis of collagen take up only the unhydroxylated forms of proline and lysine. Subsequently, some of the proline and lysine may be hydroxylated in the Golgi complex prior to incorporation into collagen molecules. The utilization of proline and lysine, as well as their hydroxylated forms, is unique among proteins, and this results in a characteristic structure. The cyclic structure of proline and hydroxyproline prevents formation of the usual right-handed α helix. However, a left-handed helix is formed with three residues per turn, - (amino acid) - (proline or lysine) - (glycine) -. Three left-handed helices twist together to form a right-handed superhelix, tropocollagen. In the process of superhelix formation, the small glycine molecules are internalized and the side chains of the other amino acids project outward. The resultant close approximation of the individual strands enables stabilization by hydrogen bonds while the projecting side chains provide a high surface charge. As a result, the stiff and strong tropocollagen molecules will form liquid-crystalline fibrils. Desmosine is a characteristic protein of elastin, which composes the elastic fibers.

64. The answer is B. *(Alberts, ed 2. pp 810-812. Junqueira, ed 6. pp 97-100. Kelly, ed 18. pp 173-175.)* Fibroblasts, chondroblasts, and osteoblasts synthesize and secrete tropocollagen. Each tropocollagen molecule is a triple helix of polypeptide chains, which, depending on the tissue, may or may not be identical. The tropocollagen molecule is secreted as a unit of 300 nm × 1.5 nm. Under the appropriate conditions, these undergo side-to-side aggregation with a 64-nm offset to form liquid-crystalline collagen fibrils, which, in turn, form the collagen fiber. The 64-nm offset gives the collagen fiber the characteristic banded pattern observed with electron microscopy. The induction of hydroxyapatite crystal growth is associated with specific sites between the tropocollagen molecules within the collagen fibrils.

65. The answer is E. *(Junqueira, ed 6. pp 107-110, 112-113. Kelly, ed 18. pp 170, 249.)* Basophils (basophilic granulocytes) and mast cells (tissue basophils) contain and release heparin and histamine. It appears that basophilic granulocytes in the blood may be the precursors to the tissue mast cells. Eosinophils produce histaminase, among other enzymes. One function of these cells may be the modulation of basophils and mast cells. Lymphocytes and plasma cells produce antibodies. Neutrophilic cells contain several populations of granules, about one-third of which are azurophilic (primarily phagosomes and lysosomes).

66. The answer is D. *(Alberts, ed 2. pp 1004-1005. Junqueira, ed 6. pp 110-112, 261. Kelly, ed 18. pp 167-168, 441.)* The cells illustrated in the photomicrograph accompanying the question are plasma cells. These cells are the end stage of differentiation of B lymphocytes. Plasma cells are characterized by eccentric nuclei with coarse granules of heterochromatin arranged in a radial pattern about the nuclear envelope. Membrane-bound ribosomes are extremely plentiful, providing the cytoplasm with a characteristic intense basophilia. This rough endoplasmic reticulum is involved in antibody production, principally immunoglobulin G (IgG). The juxtanuclear region, which does not stain, represents the Golgi complex, in which the antibodies are processed for secretion.

67. The answer is C. *(Junqueira, ed 6. pp 121-124.)* Nutritional and other influences during a finite postnatal period determine the number of fat cells that develop from mesenchymally derived lipoblasts. After this period, adipocytes do not increase in number. Thus, while the size of fat cells varies as a function of caloric intake, the number of fat cells is determined in early childhood and does not change. Brown fat is sympathetically innervated. In both brown and white fat, norepinephrine stimulates hydrolysis of triglycerides to fatty acids with the generation of heat. Insulin, among a number of other hormones, influences triglyceride metabolism.

68. The answer is E. *(Junqueira, ed 6. pp 143-144. Kelly, ed 18. p 203.)* The two forms of bone distinguishable under low magnification are compact bone and trabecular, or cancellous, bone. Trabecular bone, as shown in the photomicrograph accompanying the question, consists of a three-dimensional lattice of branching spicules or trabeculae lining a system of intercommunicating spaces filled with bone marrow. In the long bones the shaft consists of a thick-walled, hollow cylinder of compact bone; trabecular bone occurs in the marrow cavity, the metaphyses, and the epiphyses. In flat bones the inner and outer plates are composed of compact bone; the central region, the diploe, is trabecular bone.

69. The answer is D. *(Alberts, ed 2. pp 991-993. Junqueira, ed 6. pp 139-141, 419. Kelly, ed 18. pp 214-215.)* Osteoblastic activity and osteoclastic activity, as well as the body's need for calcium, are factors in bone remodeling. Osteoclasts are giant multinucleated cells that derive from the monocytic line. They are stimulated by parathyroid hormone and inhibited by calcitonin. The osteoclast surface membrane adjacent to bone proliferates greatly, forming a ruffled border that subserves its function. Osteoclasts dissolve bone by secreting lysosomal enzymes, collagenase, and H^+, producing shallow concavities (Howship's lacunae) in the surface of the bone. While osteoclasts phagocytose the bony debris of their activity, there is no evidence that they phagocytose foreign bodies as a part of the general defense system.

70. The answer is A. *(Junqueira, ed 6. pp 136, 139. Kelly, ed 18. p 206.)* A transverse system of perforating (Volkmann's) canals brings blood vessels from the endosteum and periosteum into the matrix of compact bone. The vessels of Volkmann's canals branch to form the capillaries found within the central canals of the haversian systems. Osteocytes communicate with the central canal and with each other by cytoplasmic processes within canaliculi. The osteocyte processes are joined by gap junctions that allow exchange of small molecules; larger molecules seem to diffuse along the canaliculi.

71. The answer is A. *(Alberts, ed 2. pp 614-616, 620. Junqueira, ed 6. pp 196-201, 242-244, 247-253. Kelly, ed 18. p 286.)* The photomicrograph accompanying the question is of skeletal muscle. The skeletal muscle fiber is long, cylindrical, and multinucleated, with a limiting membrane called the sarcolemma. It contains a large number of parallel, cross-striated myofibrils. The dark-staining cross striations, the A bands, are liquid crystalline and anisotropic in polarized light. Each skeletal muscle fiber is innervated at one or more neuromuscular junctions by a branch of a motor nerve. In cardiac and smooth muscle, both of which have centrally located nuclei, the motor nerves innervate a small percentage of the muscle cells. The impulse spreads through these tissues via nexuses or gap junctions. Some cardiac cells, the Purkinje fibers, are so highly modified for the conduction of the impulse that they contain far fewer contractile proteins. Cardiac muscle also is striated but can be distinguished from skeletal muscle by the presence of intercalated disks (desmosomes) between longitudinally adjacent cells.

72. The answer is B. *(Alberts, ed 2. pp 614-618. Junqueira, ed 6. pp 196-201. Kelly, ed 18. pp 267-274.)* The myosin molecule, being composed of two similar polypeptides with tails intertwined in an α helix and two projecting globular heads, is similar in structure to an antibody. The actin filament possesses a helix of two chains composed of globular actin monomers with the additional proteins tropomyosin and troponin. The liquid-crystalline array of the myosin filaments provides the anisotropy that gives the A band its name. The array of actin filaments is less ordered and nearly isotropic in polarized light, which gives the I band its name. Myosin heads (cross bridges) bind to actin in the presence of calcium and when activated by ATP. Upon binding, they undergo a conformational change, which constitutes the power stroke for contraction, and in the process release ADP. This process will recycle as long as both ATP and calcium are present.

73. The answer is C. *(Junqueira, ed 6. pp 196-201.)* When a muscle fiber is fully stretched in situ, the sarcomere length is approximately 2.25 μm and the actin filaments precisely contact the maximum number of cross bridges without entering the 0.20-μm wide bridge-free zone in the center of the sarcomere. With sarcomere shortening from 2.25 μm to 2.05 μm, the thin filaments meet in the center of the A band, obliterating the H zone. However, the number of cross bridges is unchanged, and the active force produced remains maximal over this range of shortening. Since the muscle shortens in a constant-volume manner, a decrease in sarcomere length is accompanied by an increase in sarcomere diameter.

74. The answer is D. *(Alberts, ed 2. p 621. Junqueira, ed 6. pp 200-202. Kelly, ed 18. pp 276, 283-284.)* Adenosine triphosphate (ATP) provides a direct source of energy for the conformational change within the heavy meromyosin portion of the actomyosin cross bridge that results in the generation of tension and a simultaneous release of the cross linkage. ATP also provides the energy for initial activation of the heavy meromyosin. Inasmuch as levels of ATP usually are high within the cell, activation of the contractile system is accomplished by controlling the free calcium levels. Finally, ATP provides energy needed for the sequestration of calcium by the sarcoplasmic reticulum so that contraction will cease. Depolarization of the surface membrane spreads inward along the T tubules and triggers release of calcium from the sarcoplasmic reticulum.

75. The answer is A. *(Junqueira, ed 6. pp 206-210. Kelly, ed 18. pp 288-296.)* Skeletal and cardiac muscle have identical patterns of cross striations of myofibrils including A, I, M, H, and Z bands on the muscle bundles. All the other characteristics mentioned in the question, however, help to distinguish cardiac from skeletal fibers. Cardiac muscle nuclei are situated deep in the sarcolemma; the fibers are not cylindrical units, but bifurcate, connecting with adjacent fibers to form a complex, three-dimensional network.

76. The answer is C. *(Junqueira, ed 6. pp 206-210. Kelly, ed 18. pp 288-293.)* The striated muscle cells shown in the photomicrograph accompanying the question were obtained from the left atrium of the heart. Cardiac muscle cells demonstrate cellular branching, cross striations, and centrally placed nuclei. Intercalated disks, representing cell boundaries, frequently are evident. Skeletal muscle fibers, such as are found in the diaphragm or tongue, do not branch, and the innumerable nuclei are located just beneath the sarcolemma. Smooth muscle cells, such as are found in the uterus, contain centrally placed fusiform nuclei but no cross striations.

77. The answer is B. *(Cormack, ed 9. pp 394, 400-401, 412, 416-417. Junqueira, ed 6. pp 195-197, 200-203, 210-212.)* In all types of muscle, interaction between actin and myosin is controlled by regulation of the intracellular calcium concentration. Electrical activation of the cell membrane results in release of calcium from sarcoplasmic (endoplasmic) reticulum, which binds to a regulatory protein on the actin filaments to produce a structural change that exposes myosin-binding sites. ATP-mediated uptake of calcium by the sarcoplasmic reticulum reduces the calcium concentration and results in relaxation. Smooth and cardiac muscle have gap junctions for the spread of membrane depolarization between fibers; each skeletal muscle fiber is separately innervated, sometimes more than once. Skeletal and cardiac muscle have profuse systems of T-tubules that convey the surface depolarization deep into the muscle fibers for rapid activation; smooth muscle has no T-tubules and activation is much slower. Intercalated disks are desmosomes (zonula adherens) between the ends of cardiac muscle cells that serve as anchoring points for Z-lines and prevent the cells from pulling apart during contraction; in smooth muscle actin filaments insert into these dense bodies on the inner surface of the cell membrane. Finally, below the head skeletal muscle is innervated by large somatic motor neurons from the anterior horn of the spinal cord; smooth muscle is innervated by two autonomic neurons sequentially located in the lateral horn of the spinal cord and in an intervening ganglion.

78. The answer is A. *(Alberts, ed 2. pp 1062-1064. Kelly, ed 18. p 322.)* Because endoplasmic reticulum and ribosomes are not present in the axon, proteins necessary for the maintenance of the axon and axon terminal must be transported along the axon from the soma. Soluble proteins in the cytoplasmic matrix and microtubules are transported at the slow rate of 1 to 3 mm per day. Mitochondria, vesicle-bound neurotransmitters, and insoluble proteins are transported at a fast rate of 100 to 400 mm per day. The insoluble proteins, synthesized by ribosomes attached to rough endoplasmic reticulum, are thought to be involved in membrane renewal and synthesis of synaptic vesicles. Fast axonal transport occurs in both anterograde and retrograde directions. Colchicine, which interrupts microtubule formation, blocks fast axonal transport only.

79. The answer is A. *(Junqueira, ed 6. pp 164, 173. Kelly, ed 18. pp 319-322.)* Dendrites do not have myelin sheaths. Dendritic surfaces frequently are covered with spines or gemmules that increase the surface area for synaptic contact. Axons are longer, thinner, and have more regularly shaped cross-sectional profiles than dendrites; do not contain Nissl bodies (sites of protein synthesis); and branch at more nearly right angles. The diameter of an axon, unlike that of a dendrite, does not change when branches occur. The presence along the axons of myelin sheaths, derived from oligodendroglia, gives the characteristic color to the white matter of the central nervous system. Peripheral nerve fibers are surrounded by a cellular covering of Schwann's cells, known as Schwann's sheath or neurilemma, which may or may not form myelin.

80. The answer is D. *(Kelly, ed 18. pp 312, 320, 383-384.)* Large, multipolar neurons in the cerebral cortex are pyramidal cells. Forming the stroma of the brain, the neuroglial cells, which are small, are located along the dendrites and soma of the neurons. Basket cells, Purkinje cells, and granule cells are located in the cerebellar cortex. The basket cells make profuse dendritic contact with the Purkinje cells, which have a very characteristic flask shape. The granule cells are small neurons located in the vicinity of the Purkinje cells.

81. The answer is A. *(Kelly, ed 18. pp 319-322.)* An axon is not evident in the histologic section accompanying the question. The axon arises from the axon hillock. Neither the axon nor axon hillock contains the Nissl substance (rough endoplasmic reticulum), which is dispersed throughout the soma and dendrites. Dendrites generally are wider than axons, are of nonuniform diameter, and taper to a point. Motor neurons, such as the one illustrated, usually display large amounts of euchromatin and a distinct nucleolus characteristic of high synthetic activity.

82. The answer is A. *(Junqueira, ed 6. pp 187-188. Kelly, ed 18. pp 355-356.)* The presence of large multipolar neurons with eccentrically placed nuclei and coarse granular Nissl bodies characterizes a neuron as autonomic rather than sensory. The autonomic nervous system mediates activity by two motor neurons placed in series: the first lies either in a nucleus of the brain stem or in the spinal gray matter; the second is located in a ganglion. The autonomic ganglia contain motor nerve cell bodies that convey impulses originating in the brain and spinal cord to smooth muscle and glands by way of the splanchnic nerves.

83. The answer is E. *(Cormack, ed 9. pp 361-364. Junqueira, ed 6. pp 168-171, 190-191.)* *Oligodendroglia* are analogous to the Schwann's cells of the peripheral nervous system in that they form the myelin sheaths of the axons of the central nervous system. However, unlike Schwann's cells, each oligodendrocyte participates in the myelination of multiple axons. *Astroglia* (especially protoplasmic astrocytes) have numerous processes with expanded pedicles that continuously ensheath the capillaries of the brain and abut the pial layer in a continuous layer. As such, the astrocytes contribute to the blood-brain barrier, which prevents diffusion of plasmaborne substances into the brain tissue. *Microglia* are components of the mononuclear phagocytic system. The meninges are composed of connective tissue elements.

84. The answer is C. *(Junqueira, ed 6. p 190. Kelly, ed 18. p 377.)* Cerebrospinal fluid formed in the choroid plexus circulates in the subarachnoid space and is absorbed by the venous sinuses through the arachnoid villi, some of which project into the superior sagittal sinus. Cerebrospinal fluid protects the nervous system from concussions and mechanical injuries and is important for metabolism. It circulates slowly through the ventricles of the brain and through the meshes of the subarachnoid space.

85. The answer is B. *(Alberts, ed 2. p 289. Junqueira, ed 6. pp 230-233, 248.)* Fibrous molecules of spectrin compose a component of the erythrocyte cytoskeleton and form a meshwork on the cytoplasmic side of the plasma membrane. Osmotic factors as well as interaction of spectrin with actin and other cytoskeletal proteins maintain the biconcave shape of red blood cells, which permits the flexibility necessary for passage through narrow capillaries. The biconcave shape also provides a large surface-to-volume ratio, which facilitates rapid gaseous diffusion with the shortest diffusion pathway. Polychromatophilic erythroblasts are spherical, nucleated, and still capable of mitosis.

86. The answer is A. *(Kelly, ed 18. pp 240-242.)* Lymphocytes that are the equivalent of the bursa-dependent B lymphocytes of the chicken can be identified by the presence of immunoglobulin on their surface membranes. These are the cells that ultimately differentiate into antibody-secreting plasma cells under the appropriate conditions. T lymphocytes, on the other hand, do not have readily detectable cell membrane immunoglobulin.

87. The answer is E. *(Alberts, ed 2. pp 1002-1005. Junqueira, ed 6. pp 255-256, 260-262.)* Lymphocytes originate from pluripotential liver precursor cells late in the fetal period. The precursor cells slowly proliferate postnatally, some seeding the thymus, spleen, tonsils, lymph nodes, and bone marrow. The site of lymphocyte differentiation, rather than the precursor cell, determines the specific immunological characteristics of B cells and T cells. Those lymphocytes maturing in the thymus (T cells) acquire the attributes of synthesizing surface antigens and function in cell-mediated immunity (helper, suppressor, and killer T cells). T cells do not differentiate further and may live for several years as the repository for immunological "memory." B cells mature in bone marrow, are rather short-lived, and constitute less than 20 percent of the circulating lymphocytes. Appropriate stimulus causes B cells to differentiate into plasma cells that secrete the immunoglobulins that are the basis for humoral immunity.

88. The answer is D. *(Junqueira, ed 6. pp 262-265. Kelly, ed 18. pp 453-456.)* The thymus can be readily recognized histologically by the presence of Hassall's corpuscles, which consist of a concentric array of squamous cells joined by many desmosomes containing keratohyaline granules. The thymus is the first organ to become lymphoid during embryonic life, being seeded by blood-borne stem cells from the yolk sac that then differentiate into lymphocytes within the special environment of the thymus. The thymus is divided into lobules by connective tissue septa. The cortex of the thymus is a dense mass of thymocytes and epithelial tissue, in which no sinuses or germinal centers are present. Epithelial cells are more numerous in the medulla than in the cortex.

89. The answer is A. *(Junqueira, ed 6. pp 221-222. Kelly, ed 18. pp 403-405.)* The aorta can be recognized by the presence of large numbers of elastic fibers within the vascular media. The tunica media of the human aorta contains approximately 50 concentric, fenestrated, elastic laminae interspersed with thin layers of connective tissue, fibroblasts, and smooth muscle cells. Large veins have a poorly developed tunica media.

90. The answer is C. *(Junqueira, ed 6. pp 224-225. Kelly, ed 18. p 407.)* Large veins are characterized by a thick, muscular adventitia and occasional valves. The circular muscle fibers in the tunica media are irregularly arranged and reduced in amount. The adventitia of the vein is its thickest coat and contains longitudinal muscle fibers, which strengthen the wall and prevent dilation. In arteries, the adventitia is less important than the media and contains very few muscle fibers. However, only large arteries have a very prominent internal elastic membrane. As in all vessels, vasa vasorum are present.

91. The answer is E. *(Junqueira, ed 6. pp 262-265.)* The thymus can be readily recognized histologically by the presence of Hassall's corpuscles, which consist of concentric arrays of squamous cells among the lymphocytes of the medulla. The thymus is the first organ to become lymphoid during embryonic life; it is seeded by blood-borne stem cells from the yolk sac that then differentiate into T lymphocytes within the special environment of the thymus. The thymus is enclosed in a connective tissue capsule, which gives rise to septa that divide the gland into lobules. The cortex of the thymus is a dense mass of thymocytes and epithelial tissue, in which no sinuses or germinal centers are present. The lymphocytes of the medulla are less tightly packed. The thymus does not have afferent lymphatic vessels. The prostate secretes acid phosphatase, citrate, and amylase; the thyroid parafollicular cells secrete calcitonin; the pancreatic A cells secrete glucagon; the pineal gland produces melatonin and serotonin.

92. The answer is A. *(Junqueira, ed 6. pp 306-309, 313-316. Kelly, ed 18. pp 439-445, 453-456.)* The thymus is divided into cortex and medulla and is composed primarily of epithelial cells and thymocytes. The cortex and medulla of a lymph node contain sinuses that are not present in the thymus. Therefore, the thymus does not act as a filter as does the lymph node. The thymus produces T cells in the cortical zone and those cells are associated with cell-mediated immunity. Germinal centers in the lymph nodes produce B lymphocytes. These B lymphocytes may mature into plasma cells that produce antibodies or into memory B lymphocytes, which will become plasma cells when they encounter the appropriate specific antigen.

93. The answer is C. *(Cormack, ed 9. pp 244, 367-368, 667-668, 688. Junqueira, ed 6. pp 191, 219-220, 265, 277-278, 428.)* Blood-tissue barriers are characteristically found in the retina, brain, thymus, and testis. They result primarily from continuous tight junctions between contiguous cells, thereby preventing diffusion of high-molecular-weight substances through intercellular spaces. In the brain and eye, continuous tight junctions between the endothelial cells of nonfenestrated capillaries as well as expansions of neuroglial cells against the capillaries contribute to the blood-brain barrier. In the thymus, continuous tight junctions between contiguous endothelial cells as well as ensheathment of capillaries by epithelial reticular cells contribute to the blood-thymus barrier, which prevents antigenic proteins from coming into contact with developing T cells. In the testis, continuous tight junctions between the Sertoli cells form the blood-testis barrier, which protects maturing spermatids from blood-borne materials. Current evidence indicates that blood flows freely through the sinusoids of the spleen.

94. The answer is E. *(Junqueira, ed 6. pp 273-274, 277. Kelly, ed 18. pp 467-468.)* The photomicrograph accompanying the question demonstrates a germinal center in the white pulp of the spleen. The germinal center is composed of lymphocytes and lymphoblasts and is surrounded by a cortical area of densely packed lymphocytes. The surrounding red pulp contains predominantly erythrocytes in tortuous splenic sinuses.

95. The answer is E. *(Junqueira, ed 6. pp 278-280. Kelly, ed 18. pp 468-469.)* In the spleen, the free macrophages of the red pulp ingest worn-out erythrocytes. Subsequently, iron is released from the hemoglobin molecules, bound to transferrin, and transported to bone marrow. Heme is metabolized to bilirubin, which is excreted by the liver. Another established function of the spleen is antibody production against blood-borne antigens. The spleen also serves as a reservoir for blood.

96. The answer is C. *(Junqueira, ed 6. pp 354-358. Kelly, ed 18. pp 480-481.)* The stratum germinativum is a single layer of modified columnar cells forming the boundary between the epidermis and dermis. The cells of the stratum spinosum, just superficial to the stratum germinativum, have extensive desmosomal interconnections with associated nets of tonofibrils. In addition, these cells produce membrane-coating granules that, when secreted into the intercellular space, provide a watertight seal and increase cohesiveness. It is in these two layers that mitoses occur. Above the stratum spinosum are three to five layers of spindle-shaped cells, the stratum granulosum, which contain basophilic keratohyalin granules. As these granules increase in number and the cells become further removed from the nutrient supply, they become the stratum lucidum, which is composed of several rows of flattened nonnucleated cells. Seventy-five percent of the thickness of the epidermis consists of the outermost stratum corneum, composed of cornified, nonnucleated cells.

97. The answer is B. *(Junqueira, ed 6. pp 358-360. Kelly, ed 18. p 477.)* The number of melanocytes is approximately the same in all human races. Differences in skin color are primarily due to the vascularity and the amount of pigment transferred to keratinocytes. Because the transfer of melanin from the long cytoplasmic processes to keratinocytes (cytocrine secretion) is highly efficient, the melanocytes may contain less pigment than the adjacent cells. The melanocytes, derived from the neural crest of the embryo, are located in the basal layer of the stratum germinativum and in the underlying connective tissue of the dermis.

98. The answer is B. *(Junqueira, ed 6. pp 290, 297-298, 306, 354, 450-451, 458.)* The histologic section in the photomicrograph accompanying the question shows two distinctly different types of epithelium. The esophageal mucosa on the left is nonkeratinized, stratified squamous epithelium overlying a fibrovascular submucosa and smooth muscle. The gastric mucosa on the right is simple columnar epithelium with simple glands, overlying submucosa and smooth muscle. Skin is keratinized. Both the stomach and duodenum are simple columnar epithelium. The simple columnar epithelium of the distal-most rectum contains only mucous cells. The cervical mucosa contains extensive cervical glands and the vaginal epithelium is keratinized.

99. The answer is D. *(Junqueira, ed 6. pp 290-295. Kelly, ed 18. pp 535-540.)* Characteristic cell types that occur in the superficial section of gastric fundal mucosa (shown in the photomicrograph accompanying the question) consist of parietal cells, mucous neck cells, and chief cells. The parietal (oxyntic) cells are acid-producing and lie principally in the neck region of the gastric glands. The chief (peptic) cells line the lower portions of the gastric glands and are most numerous toward the cardia; they produce pepsinogen and contain considerable amounts of basophilic, rough endoplasmic reticulum and the numerous mitochondria characteristic of a secretory cell. The mucous neck cells are few in number but contain larger mucous droplets than the cells lining the surface mucosa of the stomach. Enteroendocrine (APUD) cells are identifiable by their basal location and affinity for silver stains. The granules of the argentaffin cells contain serotonin, a vasoconstrictor that stimulates smooth muscle contraction. Gastrin cells (G cells) are found primarily in the pyloric region and control parietal cell activity. Paneth's cells appear in the small bowel.

100. The answer is A. *(Junqueira, ed 6. p 300. Kelly, ed 18. p 542.)* The presence of Brunner's glands in the submucosal layer of the intestine is an identifying feature of the duodenum. Parietal cells are unique to the stomach (with the exception of Meckel's diverticulum), whereas Peyer's patches of lymphoid tissue are most characteristic of the ileum. Chief cells and serous cells are found in numerous locations throughout the alimentary tract.

101. The answer is D. *(Junqueira, ed 6. pp 297-302. Kelly, ed 18. p 542.)* The duodenum contains short tubular glands—intestinal crypts (of Lieberkühn)—which open into the intervillous spaces. The duodenal glands (of Brunner) are compound-tubular glands that are located in the submucosa and enter the duodenal lumen through ducts that tend to open between the intestinal crypts. Brunner's glands secrete mucus. Plicae circularis, absent in the first portion of the duodenum and giving the interior of the duodenal cap a smooth appearance in an x-ray, become progressively taller in the jejunum and then much less prominent in the ileum. The duodenal villi are tall and leaf-shaped, but become progressively shorter and more club-shaped towards the ileocecal valve. Peyer's patches are much more numerous in the ileum. The number of goblet cells in the mucosa increases progressively from the duodenum to the ileocecal valve.

102. The answer is C. *(Junqueira, ed 6. pp 282, 304. Kelly, ed 18. pp 355-356, 528.)* The myenteric (Auerbach's) plexus is the location of the postsynaptic para-sympathetic neurons innervating the gut from the esophagus to the rectum. These plexuses are located between the circular and longitudinal layers of the muscularis externa and are surrounded by satellite cells, which form a blood-plexus barrier. The myenteric plexuses also contain enteric neurons that control the intrinsic motility of the gastrointestinal tract. The submucosal (Meissner's) plexuses innervate the mucosal and submucosal glands of the gastrointestinal tract. The sympathetic cell bodies are located in the paravertebral and prevertebral ganglia.

103. The answer is D. *(Junqueira, ed 6. p 300. Kelly, ed 18. pp 553-556.)* Paneth's cells are found throughout the small intestine located at the base of the crypts of Lieberkühn, are somewhat larger than the surrounding cells, and are eos-inophilic. They secrete enzymes within zymogenic granules, which plays a role in controlling intestinal bacterial populations. It appears that the abundance of these cells may be related to the nutritional status of the patient.

104. The answer is C. *(Junqueira, ed 6. pp 317-321. Kelly, ed 18. pp 590-592.)* The photomicrograph accompanying the question shows normal histologic features of human liver with a portal triad surrounded by radiating plates of hepatocytes. At points where three or more lobules join, there is usually an area of more dense connective tissue together with a bile duct (and its columnar epithelium) and one or more branches of the portal vein and of the hepatic artery. These structures form the portal triad.

105. The answer is C. *(Junqueira, ed 6. pp 229, 328.)* The γ-globulin fraction of plasma proteins is manufactured principally in the reticuloendothelial system by the plasma cells. Albumin and proteins of the clotting process, e.g., fibrinogen and prothrombin, are synthesized in the liver by hepatocytes. These blood proteins are important in maintaining proper fluid osmotic pressure. They also can serve as an emergency source of nutrition during starvation and serve as blood carriers of copper, calcium, lipids, and hormones.

106. The answer is B. *(Junqueira, ed 6. pp 324-325. Kelly, ed 18. pp 598-601.)* The bile canaliculi are dilated intercellular spaces between the hepatocytes in the hepatic plates. The presence of a junctional complex between the canalicular space and the remaining intercellular space modifies the cell surface for the transport of bile. At the periphery of the hepatic lobule, the canaliculi become small ductules (of Hering), which drain into the interlobular bile ducts.

107-108. The answers are: 107-E, 108-E. *(Cormack, ed 9. pp 255-256, 535. Junqueira, ed 6. pp 328-330.)* Bilirubin, a product of iron-free heme, is liberated during the destruction of old erythrocytes by the mononuclear macrophages of the spleen and, to a lesser extent, of the liver and bone marrow. The hepatic portal system brings splenic bilirubin to the liver, where it is made soluble for excretion by conjugation with glucuronic acid. Commonly, initial low levels of glucuronyl transferase in the under-developed smooth endoplasmic reticulum of hepatocytes in the newborn result in jaundice (neonatal hyperbilirubinemia); less commonly, this enzyme is genetically lacking. The ability of mature hepatocytes to take up and conjugate bilirubin may be exceeded by abnormal increases in erythrocyte destruction (hemolytic jaundice) or by hepatocellular damage (functional jaundice), such as in hepatitis. Finally, obstruction of the duct system between the liver and duodenum (usually of the common bile duct in the adult and rarely from aplasia of the duct system in infants) results in a back-up of bilirubin (obstructive jaundice). However, obstruction of the cystic duct, while painful, will not interfere with the flow of bile from the liver to the duodenum.

109. The answer is B. *(Junqueira, ed 6. pp 320-321. Kelly, ed 18. p 593.)* The photomicrograph accompanying the question shows one complete liver lobule and portions of several others. The central vein, indicated by the arrow, is a branch of a hepatic vein. It is surrounded by sheets of hepatocytes separated by sinusoids. The irregular areas at the periphery of the lobule are the portal areas (triads), which contain branches of the hepatic portal vein, the hepatic artery, and the bile ducts. The blood flow through the liver is from the portal area, through the hepatic sinusoids, to the central vein.

110. The answer is A. *(Junqueira, ed 6. pp 315-316, 409-410. Kelly, ed 18. p 589.)* Glucagon is the secretory product of the α cells of the endocrine pancreas. The β cells are responsible for the secretion of insulin. The α cells are less populous than β cells and generally are located about the periphery of the islet. δ Cells usually are found within α-cell clusters and may represent a modified type of α cell. Pancreatic C cells, found in the pancreatic islets of guinea pigs, are without organelles or granules and have been called both precursor cells and degenerative cells by various authors. Gastrin (G) cells, located among the mucous cells of the pylorus, promote the secretion of acid in the stomach by releasing gastrin.

111. The answer is D. *(Junqueira, ed 6. pp 342-346. Kelly, ed 18. pp 634-635.)* Ciliated cells and goblet cells function to remove inspired particulate matter from the respiratory airway. The mucus-secreting goblet cells are found as far as the terminal bronchiole. The ciliated cells extend farther into the respiratory bronchiole. It is significant that the cilia extend farther down the airways than do the mucous cells so that all mucus may be removed and not block the airway. The mucous film with adherent particulate matter is continually moved orally by the ciliary action. Since there are no cilia beyond the respiratory bronchioles, particulate matter reaching the alveolae is removed by macrophages, the dust cells.

112. The answer is A. *(Cormack, ed 9. pp 555-558. Junqueira, ed 6. pp 345-350.)* A blood-air barrier separates air in the alveolus from blood in the capillary. It is composed of both alveolar epithelium and capillary endothelium with a shared basal lamina. A major component of this barrier is a continuous tight junction between contiguous endothelial cells that retards passage of plasma onto the alveolar surface. Gaseous diffusion occurs across the blood-air barrier and any thickening of this structure, such as edema under pathologic conditions, will inhibit this vital process. The blood-air barrier is unbroken. Alveolar pores are found in the interalveolar septa and function to equalize pressure between adjacent alveoli.

113. The answer is A. *(Cormack, ed 9. pp 555-559. Junqueira, ed 6. pp 347-349.)* The type II (great alveolar or septal) cells of the lung are large pyramidal cells interspersed among the squamous type I alveolar cells. Composing about 3 percent of the alveolar surface area, they have continuous tight junctions along their contiguous borders with the type I cells and therefore contribute to the blood-air barrier. These cells contain lamellar bodies composed of phospholipid-rich pulmonary surfactant, which coats the alveolar surface to reduce surface tension and thereby prevent alveolar collapse.

114. The answer is A. *(Junqueira, ed 6. pp 369-378. Kelly, ed 18. pp 645-647.)* All nephrons begin in cortical tissue; hence all glomeruli are confined to this zone. The proximal and distal convoluted tubules are also located in the cortex. The proximal straight tubule descends into the medulla as the descending limb of the loop of Henle. Deep within the medulla the nephron turns upward to form the distal straight tubule. As the distal tubule returns to the cortex, it becomes convoluted and comes to lie adjacent to its originating renal corpuscle, where it forms the macula densa of the juxtaglomerular complex. The nephron then continues as the collecting tubule toward the medulla. The arcuate arteries arch over the bases of the medullary pyramids as they branch from the interlobar arteries in the cortex. Blood passing through the glomeruli then drains into the vasa rectae within the medulla before joining the renal veins in the cortex.

115. The answer is E. *(Junqueira, ed 6. pp 374-375, 384. Kelly, ed 18. pp 656-665.)* The kidney regulates the chemical composition of the blood through the various cell types of the nephron. The filtration barrier of the glomerulus is formed by the fenestrated capillary endothelium, the basal lamina, and the filtration slits between the processes of the podocytes. This barrier allows filtration of the blood while maintaining its colloid osmotic pressure. The brush border of the cuboidal cells of the proximal convoluted tubule provides an augmented surface area for resorption of essential solutes and water from the glomerular filtrate, whereas the basal membrane infoldings provide an augmented surface for active transport of these substances out of the cell into the bloodstream. Numerous mitochondria associated with the basal membrane provide the energy necessary for active transport. The squamous cells of the descending limb of the loop of Henle are very permeable to water and ions. Since the efferent glomerular arteriole runs counter to the loop of Henle, there is countercurrent exchange of water from the hypotonic ultrafiltrate into the hypertonic blood of the capillaries. The low cuboidal cells of the ascending limb of the loop of Henle are impermeable to water, but active transport of ions out of the tubule maintains the hypertonicity of the medulla. The simple cuboidal cells of the distal convoluted tubule are sensitive to circulating aldosterone levels, so they regulate the balance between sodium and potassium. As the distal convoluted tubule passes by the afferent glomerular arteriole, its epithelium is modified as the macula densa. The cuboidal cells of the collecting tubules are variably permeable to water, depending on the circulating levels of antidiuretic hormone (ADH). When ADH is high, the flow of water across the cells into the hypertonic medulla concentrates the urine and conserves fluid.

116. The answer is C. *(Junqueira, ed 6. pp 373-378. Kelly, ed 18. p 662.)* The distal tubule of the kidney is noted for its lack of a brush border, a prominent feature in the proximal tubule. Other histologic characteristics that help to differentiate distal from proximal tubules include a shallower epithelium, more densely packed cells, a less acidophilic cytoplasm, and nuclei that lie closer to the lumen.

117. The answer is A. *(Junqueira, ed 6. pp 378, 380-381. Kelly, ed 18. pp 662, 667.)* The macula densa of the distal convoluted tubule is in direct contact with the juxtaglomerular cells of the afferent glomerular arteriole. The cells of the macula densa and the juxtaglomerular cells of the afferent glomerular arteriole form the juxtaglomerular apparatus, which is instrumental in the maintenance of blood volume and blood pressure. The juxtaglomerular cells, acting as baroreceptors in the afferent arterioles, produce renin, which acts on a precursor (angiotensinogen) in the blood to form the active vasopressor angiotensin. The macula densa senses levels of sodium in the provisional urine and interacts with the juxtaglomerular cells. Because angiotensin also promotes the release of aldosterone from the adrenal cortex, low urine sodium concentrations result in augmented water absorption in the distal convoluted tubule and the collecting tubules.

118. The answer is C. *(Cormack, ed 9. pp 224, 573-574. Junqueira, ed 6. pp 249, 380, 387.)* In response to decreased blood pressure in the afferent glomerular arteriole, increased chloride concentration in the distal convoluted tubule, or sympathetic nerve stimulation, the juxtaglomerular cells secrete renin into the circulation. Renin reacts with a plasma α globulin (angiotensinogen) to produce angiotensin I, which is converted in the lung to vasoactive angiotensin II. Angiotensin II also stimulates the adrenal zona glomerulosa to produce aldosterone, which promotes sodium, chloride, and water uptake by the distal tubule, thereby raising blood volume and pressure. The renal cortex is the principal source of erythropoietin. The stimuli for production appear to be decreased partial pressure of oxygen (indicative of insufficient erythrocytes) and high chloride concentration in the distal tubule (indicative of decreased blood volume). While the cellular source is unknown, the most likely candidates are the juxtaglomerular cells and the lacis cells, both of which contain granules. Glucocorticoids and mineralocorticoids, as well as sex hormones, are products of the adrenal cortex.

119. The answer is A. *(Junqueira, ed 6. pp 387-388. Kelly, ed 18. pp 145-149, 677-679.)* The photomicrograph accompanying the question shows a section of transitional epithelium from the ureter. Similar epithelium covers fibromuscular tissue found in the urinary bladder, renal pelvis, and proximal urethra. The collecting ducts within the renal medulla are lined by a *single* layer of cuboidal cells. The transitional epithelium is two or three layers thick in the renal pelvis and extends to six layers thick in the undistended bladder. This epithelium is reduced to three layers as the bladder distends.

120. The answer is A. *(Junqueira, ed 6. pp 387-388. Kelly, ed 18. pp 145-149, 677-679.)* A characteristic feature of transitional epithelium, which lines the ureters and urinary bladder, is its impermeability to water. The plasma membrane at the luminal surface of these cells is scalloped and infolded. Its outer osmophilic lamella is thickened, a fact that may account for its impermeability.

121. The answer is D. *(Junqueira, ed 6. pp 422-424. Kelly, ed 18. pp 689-696.)* From the periphery toward the lumen of seminiferous tubules, spermatogenesis proceeds over a period of about 64 days from spermatogonia to primary—then secondary—spermatocytes, thence to spermatids. The spermatids undergo transformation (spermiogenesis) into spermatozoa. Sertoli, or sustentacular, cells are not part of the spermatogenic cell line.

122. The answer is D. *(Alberts, ed 2. pp 845-848.)* Gametogenesis uses meiosis to admix the parental genetic material and to produce a haploid gamete. There is pairing of homologous chromosomes and chromosomal duplication during prophase I. The paired homologues align in the metaphase and crossing-over occurs between sister chromatids. Also at this stage the independent assortment of maternal and paternal genetic material occurs. Because the chromosomal replication results in a tetraploid chromosomal number, division I produces cells with the diploid number. After division I the daughter cells enter a second M phase of the cell cycle without passing through the G_1 phase and S phase. Thus, the result of division II is a chromosomal reduction to the haploid number.

123. The answer is A. *(Junqueira, ed 6. pp 396, 431-432. Kelly, ed 18. pp 704-705.)* Production of testicular endocrine hormones is a function of the interstitial cells (of Leydig). Testosterone, the main androgenic steroid hormone secreted by the Leydig cells, acts locally on the seminiferous tubule and remotely on, *inter alia,* the accessory reproductive glands. Spermatogonia require high concentrations of androgen in order to proliferate spermatids, which, in turn, require androgen for their transformation to sperm. Sertoli cells are sustentacular, transferring testosterone, among other nutrients, to the spermatids. Myoepithelial cells are smooth muscle cells found in sweat, mammary, lacrimal, and salivary glands.

124. The answer is D. *(Junqueira, ed 6. pp 424-427. Kelly, ed 18. pp 699-702.)* During maturation of the spermatid to the spermatozoon, termed *spermiogenesis,* numerous complex morphologic changes occur. During the Golgi phase, an acrosomal vesicle develops from the Golgi apparatus. This vesicle is redistributed over the surface of the anterior pole of the nucleus to form the acrosomal cap. The contained hydrolytic enzymes separate the cells of the corona radiata surrounding the ovum and digest the zona pellucida, enabling fertilization to occur. Concurrently with the Golgi phase, the two centrioles migrate to the posterior pole; from one centriole the flagellum develops. The mitochondria migrate toward the developing flagellum and become oriented in a spiral around the proximal portion of the tail to form the middle piece of the spermatozoon. This mitochondrial accumulation provides the ATP necessary for sperm motility. The nucleus condenses; the excess cytoplasm is extruded as a residual body; and the spermatozoon is mature. However, the spermatozoon does not become motile until a source of metabolic energy is provided. Although motility begins in the epididymis, the secretions of the seminal vesicles and the prostate gland contribute the major nutrients necessary for sperm metabolism and motility.

125. The answer is D. *(Junqueira, ed 6. p 435. Kelly, ed 18. pp 712-713.)* The thick secretion from the seminal vesicles contributes substantially to the ejaculate volume that conveys the spermatozoa. The high fructose content of secretions of the seminal vesicles provides the primary metabolic energy source for spermatozoal motility. The flavens that are contributed to the ejaculate by the seminal vesicles fluoresce strongly in ultraviolet light, a phenomenon that supplies a useful forensic test for the presence of semen.

126. The answer is C. *(Junqueira, ed 6. pp 435-437. Kelly, ed 18. pp 713-715.)* The glandular architecture of the prostate is very irregular, exhibiting tubular, alveolar, and saccular forms varying considerably in size. Papillae that project into the lumen may appear as isolated islands on cut sections. In addition, the lumina of the prostate gland may contain characteristic prostatic concretions, the number of which increases with age. The thyroid, however, has a more regular, follicular appearance. The adrenal medulla does not have glandular lumina. Sections of a uterine tube or gallbladder would allow evidence of the central luminal surface.

127. The answer is E. *(Alberts, ed 2. pp 856-857. Junqueira, ed 6. p 444. Kelly, ed 18. pp 739-740.)* Follicle-stimulating hormone (FSH) and luteinizing hormone (LH) produced in the adenohypophysis result in growth and maturation of the ovarian follicle. Under FSH stimulation, the theca cells proliferate, hypertrophy, and begin to produce estrogen. A midcycle surge of LH appears to trigger the resumption of meiosis and to cause the FSH-primed follicle to rupture and discharge the ovum. Under the influence of LH, the ruptured follicle is transformed to a corpus luteum, which produces progesterone.

128. The answer is D. *(Alberts, ed 2. pp 856-857. Junqueira, ed 6. p 444. Kelly, ed 18. p 734.)* The secondary oocyte enters the second meiotic division just prior to ovulation and arrests at metaphase. Fertilization by a spermatozoon provides the stimulation for the division of chromatin to the haploid number. By the time the fertilized ovum reaches the uterus, the progesterone produced by the corpus luteum has initiated the secretory phase in the endometrium. Once implantation occurs and the chorion develops, human chorionic gonadotropin (hCG) is synthesized and the corpus luteum is maintained.

129. The answer is C. *(Junqueira, ed 6. pp 440-441. Kelly, ed 18. pp 730-733.)* The germinal epithelium is the outer layer of the ovary and is not involved in follicle development. By the fourth prenatal month, the ovary contains approximately five million oocytes surrounded by granulosa cells, thus forming the primordial follicle. As ovulation approaches, the granulosa cells become cuboidal or columnar, forming the granulosa layer. The stroma around the follicle changes as development continues, and its inner zone becomes the highly vascular theca interna; the outer, more dense connective tissue remains as the theca externa. The cluster of cells surrounding the ovum, the cumulus oophorus, is undercut, and the egg, with a surrounding halo of cells called the corona radiata, floats free in the antrum and finally passes through the ruptured follicle wall into the oviduct.

130. The answer is C. *(Junqueira, ed 6. pp 444-445. Kelly, ed 18. pp 734-738.)* The structure depicted is a corpus luteum. Ovulation appears to be stimulated by a surge of luteinizing hormone (LH) that is produced by the pituitary gland. With the release of liquor folliculi upon ovulation, there is collapse and folding of the follicular wall. Under the influence of LH, the granulosa cells enlarge, become epithelioid, and differentiate into granulosa lutein cells; the cells of the theca interna differentiate into theca lutein cells. These cells now produce estrogen, which maintains the secretory or luteal phase of the uterine endometrium, as well as progesterone, which both stimulates secretion of the endometrial glands and inhibits pituitary production of LH. If fertilization and implantation do not occur, the decrease in LH results in degeneration of the corpus luteum within 14 days and the concomitant decline in estrogen results in endometrial degeneration with menstruation. If fertilization and implantation do occur, the production of human chorionic gonadotropin (hCG) by the developing placenta maintains the corpus luteum and menstruation does not occur.

131. The answer is A. *(Junqueira, ed 6. pp 448-450. Kelly, ed 18. pp 748-751.)* The spiral arteries of the endometrium (labeled A in the diagram accompanying the question) are dependent on specific estrogen/progesterone ratios for their development. They pass through the basalis layer of the endometrium into the functional zone, and their distal ends are subject to degeneration with each menses. The straight arteries (B) are not subject to these hormonal changes. In the proliferative phase the endometrium is only 1 to 3 mm thick, and the glands are straight, with the spiral arteries only lightly coiled. This diagram of the early secretory phase shows an edematous endometrium that is 4 mm thick, with glands that are large, beginning to sacculate in the deeper mucosa, and coiled for their entire length. In the late secretory phase, the endometrium becomes 6 to 7 mm thick.

132. The answer is D. *(Junqueira, ed 6. pp 454-457. Kelly, ed 18. p 757.)* A fertilized ovum reaches the uterus about 4 days after fertilization. At that time, it has developed into a multicellular, hollow sphere referred to as a blastocyst. The blastocyst soon adheres to the secretory endometrium and differentiates into an inner cell mass that will develop into the embryo and a layer of primitive trophoblast. The expanding trophoblast penetrates the surface endometrium and erodes into maternal blood vessels. Eventually, it develops two layers, an inner cytotrophoblast and an outer syncytiotrophoblast. Solid cords of trophoblast form the chorionic villi, which then are invaded by fetal blood vessels.

133. The answer is D. *(Cormack, ed 9. pp 598-600, 605-606, 610, 627. Junqueira, ed 6. pp 396, 405-406, 413, 432.)* The cells of the adenohypophysis produce hormones that regulate the functions of numerous organs and systems throughout the body. Release of the anterior pituitary hormones is controlled by negative or positive feedback mediated by hypothalamic releasing hormones secreted by the hypothalamus. After hypophysectomy, loss of adrenocorticotropin (ACTH) results in lack of stimulation and reduced size of the glucocorticoid-producing cells of the adrenal zona fasciculata. Loss of thyrotropin (TSH) results in lack of stimulation and reduced activity of the thyroid follicular cells. Loss of follicle-stimulating hormone (FSH) results in failure of maturation of the germ cells so that spermatogenesis and growth of ovarian follicles ceases. The parathyroid chief (principal) cells produce parathyroid hormone (PTH) in response to low plasma calcium titers.

134. The answer is A. *(Junqueira, ed 6. p 412. Kelly, ed 18. p 797.)* The parafollicular cells of the thyroid gland, which are very rich in mitochondria, have been shown to be responsible for the secretion of thyrocalcitonin (or more simply, calcitonin). The thyroid follicles are lined with simple epithelium that secretes gelatinous colloid. The colloid contains the hormone thyroglobulin, which is made up of iodinated amino acids such as thyroxine (T_4) and triiodothyronine (T_3). Some researchers believe the follicles also secrete a protease enzyme that splits the thyroglobulin.

135. The answer is D. *(Junqueira, ed 6. pp 414-416. Kelly, ed 18. pp 798-801.)* Thyroxine is produced by the thyroid gland, a structure composed of follicles filled with colloid material and lined by a low columnar or cuboid epithelium. Although relatively little connective tissue is seen between the follicles in a group, prominent bands of connective tissue arise from the capsule of the thyroid and penetrate the gland, dividing it into groups of follicles. Cortisone is secreted by the adrenal gland; growth hormone is produced in the pars distalis of the pituitary. Vasopressin is produced by the hypothalamic nuclei of the brain, and parathormone is produced by the parathyroid glands.

136. The answer is B. *(Junqueira, ed 6. pp 479-483. Kelly, ed 18. pp 841, 849, 856.)* The cell bodies of the rod and cone cells are located in the outer nuclear layer of the retina. The fovea centralis, a shallow depression at the posterior pole of the optic axis in the middle of the macula lutea, is composed entirely of cone cells and is the region of highest visual acuity. The rod cells begin to appear at the edge of the fovea centralis and increase in number so that a 4:1 ratio of rods to cones is reached at the edge of the macula. The ora serrata marks the outer boundary of the sensory portion of the retina. The optic disk (papilla), the site of convergence of the axons of the ganglion cells to form the optic nerve, is devoid of visual receptor cells and is thus a blind spot.

137-139. The answers are: 137-D, 138-A 139-B. *(Alberts, ed 2. pp 792-801. Kelly, ed 18. pp 119-124, 128-132.)* There are three major categories of cell junctions. Interconnections between either belt or spot desmosomes hold cells together by mechanical means and also provide anchoring sites for cytoskeletal elements.

Gap junctions contain proteinaceous channels (connexons) that enable both electrical intercellular communication by permitting the flow of ions as well as chemical intercellular communication through exchange of metabolites.

Tight junctions closely appose plasma membranes of adjacent cells and thereby form a barrier impermeable to aqueous diffusion. Frequently more than one type of junction lies in close proximity to form a junctional complex.

140-143. The answers are: 140-B, 141-A, 142-D, 143-A. *(Alberts, ed 2. pp 633-634, 652-656, 797-798. Junqueira, ed 6. pp 43-45, 68-73.)* Spot desmosomes (macula adherens) hold epithelial cells together and serve as anchor sites for keratin tonofilaments (cytokeratin). The tonofilaments extend across the cell to form a structural framework within the cytoplasm. The maculae adherentes of each cell result in a transfer of force from the apposing tonofilaments within one cell to those of the next and throughout the epithelial sheet.

Belt desmosomes (zonula adherens) form a band about the apical end of the cell and serve as an anchor for the terminal web of actin filaments. The terminal web provides support for the microvilli and the apical region of the cell.

The mitotic spindle consists of microtubules composed of tubulin. Polar fibers extend from the spindle poles to the equator. Kinetochore fibers attach to the centromere of each chromatid. The movement of the chromosomes appears to be the result of interaction between the tubulin of the two microtubule populations.

Within each microvillus is a cluster of 20 to 30 actin filaments. The proximal ends of these filaments intermingle with the terminal web of actin filaments that lies just beneath the microvilli; the distal ends attach to the inner surface of the plasma membrane. The actin filaments within the microvilli are polarized and probably interact with myosin dimers to effect limited movement.

144-148. The answers are: 144-C, 145-B, 146-C, 147-D, 148-A. *(Kelly, ed 18. pp 390-395.)* Continuous capillaries, characterized by complete layers of endothelium and basal lamina, are found in muscle, connective tissue, brain parenchyma, and exocrine glands—among other locations.

Fenestrated capillaries, characterized by 50- to 100-nm porous regions (the inner and outer plasmalemmae are apposed without intervening cytoplasm) covered by basal lamina, are found in endocrine glands, the renal glomerulus, the choroid plexus of the brain, and the ciliary body.

Sinusoids, characterized by larger fenestrae that are not covered by basal lamina, are found in the hepatic parenchyma as well as in lymphoid and myeloid tissues.

149-154. The answers are: 149-A, 150-C, 151-B, 152-D, 153-D, 154-C. *(Cormack, ed 9. pp 496-501. Junqueira, ed 6. pp 292-297.)* Parietal *(oxyntic) cells* secrete HCl in response to vagal stimulation and also produce intrinsic factor. These cells are located between the mucous neck cells in the upper half of the gastric glands of the fundus and body of the stomach. *Chief (zymogenic) cells* lie in the lower regions of the gastric glands in the fundus and body of the stomach. They secrete pepsinogen and gastric lipase in response to vagal stimulation. The mucous neck cells, located in the gastric glands throughout the stomach, produce mucus while enteroendocrine (enterochromaffin) cells are associated with production of serotonin and endorphin. In the pyloric glands interspersed among the mucous cells are gastrin (G) cells, which produce gastrin and thereby control HCl secretion. The glands of the cardia primarily produce mucus. The stomach does not have villi and there are few, if any, absorptive cells in the stomach, although some substances, such as ethanol, diffuse across the gastric mucosa.

155-158. The answers are: 155-C, 156-E, 157-A, 158-D. *(Alberts, ed 2. pp 214, 345-346, 436-437, 511-513, 541-544.)* Oxidative phosphorylation occurs primarily in the mitochondria (C in the photomicrograph accompanying the questions) of mammalian cells. These structures are responsible for producing most of the ATP, which is the principal energy source for cell function. Cells that are metabolically active, such as the cardiac contractile cells, the renal absorptive cells of the proximal convoluted tubule, and the pancreatic secretory cells, have large numbers of mitochondria.

The site of messenger RNA (mRNA) synthesis is euchromatin (E), which represents the uncoiled and metabolically active form of DNA. It is thought that perichromatin granules may represent mRNA because of their abundance in a synthetically active cell. mRNA, representing complementary copies of the DNA nucleotide sequences, codes for protein structures. These filamentous coded sequences pass through the nuclear pores and are translated on the cytoplasmic ribosomes to yield the specific protein.

The nucleolus (A) consists of fibrils, nucleolar chromatin, ribosomal RNA (rRNA) granules, and nucleoproteins. The nucleolar chromatin contains the genes from which rRNA is transcribed and is thus the site of ribosome synthesis. Because cytoplasmic ribosomes are the site of protein synthesis, a cell especially active in growth or protein synthesis will have one or more very prominent nucleoli. Although it has been proved that ribosomes are synthesized in the nucleolus, it is unclear just how the ribosomes (which are approximately 20 μm) leave the nucleus through the pores and become attached to endoplasmic reticulum.

The microsomal fraction of a cell homogenate contains small membranous vesicles studded with rRNA. They are called *microsomes* because they were originally thought to be discrete cellular structures. It later became evident that the microsomes are fragmented rough endoplasmic reticulum (D) with attached ribosomes. The early stages of protein synthesis are associated with this cellular fraction and, hence, with rough endoplasmic reticulum.

159-163. The answers are: 159-A, 160-C, 161-A, 162-B, 163-D. *(Alberts, ed 2. pp 808-815. Junqueira, ed 6. pp 95-100.)* Tropocollagen is the principal protein secreted by fibroblasts. It consists of three polypeptides arranged in a triple-stranded helix. There are four types of tropocollagen, labeled I through V, which differ in the amino acid sequences of their three constituent polypeptide strands.

Type I collagen is synthesized by fibroblasts of connective tissue proper, ligaments, and tendons, as well as the chondroblasts of fibrocartilage and the osteoblasts of bone. This type forms the typical collagen fibrils that aggregate into fibers and pack densely to form bundles and accounts for 90 percent of the body collagen. Type II collagen is synthesized by chondroblasts of hyaline, an elastic cartilage. It forms collagen fibrils that pack loosely and do not aggregate into fibers. Type III collagen is synthesized by reticular cells and has a higher concentration of hexoses. The fibrils aggregate to form thin fibers arranged into a loose meshwork such as that found in hemopoietic tissue, lymphoid tissue, smooth muscle, and nerve. Type IV collagen is secreted by epithelial, endothelial, muscle, and neurilemma cells. This type does not aggregate to form fibers; it forms basal lamina of the basement membrane.

164-167. The answers are: 164-B, 165-D, 166-C, 167-E. *(Junqueira, ed 6. pp 110-113, 233-242. Kelly, ed 18. pp 167-168, 239, 249-251.)* Blood platelets (thrombocytes) are anucleate corpuscles that originate from the megakaryocytes of bone marrow. They have a tendency to agglutinate and are instrumental in clot formation. Platelets contain granules of serotonin, which, on traumatic rupture, produce vasoconstriction to minimize bleeding. The release of thromboplastin initiates conversion of prothrombin to thrombin, which, in turn, converts fibrinogen to fibrin. Fibrin is a major constituent of the blood clot.

Neutrophils (polymorphonuclear leukocytes), constituting 70 percent of the white blood cells, are highly chemotactic and phagocytic. The specific granules contain alkaline phosphatase, whereas the azurophil granules contain lysosomal enzymes, peroxidase, and lysozyme for the breakdown of bacterial walls. These cells, constituting the first line of defense against bacterial invasion, increase many-fold in the presence of bacterial infection.

Eosinophilic leukocytes normally constitute 1 to 4 percent of the white blood cells. The eosinophil granules, for which the cell is named, contain peroxidase and function as lysosomes. The granules also contain an arginine-rich crystalloid inclusion. These cells, which increase markedly during allergic reaction, selectively phagocytize antigen-antibody complexes.

Plasma cells produce and secrete antibodies. The euchromatin and numerous nucleoli, as well as the intense basophilia of the profuse rough endoplasmic reticulum, indicate active protein synthesis. The synthesized antibodies are formed into granules in a prominent Golgi complex. The granules move to the plasma cell membrane where they are released into the extracellular fluid and blood by exocytosis. The activity of plasma cells, which derive from B lymphocytes, increases during bacterial and viral infections.

168-171. The answers are: 168-C, 169-B, 170-D, 171-A. *(Kelly, ed 18. pp 874-881.)* The tectorial membrane is an epithelial, cuticular substance that is flexible, delicate, fibrillar, and gelatinous. It fills about one-fourth of the spiral duct and extends into the scala media. It is the alternation of position of the hair cells in relation to the tectorial membrane that is the stimulus transmitted to the brain as sound.

The limbus spiralis is a thickened periosteum overlying the bony spiral lamina. Its apical convex surface is covered by columnar epithelium and is continuous with the tectorial membrane; its lower surface is covered with cuboidal cells.

Below the limbus spiralis is the osseous lamina, which contains the spiral ganglion; the spiral ganglion lies in the bony spiral lamina. The ganglion cells are bipolar with peripheral and central processes. It is the axons of the cells within the spiral ganglion that carry impulses to the brain. The nerve fibers join vestibular branches to form CN VIII.

The cochlear duct is a membranous tube that communicates with the saccule. The roof is covered by the vestibular membrane; the basal surface is the spiral organ of Corti. The vestibular membrane separates the scala media from the scala vestibuli.

172-175. The answers are: 172-E, 173-A, 174-D, 175-B. *(Junqueira, ed 6. pp 285-289. Kelly, ed 18. pp 518-519.)* The pulp of a mature tooth (labeled D in the diagram) consists primarily of loose connective tissue rich in vessels and nerves. Odontoblasts, which are derived from the neural crest, lie at the edge of the pulp cavity and secrete collagen, which mineralizes to become dentin (B). Mineralization of the matrix occurs around the process of odontoblasts and forms dentinal tubules. Ameloblasts, ectodermal derivatives, lay down an organic matrix and secrete enamel, initially onto the surface of the dentin. As hydroxyapatite crystals form at the apices of ameloblast processes (Tomes' processes), rods of enamel grow peripherally and the ameloblasts resorb the organic matrix so that the enamel layer (A) is almost entirely mineral. Upon eruption of the tooth, enamel deposition is complete and the ameloblasts are shed. Cementum (E) has a composition similar to that of bone, is produced by cells similar in appearance to osteocytes, and covers the dentin of the root. The periodontal ligament (C) consists of coarse collagenous fibers running between the alveolar bone and the cementum of the tooth and separates the tooth from the alveolar socket. Although the periodontal ligament suspends and supports each tooth, the membrane permits physiologic movement within the limits provided by the elasticity of the tissue.

Gross Anatomy: Thorax

DIRECTIONS: Each question below contains four or five suggested responses. Select the **one best** response to each question.

176. Knowledge of the lymphatic drainage of the breast is clinically important because of the high incidence of breast tumors. The *major* pathway of lymphatic drainage from the mammary gland is along lymphatic channels that parallel

(A) subcutaneous venous networks to the contralateral breast and to the abdominal wall
(B) tributaries of the axillary vessels to the axillary nodes
(C) tributaries of the intercostal vessels to the parasternal nodes and posterior mediastinal nodes
(D) tributaries of the internal thoracic (mammary) vessels to the parasternal (internal thoracic) nodes
(E) tributaries of the thoracoacromial vessels to the apical (subclavicular) nodes

177. A patient who has undergone a radical mastectomy with extensive axillary dissection suffers winging of the scapula when the anteriorly extended arm is pressed against a fixed object. This indicates injury to which of the following nerves?

(A) Axillary
(B) Long thoracic
(C) Lower subscapular
(D) Supraclavicular
(E) Thoracodorsal

178. All the following correctly pertain to the left costodiaphragmatic recess EXCEPT

(A) it accommodates lung tissue during inspiration
(B) it extends below the twelfth rib posteriorly
(C) it is formed by the apposition of diaphragmatic and mediastinal pleura
(D) it is maximal upon forced expiration
(E) it is the most dependent (lowest) part of the pleural cavity when a person is sitting

179. Pain referred to the right side of the neck and extending laterally from the right clavicle to the tip of the right shoulder is most likely to involve the

(A) cervical cardiac accelerator nerves
(B) posterior vagal trunk
(C) right intercostal nerves
(D) right phrenic nerve
(E) right recurrent laryngeal nerve

Questions 180-182

A child suspected of aspirating a small cloth-covered metal button is seen in the emergency room. While the child does not complain of pain, there is frequent coughing.

180. Anticipating absence of breath sounds, the examining physician listens with a stethoscope to the right lung. Aspirated small objects tend to lodge in the right inferior lobar bronchus for all the following reasons EXCEPT

(A) the left main stem (primary) bronchus is more horizontal than the right
(B) the right inferior lobar bronchus nearly continues the direction of the trachea
(C) the right lung has no middle lobe
(D) the right main stem (primary) bronchus is of greater diameter than the left

181. The breath sounds appear normal on the right side and, to the surprise of the examining physician, there is absence of breath sounds over the lower lobe of the left lung. A posteroanterior (PA) radiograph confirms that the button is in the left lower lobe bronchus. One probable explanation for the object's presence in this location is

(A) left diaphragmatic hernia
(B) left pneumothorax
(C) normal anatomy
(D) paralysis of the left hemidiaphragm
(E) situs inversus

182. The afferent nerves from the inferior lobar bronchus that carry the stimulation producing the cough include the

(A) phrenic nerve
(B) spinal nerves T1 through T4
(C) superior laryngeal nerve
(D) thoracic splanchnic nerves
(E) vagal fibers in the pulmonary plexus

(End of question set)

Questions 183-185

A 28-year-old woman comes into the emergency room exhibiting dyspnea and mild cyanosis, but no signs of trauma. Her chest x-ray is shown below.

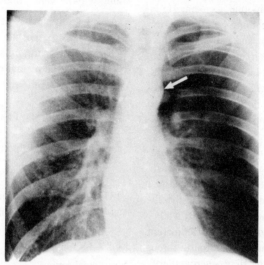

183. The most obvious *abnormal* finding in this patient's inspiratory postero-anterior chest x-ray (viewed in the anatomical position) is a

(A) bilateral extension of the pleural cavities above the first rib
(B) grossly enlarged heart
(C) left pneumothorax (collapsed lung)
(D) paralysis of the left hemidiaphragm
(E) right hemothorax (blood in the pleural cavity)

184. The pronounced mediastinal shift to the right includes all the following structures EXCEPT the

(A) aorta
(B) esophagus
(C) heart
(D) sternum
(E) trachea

185. The structure labeled by the arrow in the x-ray is the

(A) arch of the aorta
(B) auricle of the left atrium
(C) collapsed lung
(D) edge of the manubrium
(E) left main stem bronchus

(End of question set)

Questions 186-190

A 23-year-old, semiconscious man is brought to the emergency room following an automobile accident. He is tachypneic (breathing rapidly) and cyanotic (blue lips and nail beds). The right lower anterolateral thoracic wall reveals a small laceration and flailing (moving *inward* as the rest of the thoracic cage expands during inspiration). Air does not appear to move into or out of the wound, and it is assumed that the pleura has not been penetrated. After the patient is placed on immediate positive pressure endotracheal respiration, his cyanosis clears and the abnormal movement of the chest wall disappears. Radiographic examination confirms fractures of the fourth through eighth ribs in the right anteroaxillary line and of the fourth through sixth ribs at the right costochondral junction. There is no evidence that bony fragments have penetrated the lungs or of pneumothorax (collapsed lung).

186. In this patient, the initial cyanosis—incomplete oxygenation of the blood owing to perfusion of the right lung without ventilation—is a result of

(A) bilateral inability of the pleural cavities to expand
(B) inability of the right chest wall to expand the pleural cavity
(C) paralysis of the right hemidiaphragm
(D) paralysis of the thoracic musculature
(E) shunting of all blood through the normal lung

187. The primary action of thoracic cavity enlargement during inspiration can be accomplished by all the following EXCEPT the

(A) diaphragm
(B) external intercostal muscles
(C) interchondral portions of the internal intercostal muscles
(D) sternomastoid muscle
(E) transverse thoracic muscle

188. The small superficial laceration, once it is ascertained that it has not penetrated the pleura, is sutured and the chest bound in bandages; positive pressure
endotracheal respiration is maintained. Several hours later, the patient's cyanosis
returns. The right side of the thorax is found to be more expanded than the left,
yet moves less during respiration. Chest x-rays are shown below. A negative pressure drain (chest tube) has to be inserted into the pleural space. Effective locations
for the drain include the

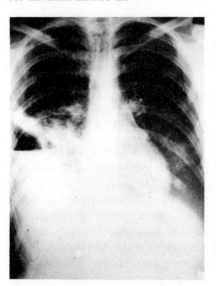 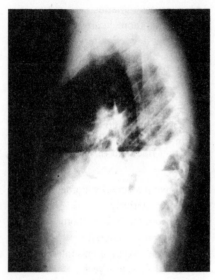

(A) apex between the clavicle and first rib
(B) costomediastinal recess on the left, adjacent to the xiphoid process
(C) right fourth intercostal space in the midclavicular line (just below the nipple)
(D) right seventh intercostal space in the midaxillary line
(E) right eighth intercostal space in the midclavicular line (about 4 inches below
the nipple)

189. One liter of blood is withdrawn from the pleural cavity; the patient's cyanosis immediately clears and signs of the mediastinal shift disappear. Possible sources of the bleeding that produces the hemothorax include all the following EXCEPT the

(A) intercostal arteries
(B) internal thoracic artery
(C) lateral thoracic artery
(D) musculophrenic artery
(E) vessels associated with the lung parenchyma

190. The intercostal neurovascular bundle is particularly vulnerable to injury from fractured ribs because it is located

(A) above the superior border of the ribs, anteriorly
(B) beneath the inferior border of the ribs, posterolaterally
(C) between external and internal intercostal muscle layers
(D) deep to the posterior intercostal membrane
(E) superficial to the ribs, anteriorly

(End of question set)

191. Pulmonary disease sometimes can be localized to a bronchopulmonary segment, in which event segmental resection may be feasible. Characteristics of a bronchopulmonary segment that assist in its surgical definition include all the following EXCEPT

(A) an apex directed toward the hilum of the lung
(B) a central segmental artery
(C) a central tertiary or segmental bronchus
(D) a central vein

Questions 192-195

A 38-year-old man is seen in the emergency room complaining of severe chest pain. He tends to sit leaning forward. Upon physical examination he is noted to be tachypneic (breathing rapidly); he has a rapid pulse rate, and on auscultation of the chest his valve sounds appear "distant." A radiograph shows a globular heart shadow. All evidence indicates pericarditis with pericardial effusion.

192. The pain originating in the parietal pericardium travels by way of

(A) the cardiac plexus
(B) greater splanchnic nerves
(C) intercostal nerves
(D) vagus nerves
(E) none of the above

193. The heart sound associated with closure of the mitral valve is heard most distinctly

(A) immediately to the left of the sternal angle (of Louis)
(B) immediately to the right of the sternal angle (of Louis)
(C) just inferior to the left nipple
(D) just inferior to the right nipple
(E) over the xiphoid process

194. Pericardiocentesis (to drain the exudate) via the costoxiphoid approach passes through which of the following structures?

(A) The interchondral portion of an internal oblique muscle
(B) The left pleura
(C) The rectus sheath and rectus abdominis muscle
(D) The visceral pericardium
(E) None of the above

195. Vessels at high risk during the costoxiphoid approach include

(A) the anterior interventricular artery
(B) the left internal thoracic artery
(C) the right coronary artery
(D) the right marginal artery
(E) none of the above

(End of question set)

196. The major venous return system of the heart, the coronary sinus, empties into the

(A) inferior vena cava
(B) left atrium
(C) right atrium
(D) right ventricle
(E) superior vena cava

197. All the following veins drain into the coronary sinus EXCEPT the

(A) anterior cardiac veins
(B) great cardiac vein
(C) middle cardiac vein
(D) oblique vein of the left atrium
(E) small cardiac vein

198. The sinoatrial node in the heart receives its blood supply principally from

(A) the anterior interventricular branch of the left coronary artery
(B) the circumflex branch of the left coronary artery
(C) the posterior interventricular branch of the right coronary artery
(D) the right coronary artery
(E) none of the above

199. The first (S1 or "Lub") heart sound and the second (S2 or "Dup") heart sound originate, respectively, from the

(A) closure of the pulmonary valve followed by closure of the aortic valve
(B) closure of the tricuspid valve followed by closure of the mitral valve
(C) closure of the atrioventricular valves followed by closure of the semilunar valves
(D) closure of the atrioventricular valves followed by opening of the semilunar valves
(E) opening of the atrioventricular valves followed by closure of the atrioventricular valves

Questions 200-209

A 64-year-old man is brought into the emergency room after experiencing more than 3 hours of increasing chest pain that was unrelieved by rest, antacids, or nitroglycerin. On physical examination he is found to be acyanotic (normal blood oxygenation), tachypneic (rapid breathing), tachycardiac (rapid pulse rate) with a regular rhythm, and diaphoretic (sweating). He complains of nausea without vomiting. Further questioning reveals a 2-year history of exertional angina pectoris (pressing chest pain that often radiated along the inner aspect of the left arm when the patient climbed one flight of stairs). Propranolol, which reduces the response of the heart to stress, and nitroglycerin, which dilates systemic veins as well as coronary arteries, had been prescribed previously.

200. This patient's tachycardia probably is mediated by reflex arcs associated with decreased cardiac output and possible reduced blood pressure. The visceral efferent (motor) pathway of this cardiac response is mediated by the

(A) carotid branches of the glossopharyngeal nerves
(B) greater splanchnic nerves
(C) phrenic nerves
(D) sympathetic cervical and thoracic cardiac fibers
(E) vagus and recurrent laryngeal nerves

201. The superficial and deep cardiac plexuses, located in the middle mediastinum, receive contributions from all the following EXCEPT the

(A) cervical sympathetic ganglia
(B) phrenic nerves
(C) recurrent laryngeal nerves
(D) upper thoracic sympathetic ganglia
(E) vagus nerves

202. In angina pectoris, the pain radiating down the left arm is mediated by increased activity in afferent (sensory) fibers contained in

(A) the carotid branch of the glossopharyngeal nerves
(B) the greater splanchnic nerves
(C) the phrenic nerves
(D) the vagus nerve and recurrent laryngeal nerves
(E) none of the above

203. Angina pectoris, which can be explained on the basis of anatomic pathways, is an example of

(A) imagined pain
(B) psychomotor neurosis
(C) referred pain
(D) somatic pain
(E) none of the above

204. The patient is admitted to a coronary care unit for tests and observation. An electrocardiogram reveals a pattern consistent with a small ventricular posteroseptal infarct from ischemic necrosis resulting from inadequate blood supply. Despite the rapid heart beat, its regularity indicates that the infarct has involved only

(A) a localized region of ventricular myocardium
(B) both atrioventricular node and bundle
(C) the atrioventricular bundle
(D) the atrioventricular node
(E) the sinoatrial node

205. In the diagram of a normal heart shown below, the coronary artery most likely to be involved in a posteroseptal infarct (as in this patient) is indicated by which letter?

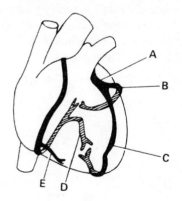

(A) A
(B) B
(C) C
(D) D
(E) E

206. The "margin of safety" provided by the coronary circulation is less than for other parts of the body for which of the following reasons?

(A) Blood flows through the coronary circulation only during diastole (cardiac relaxation)
(B) The coronary arteries arise from the truncus arteriosus just before the semilunar valves
(C) The leaflets of the semilunar valves impede the flow of blood into the coronary circulation
(D) The right coronary artery normally arises from the pulmonary trunk, whereas the left normally arises from the aorta
(E) None of the above

207. The patient recovers and is discharged from the hospital. Even with rest and increased doses of propranolol, however, his angina pectoris persists and, in fact, the attacks progress to angina decubitis (angina occurring at rest). On his readmission to the hospital, coronary angiography is ordered. From this angiogram, the coronary circulation may best be described as

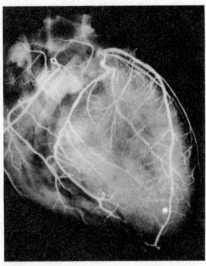

©SAWYER'S Inc., 1958, Portland, Ore. USA

(A) balanced
(B) left preponderant
(C) right dominant
(D) right preponderant
(E) impossible to determine

208. The coronary angiogram (see previous question) indicates that the right coronary artery is free of pathology. The left coronary artery is found to be 70 to 80 percent occluded at three points proximal to its bifurcation into the circumflex and anterior descending arteries. Without surgery and with the coronary distribution pattern shown previously, the prognosis for recovery of this patient to a normally active life is considerably reduced because

(A) all branches of the coronary arteries are end-arteries, precluding the chance that anastomotic connections will occur
(B) the anterior and posterior papillary muscles of the tricuspid valve may be damaged
(C) the blood supply to the sinoatrial node is inadequate
(D) the development of effective collateral circulation between anterior and posterior interventricular arteries is not possible in this case
(E) of none of the above

209. To improve the blood flow to the interventricular septum, a coronary bypass procedure is elected. A section of superficial vein, removed from the lower portion of the patient's leg, is grafted from the aorta to the coronary artery just distal to the site of occlusion. In coronary bypass surgery, which of the following statements is true?

(A) The proximal end of the vein is anastomosed to the aorta
(B) The distal end of the vein is anastomosed to the aorta
(C) The orientation is unimportant because aortic pressure is always higher than venous pressure
(D) The orientation is unimportant because the vein is being used as an artery
(E) The orientation would be important only if a coronary vein were being bypassed

210. A malignant tumor extending from the apical lobe of the right lung may produce all the following signs EXCEPT

(A) bilateral engorgement of the external jugular veins and facial edema
(B) decreased axillary pulse pressure
(C) dilated pupils
(D) paradoxical movement of the right hemidiaphragm
(E) vocal hoarseness

211. Structures that normally transit the diaphragm by way of the esophageal hiatus include the

(A) aorta
(B) azygos vein
(C) hemiazygos vein
(D) right vagus nerve
(E) thoracic duct

(End of question set)

DIRECTIONS: The group of questions below consists of four lettered headings followed by a set of numbered items. For each numbered item select

A	if the item is associated with	(A) **only**
B	if the item is associated with	(B) **only**
C	if the item is associated with	**both** (A) and (B)
D	if the item is associated with	**neither** (A) nor (B)

Each lettered heading may be used **once, more than once, or not at all.**

Questions 212-216

(A) Gray ramus communicans
(B) White ramus communicans
(C) Both
(D) Neither

212. Parasympathetic neurons

213. General visceral afferent neurons

214. Unmyelinated neurons

215. Every spinal nerve

216. Neurons that terminate on sweat glands and smooth muscle

DIRECTIONS: The group of questions below consists of lettered headings followed by a set of numbered items. For each numbered item select the **one** lettered heading with which it is **most** closely associated. Each lettered heading may be used **once, more than once, or not at all.**

Questions 217-220

Movements of the chest wall and diaphragm produce changes in thoracic volume and pulmonary ventilation. For each respiratory muscle action described below, select the factor to which it is most nearly related.

(A) A factor in quiet inspiration
(B) A factor in quiet expiration
(C) An accessory factor in exertional inspiration
(D) A factor in exertional expiration
(E) Not a factor in respiration

217. Contraction of the interchondral (parasternal) portion of the internal intercostal muscles

218. Contraction of the rectus abdominis muscle

219. Contraction of the sternocleidomastoid muscle

220. Contraction of the internal oblique muscle

Gross Anatomy: Thorax

Answers

176. The answer is B. *(Hollinshead, ed 4. pp 176-177.)* The lymphatic drainage of the mammary gland, which follows the pathway of its blood supply, generally travels parallel to the tributaries of the axillary, internal thoracic (mammary), and thoracoacromial vessels. A tendency for the lateral and inferior portions of the breast to drain toward the axillary nodes accounts for approximately 75 percent of the lymphatic drainage. The medial portion tends to drain along the anterior intercostal vessels toward the internal thoracic (parasternal) lymphatic chain, whereas the superior portion tends to drain along the branches of the thoracoacromial artery toward the apical (subclavicular) nodes. Finally, the more superficial regions of the breast may drain along subcutaneous lymphatics to the contralateral breast and superior abdominal wall.

177. The answer is B. *(Hollinshead, ed 4. pp 185-186.)* The serratus anterior muscle (protractor and stabilizer of the scapula) is innervated by the long thoracic nerve (of Bell), which arises from the roots C5 through C7. During axillary dissection in a radical mastectomy, this nerve usually is spared in order to maintain shoulder function in the absence of the pectoralis major muscle. The supraclavicular nerves are sensory branches of the cervical plexus, and the axillary nerve, deep in the brachial portion of the axilla, innervates the deltoid muscle. The thoracodorsal nerve, which arises from the posterior cord of the brachial plexus, innervates the latissimus dorsi muscle. The lower subscapular nerve innervates the teres major muscle and a small portion of the subscapularis muscle.

178. The answer is C. *(Hollinshead, ed 4. p 485.)* The costomediastinal recess is formed by the apposition of diaphragmatic and mediastinal pleura. The costodiaphragmatic recess is formed by the apposition of diaphragmatic pleura and costal pleura. It provides a potential space into which the lung can expand upon inspiration and is therefore maximal upon full expiration. As the most dependent portion of the pleural cavity, it collects fluids when the patient is sitting or standing.

179. The answer is D. *(April, ed 2. p 126.)* The phrenic nerve, which arises from cervical nerves C3 through C5, mediates sensation from the diaphragmatic pleura and peritoneum, as well as from the pericardium, in addition to carrying motor fibers to the diaphragm. As such, pain from the diaphragmatic pleura or peritoneum, as well as from the parietal pericardium, may be referred to dermatomes between C3 and C5, inclusive. These dermatomes correspond to the clavicular region and the anterior and lateral neck, as well as to the anterior, lateral, and posterior aspects of the shoulder.

180. The answer is C. *(Hollinshead, ed 4. p 495.)* Large aspirated objects tend to lodge at the carina. Smaller objects usually lodge in the right inferior lobar bronchus because the right main stem (primary) bronchus is generally more vertical in its course than the left and of greater diameter. In addition, the takeoff angle of the right lower lobe bronchus is less acute than that of the right middle lobe, thereby nearly continuing the direction of both the right main stem bronchus and trachea. Blockage of the airway will produce absence of breath sounds within the lobe and eventual atelectasis.

181. The answer is E. *(April, ed 2. pp 129-130, 152.)* Situs inversus with dextrocardia, occurring in approximately 1 out of every 10,000 persons, is usually accompanied by reversal of the lungs and bronchial tree. While localization of an aspirated foreign body depends to a significant degree on body position at the moment of aspiration, a foreign body lodged in the left lung cannot be explained on the basis of normal anatomy. A preexisting right pneumothorax, right hemothorax, diaphragmatic hernia, or even paralysis of the right hemidiaphragm could result in the aspirated object's being sucked into the more functional left lung, but not if any of these occurred on the left side.

182. The answer is E. *(April, ed 2. pp 132, 539-540.)* The vagus nerve provides the afferent limb of the cough reflex. The inferior laryngeal branch of the vagus nerve innervates the inferior surface of the vocal folds, the trachea, and the bronchial tree. The superior laryngeal (recurrent) branch of the vagus nerve innervates the region of the larynx from the inferior surface of the epiglottis to the superior surface of the vocal folds. The thoracic and abdominal spinal nerves as well as the phrenic nerve provide, in part, the efferent limb of the cough reflex.

183. The answer is C. *(April, ed 2. pp 127-128, 137. Hollinshead, ed 4. pp 486-487, 511.)* The patient has a left pneumothorax. The lucidity of the left pleural cavity with the lack of pulmonary vessels indicates that the left lung has collapsed into a small dense mass adjacent to the mediastinum. Such a nontraumatic pneumothorax may result from the rupture of a pulmonary bleb, especially in a young person. The right lung is normal. There is no pleural fluid level indicative of hemothorax and the near symmetry of the domes of the two hemidiaphragms upon inspiration indicates normal function of the phrenic nerves. The pleural cavities normally extend superior to the first rib into the base of the neck. The heart, measuring less than one-half of the chest diameter, is of normal size.

184. The answer is D. *(Hollinshead, ed 4. pp 555, 557.)* All the soft tissue structures of the middle and posterior mediastinum are somewhat mobile. In the event of a hemothorax or tension pneumothorax, the contents of the middle and posterior mediastinum, including the heart, trachea, aorta, and esophagus, may be pushed to the contralateral side. Treatment in this case involves withdrawing the air with a needle.

185. The answer is A. *(Hollinshead, ed 4. pp 525-526.)* The convex radiopaque shadow indicated by the arrow in the radiograph accompanying the question is produced by the arch of the aorta as it swings posteriorly from the superior mediastinum to become the descending aorta in the posterior mediastinum. The edge of the manubrium produces a concave shadow; the left main stem bronchus usually is visible by its lucency, unless stained with contrast material. Approximately midway in the left pulmonary cavity, the collapsed lung may be seen. Unless contrast material is injected into the heart, the auricles of the left or right atria are not visible.

186. The answer is B. *(April, ed 2. pp 132-133.)* Inability of the thorax to expand and effectively lower intrathoracic (and hence, intrapleural) pressure on the affected side results in inadequate ventilation of the lung. Normal perfusion of an unventilated lung results in cyanosis owing to increased amounts of reduced hemoglobin in the arterial blood. Paralysis of either the right hemidiaphragm or the right thoracic musculature alone would not normally produce cyanosis; at any rate, there is no indication that either of these factors is involved in the patient presented in the question.

187. The answer is E. *(April, ed 2. pp 114-118.)* The increase in anterior and lateral chest diameter during inspiration is attributable in part to the external intercostal muscles; chest cavity expansion inferiorly is effected by contraction (downward movement) of the diaphragm. Patients with severe pulmonary disease also use their posterior serratus muscles, as well as the scalene, sternomastoid, and minor pectoral muscles, to increase inspiratory capacity. Only the small interchondral portions of the internal intercostal layer are inspiratory. The internal intercostal and transverse thoracic muscles are used primarily in *forced* expiration, whereas *passive* expiration is provided by the elastic recoil of the costal cartilages and the elastic resiliency of the lung parenchyma.

188. The answer is D. *(April, ed 2. p 128.)* The usual location of choice for a chest tube drain is in the midaxillary or posteroaxillary line—that is, the vertical line commencing at the posterior axillary fold, at the approximate level of the seventh intercostal space. This location is the lowest region of the pleural cavity in the supine position; it is also an appropriate location for a thoracocentesis. The needle is usually inserted just below the level at which percussive dullness occurs.

189. The answer is C. *(Hollinshead, ed 4. pp 478-479, 570.)* Hemothorax (blood in the pleural cavity) may be derived from tearing or laceration of the internal thoracic artery, musculophrenic artery, intercostal arteries, the aorta and its great vessels, and the great veins of the mediastinum. Combined pneumothorax and hemothorax can result from tears of the lung parenchyma. The lateral thoracic artery lies external to the thoracic wall, which makes it a very unlikely source.

190. The answer is B. *(Hollinshead, ed 4. pp 471, 477.)* The upper two posterior intercostal arteries arise from the costocervical trunk; the remaining arteries arise from the descending thoracic aorta. The posterior intercostal arteries anastomose with the anterior intercostal arteries, which arise from the internal thoracic artery. Laterally, the intercostal neurovascular bundle lies in the costal groove along the internal surface of the inferior border of each rib and between the inner and outer layers of the internal intercostal muscle. Indeed, scalloping of the inferior edge of the rib is a radiographic indication of increased collateral circulation through the intercostal arteries resulting from a circulatory deficit elsewhere. Just as a subcostal location offers protection to the intercostal neurovascular bundle, fracture of a rib may involve tearing of these structures. Thoracocentesis usually is performed adjacent to the upper border of the ribs in order to avoid the intercostal neurovascular bundle.

191. The answer is D. *(Hollinshead, ed 4. p 506.)* Bronchopulmonary segments, the anatomic and functional units of the lung, are roughly pyramidal in shape, have apices directed toward the hilum of the lung, and are separated from each other by connective tissue septa. Each bronchopulmonary segment is supplied by one tertiary or segmental bronchus, along with a branch of the pulmonary artery. Although the segmental bronchus and artery tend to be centrally located, the veins do not accompany the arteries but tend to be located subpleurally and between bronchopulmonary segments. Indeed, at surgery the intersegmental veins are useful in defining intersegmental planes.

192. The answer is C. *(April, ed 2. pp 136-137.)* The parietal pericardium is innervated primarily by branches from the intercostal nerves and the phrenic nerves. The afferent innervation of the visceral pericardium (epicardium) is by way of the middle and lower cervical sympathetic nerves (cardiac accelerator nerves) as well as the upper four thoracic sympathetic pathways (thoracic splanchnic nerves), all of which pass through the cardiac plexus. The greater splanchnic nerve, arising from levels T5 through T9, innervates abdominal viscera. A rule of thumb for the vagus nerve is that in the thorax and abdomen it carries reflex afferents only.

193. The answer is C. *(Hollinshead, ed 4. pp 543-544.)* The sounds associated with closure of the valves of the heart project to specific regions of the chest wall, where they can be auscultated clearly. The mitral valve sound projects to the fifth intercostal space just inferior to the left nipple. This point is superficial to the apex of the heart and a pulse may both be seen and palpated here. The tricuspid valve sounds project most clearly just to the right of the sternum in the fifth intercostal space. The pulmonary and aortic valves project, respectively, to the left and right of the sternal angle (of Louis) at the level of the second intercostal space.

194. The answer is C. *(April, ed 2. pp 136-137. Hollinshead, ed 4. p 522.)* In the costoxiphoid approach to the pericardial cavity, a needle angled upward and toward the left passes between the xiphoid process and the costal margin, through the rectus sheath and rectus abdominis muscle, and through the fibrous and serous layers of the parietal pericardium. Because the line of pleural reflection swings away from the midline anteroinferiorly on the left side, the needle should not enter either the left pleural cavity or the left lung. The parasternal approach to the pericardial cavity will pass through the external intercostal membrane and the interchondral portion of an internal intercostal muscle.

195. The answer is E. *(Hollinshead, ed 4. pp 479, 533-536.)* At the level of the costoxiphoid angle, the internal thoracic artery has bifurcated into the musculo-phrenic and superior epigastric arteries, the former coursing laterally along the costal margin and the latter entering the rectus sheath somewhat lateral to the tract of the needle. Because the heart is tilted on its right side, the right coronary artery lies directly behind and is protected by the sternum. The right marginal branch of the right coronary artery courses anteriorly along the diaphragmatic surface of the heart, anterior and superior to the needle track. The anterior interventricular (descending) artery, coursing to the apex of the heart under the left nipple, is well out of harm's way.

196. The answer is C. *(Hollinshead, ed 4. p 536.)* With the exception of the anterior surface of the right ventricle, blood returning from the coronary circulation collects in the coronary sinus, which, in turn, empties directly into the right atrium. During right ventricular systole, venous blood is stored in the right atrium, and during ventricular diastole, blood flows from the right atrium to the right ventricle.

197. The answer is A. *(Hollinshead, ed 4. pp 536-537.)* The anterior cardiac veins drain the anterior aspect of the right ventricle directly into the right atrium. The smallest cardiac (thebesian) veins (venae cordis minimae), which drain the endo-cardium, open directly into the various chambers of the heart, principally the atria, but also into the ventricles.

198. The answer is D. *(Hollinshead, ed 4. p 535.)* The right coronary artery usually supplies the structures of the right atrium, including the sinoatrial node, right ventricle, and the posterior portion of the interventricular septum. Coronary occlusions involving the right coronary artery are, therefore, often accompanied by rhythm disturbances. The left coronary artery usually supplies the left atrium, left ventricle, and the anterior portion of the interventricular septum, including the region of the atrioventricular bundle (of His).

199. The answer is C. *(April, ed 2. pp 147-149.)* Heart sounds originate from the closure of the atrioventricular and semilunar valves as a result of relative pressure reversals during the cardiac cycle. The first heart sound, heard just after the ventricles begin to contract, occurs when the ventricular pressures exceed atrial pressures, thereby closing the atrioventricular valves. Reverberation within the ventricles causes this S1 sound ("Lub") to have a low frequency and a relatively long duration. The second heart sound is heard at the beginning of ventricular diastole, when the aortic and pulmonary pressures exceed the respective ventricular pressures and snap shut the aortic and pulmonary semilunar valves. This S2 ("Dup") is relatively sharp when both aortic and semilunar valves close together. However, deep inspiration, which lowers intrathoracic pressure, results in delayed closing of the pulmonary valve, producing a split S2. Ventricular systole occurs approximately between the S1 and S2 heart sounds and diastole between S2 and S1. Occasionally, a low, rumbling third heart sound may be heard during diastole and is attributable to ventricular filling. Stenosis or insufficiency of the valves produces turbulence and backflow, respectively, which are heard as murmurs.

200. The answer is D. *(Hollinshead, ed 4. p 538.)* The *afferent* limb of the cardiac reflex is mediated by the carotid branch of the glossopharyngeal nerve (CN IX) from the aortic body and sinus as well as by the vagus nerve (CN X) from the aortic body. The *efferent* limb, which is carried by the sympathetic division of the autonomic nervous system, mediates increases in heart rate and strength of heart beat through release of norepinephrine at the postganglionic effector site. The sympathetic cardiac accelerator fibers, affecting primarily the ventricles, are derived from the superior, middle, and inferior cervical ganglia (cervical cardiac nerves) as well as from the upper four thoracic ganglia (thoracic cardiac nerves), whence they converge on the cardiac plexus before reaching the heart. Parasympathetic fibers derived from CN X and its recurrent laryngeal branch decrease heart rate and stroke volume through release of acetylcholine, principally in the vicinity of the sinoatrial node.

201. The answer is B. *(Hollinshead, ed 4. pp 538-539.)* The cardiac plexus receives its innervation from multiple sources. Parasympathetic innervation is derived from the vagus nerves and their recurrent (inferior) laryngeal branches. The sympathetic innervation is derived from the superior, middle, and inferior cervical ganglia (cervical cardiac nerves) as well as from the upper four thoracic paravertebral ganglia (thoracic cardiac nerves). The superficial and deep cardiac plexuses also contain visceral afferent fibers. The phrenic nerve innervates the diaphragm only.

202. The answer is E. *(Hollinshead, ed 4. p 539.)* Afferent innervation from the heart and coronary arteries travels to the cardiac plexus along the sympathetic pathways. Once the afferent fibers pass through the cardiac plexus, they run along the cervical and thoracic cardiac nerves to the cervical and upper four thoracic sympathetic ganglia. Having traversed these ganglia, the fibers gain access (via the white rami communicantes) to the upper four thoracic spinal nerves and the corresponding levels of the spinal cord. The visceral afferent fibers associated with the vagus nerve are associated with reflexes and do not carry nociceptive information. The greater, lesser, and least splanchnic nerves convey visceral afferents from the abdominal region.

203. The answer is C. *(Hollinshead, ed 4. p 539.)* Angina pectoris is an example of referred pain. As a consequence of the afferent sympathetic pain pathway, pain originating in the heart or coronary arteries is referred to (appears as if originating from) the upper thoracic dermatomes (T1-T4); these dermatomes include the medial aspect of the upper extremity and the thorax from the sternal angle to the tip of the xiphoid process.

204. The answer is A. *(Hollinshead, ed 4. pp 533-535, 540-541.)* Severe ischemia (resulting in oxygen deprivation) in the vicinity of the sinoatrial node, atrioventricular node, or atrioventricular bundle would severely affect the regularity of cardiac rhythm by blocking transmission of the cardiac impulse. The region of the sinoatrial node receives blood from the nodal (caval) branch of the right coronary artery. If the sinoatrial node is involved, electronic pacing of the heart may be accomplished by an implanted pacemaker. The regions of the atrioventricular node and atrioventricular bundle are supplied by branches of the right coronary artery. Localized destruction of the atrioventricular node or atrioventricular bundle produces atrioventricular heart block in which the ventricles continue to beat irregularly and at a slower rate than the atria.

205. The answer is D. *(Hollinshead, ed 4. p 535.)* The artery labeled D in the diagram accompanying the question represents the posterior interventricular (descending) artery, which supplies blood to the posterior portions of the interventricular septum as well as to the posterior wall of the right ventricle. This artery usually is a branch of the right coronary artery, and the diagnosis of this patient's disorder is consistent with the results of the ECG, which indicates a posterior septal infarct. The anterior interventricular artery (C) arises from the left coronary artery (A) and supplies the anterior portion of the interventricular septum and the anterior walls of both ventricles. The posterior interventricular artery (D) usually anastomoses with the anterior interventricular artery (C) near the apex of the heart. The circumflex artery (B) circles toward the back of the heart in the coronary sulcus and may occasionally give rise to the posterior interventricular artery (D). The right marginal artery (E) is a branch of the right coronary artery.

206. The answer is A. *(April, ed 2. p 140.)* During ventricular systole, there is no pressure gradient between the aorta and ventricular walls; therefore, flow through the coronary circulation can occur only during diastole (relaxation), or approximately half the cardiac cycle. This intermittent nature of coronary blood supply means that, compared with other vital organs, the heart has a correspondingly reduced margin of safety.

207. The answer is B. *(April, ed 2. pp 139-140.)* In balanced coronary circulation, the right coronary artery terminates as the posterior interventricular (descending) artery, whereas the circumflex branch of the left coronary artery terminates before reaching the posterior interventricular sulcus. If, as in the patient described in the question, the circumflex artery gives rise to the posterior interventricular artery in addition to the usual anterior interventricular artery, the circulation is described as left preponderant. If the right coronary artery, in addition to providing the posterior interventricular artery, crosses to the left margin of the heart, the circulation is described as right preponderant.

208. The answer is D. *(April, ed 2. pp 139-140.)* Even though coronary arteries are described as end-arteries, collateral circulation can and does develop if obstruction of a major coronary vessel or branch develops over an extended period, as in arteriosclerotic occlusion. Because in the left preponderant heart both the anterior interventricular and posterior interventricular arteries are derived from the left coronary artery, and since the patient described in the question displays radiographic evidence of partial obstruction proximal to the bifurcation of the left coronary artery into circumflex and anterior interventricular branches, development of adequate collateral circulation to the interventricular septum is not possible without surgical intervention.

209. The answer is B. *(Hollinshead, ed 4. pp 75-76, 536.)* In a coronary bypass procedure, the *distal* end of the vein graft is anastomosed to the aorta so that the presence of a valve or valve leaflets in the graft will not obstruct the flow of coronary blood. In recent years, the reversed saphenous vein graft from the calf has been the choice for this procedure. This vein is closer in size to the coronary arteries than one taken from the thigh.

210. The answer is C. *(April, ed 2. p 128.)* A tumor in the upper lobe of either lung may involve a number of important structures. Compression of a subclavian artery will result in diminished pulse pressure and a cooler extremity. Compression of a recurrent laryngeal nerve paralyzes the musculature of the larynx with resultant hoarseness. Compression of the brachiocephalic vein impedes venous return from the head, neck, and upper extremities with resultant venous engorgement and edema. Compression of the phrenic nerve paralyzes the hemidiaphragm so that paradoxical diaphragmatic movements occur; i.e., the diaphragm rises passively during inspiration and falls during expiration. Compression of the stellate ganglion or sympathetic chain produces Horner's syndrome, one sign of which is pupillary constriction.

211. The answer is D. *(Hollinshead, ed 4. pp 565-566, 570-573, 682-683.)* The esophageal hiatus, in addition to allowing passage of the esophagus, also passes the left (anterior) and right (posterior) vagal trunks. The aortic hiatus transmits the aorta, the thoracic duct, and occasionally an azygos or hemiazygos vein. Usually the azygos and hemiazygos veins either pass lateral to or through a crus of the diaphragm along with the respective left and right sympathetic chains. The phrenic nerves usually penetrate the diaphragm to gain access to the inferior surface; however, the right phrenic may accompany the inferior vena cava through the caval hiatus.

212-216. The answers are: 212-D, 213-B, 214-A, 215-A, 216-A. *(Hollinshead, ed 4. pp 59-62.)* Sympathetic outflow occurs between the first thoracic and second lumbar segments of the spinal cord. The presynaptic sympathetic neurons, which originate in the lateral cell columns of the spinal cord, pass along the thoracic and upper lumbar spinal nerves. These myelinated neurons leave the respective spinal nerves by white rami communicantes, which convey the sympathetic neurons to the chain of sympathetic ganglia.

Some of the presynaptic fibers pass through the chain as splanchnic nerves to reach prevertebral ganglia. Others may ascend into the cervical portion of the chain or descend into the lower lumbar and sacral portions of the sympathetic chain before synapsing. Visceral afferent neurons conveying sensation from the viscera reach the sympathetic chain via the splanchnic nerves and then enter the spinal nerve via a white ramus communicans.

The cell bodies of postsynaptic sympathetic neurons compose the sympathetic ganglia. These neurons receive input from the presynaptic neurons and send unmyelinated axons back to the spinal nerve along gray rami communicantes.

Each spinal nerve receives a gray ramus communicans from the sympathetic chain. These gray rami contain neurons that control the sweat glands, the arrector pili (pilomotor) muscles, and the musculature of the blood vessels that lie in the dermatomic and myotomic distributions of each spinal nerve.

217-220. The answers are: 217-A, 218-D, 219-C, 220-D. *(April, ed 2. pp 121-122.)* In quiet inspiration, the external intercostals and the interchondral (parasternal) portion of the internal intercostals function to elevate the ribs and thereby increase the transverse diameter of the thoracic cage. Concomitantly, contraction of the diaphragm increases the vertical diameter of the thoracic cage. The relative contribution of each group of muscles is dependent on the sex and age of the person. Generally, children and older men use the diaphragm and abdominal musculature; women, especially if pregnant, tend to breath thoracically.

Exertional expiration is accomplished by contraction of the internal intercostal muscles, thereby decreasing the transverse diameter of the thoracic cage, as well as by contraction of the abdominal musculature, including the rectus abdominis, external and internal oblique muscles, transversus abdominis muscle, and quadratus lumborum. In addition, the perineal muscles may tense. Contraction of the abdominal muscles moves the viscera under the diaphragm, forcing it upward into the thorax, thereby decreasing thoracic volume.

In quiet expiration, muscular activity is unnecessary. Normal relaxed expiration is accomplished by the elastic recoil of the lungs, which tends to collapse the alveoli and expel the contained air. This action is assisted by the elastic recoil of the thoracic cage in response to the twisting and bending of the costal cartilages during inspiration.

Exertional or forced inspiration is assisted by the action of the sternocleidomastoid muscle, which inserts onto the sternum and clavicle, as well as the anterior, middle, and posterior scalenes, which insert onto the first rib. Contraction of these muscles, with the head and shoulders thrown back, elevates and fixes the ribs. In this posture, the pectoralis major and minor muscles also contribute to rib elevation.

Gross Anatomy: Abdomen

DIRECTIONS: Each question below contains four or five suggested responses. Select the **one best** response to each question.

Questions 221-230

A 46-year-old bakery worker is admitted to a hospital in acute distress. She has experienced severe abdominal pain, nausea, and vomiting for 2 days. The pain, which is sharp and constant, began in the epigastric region and radiated bilaterally around the chest to just below the scapulas. Subsequently, the pain became localized in the right hypochondrium. The patient, who has a history of similar "attacks" after hearty meals over the past 5 years, is moderately overweight and the mother of four. Palpation reveals marked tenderness in the right hypochondriac region and some rigidity of the abdominal musculature. An x-ray without contrast medium shows numerous calcified stones in the region of the gallbladder. The patient shows no sign of icterus (jaundice).

221. Diffuse pain referred to the epigastric region and radiating circumferentially around the chest is the result of afferent fibers that travel via which of the following nerves?

(A) Greater splanchnic
(B) Intercostal
(C) Phrenic
(D) Vagus
(E) None of the above

222. In the patient described, the subsequent localization of the pain in the right hypochondriac region is the result of inflammatory stimulation of fibers that are extensions of which of the following nerves?

(A) Greater splanchnic
(B) Intercostal
(C) Phrenic
(D) Vagus
(E) None of the above

223. The patient receives a general anesthetic in preparation for a cholecystectomy. A right subcostal incision is made, beginning near the xiphoid process and running along and immediately beneath the costal margin to the anterior axillary line, transecting the rectus abdominis muscle and rectus sheath.

At the level of the transpyloric plane, the anterior wall of the sheath of the rectus abdominis muscle receives contributions from the

(A) aponeuroses of the internal and external oblique muscles
(B) aponeuroses of the transversus abdominis and internal oblique muscles
(C) aponeuroses of the transversus abdominis and internal and external oblique muscles
(D) transversalis fascia
(E) transversalis fascia and aponeurosis of the transversus abdominis muscle

224. At this level of incision, ligation of the superior epigastric artery probably will result in little, if any, necrosis of the rectus abdominis muscle because the superior epigastric artery anastomoses with the

(A) deep circumflex iliac artery
(B) inferior epigastric artery
(C) intercostal arteries
(D) internal thoracic artery
(E) musculophrenic artery

225. Exploration of the peritoneal cavity discloses a greatly distended gallbladder. Numerous stones could be palpated. A finger was inserted into the epiploic foramen (of Winslow), and the common bile duct was palpated for stones. Structures that bound the epiploic foramen include all the following EXCEPT the

(A) caudate lobe of the liver
(B) common bile duct
(C) hepatic vein
(D) inferior vena cava
(E) superior part of the duodenum

226. The lesser omentum is incised close to its free edge, and the biliary tree is identified and freed by blunt dissection. The liquid contents of the gallbladder are aspirated with a syringe, the fundus incised, and the stones removed. The entire duct system is carefully probed for stones, one of which is found to be obstructing a duct. In view of the observation that the patient is not jaundiced, the most probable location of the obstruction is

(A) the common bile duct
(B) the common hepatic duct
(C) the cystic duct
(D) within the duodenal papilla proximal to the juncture with the pancreatic duct
(E) within the duodenal papilla distal to the juncture with the pancreatic duct

227. The biliary duct system is carefully dissected. The cystic artery and cystic duct both are identified, ligated, and divided, the duct at a point about an eighth of an inch from its juncture with the common hepatic duct. The gallbladder is then freed from the inferior surface of the liver by blunt dissection and removed. However, the operative field suddenly fills with arterial blood. In order to locate and ligate the bleeder, hemorrhage should be controlled by

(A) ligating the common hepatic artery
(B) ligating the proper hepatic artery distal to the origin of the right gastric and gastroduodenal arteries
(C) ligating the left hepatic artery, especially if there are additional (aberrant) left hepatic arteries present
(D) ligating the hepatic portal vein
(E) temporarily compressing the hepatic pedicle

228. It is ascertained that an accessory right hepatic artery inadvertently had been torn. There is no choice but to ligate the accessory artery. The effect of this ligation most probably will be

(A) ischemic necrosis of the quadrate lobe of the liver
(B) ischemic necrosis of a discrete portion of the right lobe of the liver
(C) no necrosis in any lobe because of the integrity of the hepatic portal vein
(D) no necrosis in any lobe because of extrahepatic collateral blood supply
(E) no necrosis in any lobe because of intrahepatic collateral blood supply

229. Before closure of the incision, it is felt that a drain should be left in place in the abdominal cavity so that any leakage of bile from the sutured stump or from inadvertent injury to the duct system can be detected. This drain would most advantageously be located in the

(A) omental bursa
(B) pelvic cavity
(C) pouch of Morison
(D) right paracolic gutter
(E) right subphrenic recess

230. The subcostal incision, which parallels the anterior costal margin, is closed in layers. The patient is allowed up on her first postoperative day; on the third day the drain (which shows no bile leakage) is withdrawn, and on the tenth day the patient is discharged. As a result of the location and direction of the incision, one might expect healing to result in

(A) loss of blood supply and necrosis of a portion of the rectus abdominis muscle
(B) significant paralysis of a portion of the rectus abdominis muscle
(C) minimal scarring
(D) negligible possibility of subsequent abdominal herniation
(E) none of the above

(End of question set)

Questions 231-238

A 37-year-old man with a history of alcohol abuse was seen in the emergency room complaining of "stomach cramps" in the region of the umbilicus. He reported several recent incidents of vomiting that contained no noticeable blood, although he had in the past vomited bright red blood. He insisted that he had been "on the wagon" for the past several months. Physical examination revealed a mass about the umbilicus with indications of periumbilical peritoneal inflammation. His white blood cell count was high and he had a temperature of 39.4°C (103°F). He was admitted to the surgical service for emergency reduction of an umbilical hernia with suspected strangulation.

231. The crampy abdominal pain referred to the umbilical region and knowledge of peritoneal structure would lead the examining physician to suspect that the strangulated section of gut was most likely the

(A) ascending colon
(B) descending colon
(C) small intestine
(D) sigmoid colon
(E) stomach

232. At surgery a loop of herniated gut appeared ischemic and was strangulated. While enlarging the hernial defect superiorly in the midline so that the loop of gut could be replaced into the abdominal cavity, profuse dark bleeding occurred. The source of the bleeding was not readily apparent, but the surgeon should have suspected that the origin was most likely due to severing the

(A) inferior epigastric artery
(B) dilated paraumbilical veins
(C) superior epigastric artery
(D) inferior mesenteric artery
(E) veins of Retzius, connecting secondarily retroperitoneal structures to veins of the abdominal wall

233. In portal hypertension where blood flow through the liver is impeded, in addition to via the *caput medusae,* blood may return to the systemic circulation via all the following EXCEPT the

(A) esophageal veins
(B) inferior hemorrhoidal veins
(C) middle hemorrhoidal veins
(D) veins associated with the transverse colon
(E) veins of Retzius associated with the descending colon

234. As standard prophylaxis, the small intestine was inspected unsuccessfully for the presence of an ileal diverticulum. All the following statements pertain to Meckel's diverticulum EXCEPT

(A) it is a remnant of the urachus
(B) it is found on the antimesenteric side of the gut
(C) it is located within 3 feet of the ileocecal valve
(D) it is present in 3 percent of the population
(E) it is usually lined by gastric mucosa

235. Next, the appendix was located and removed as prophylaxis. The vermiform appendix is best located by following the

(A) anterior cecal artery
(B) descending branch of the right colic artery
(C) ileum to the ileocolic juncture
(D) posterior cecal artery
(E) teniae coli of the ascending colon

236. After the herniated segment of gut was placed into the abdominal cavity, its color changed from purple to pink, indicating that the vasculature was functional. The small intestine normally receives significant collateral circulation from the

(A) descending branch of the left colic artery
(B) renal arteries
(C) splenic artery
(D) superior pancreaticoduodenal artery
(E) none of the above

237. On manual exploration of the abdominal cavity, the liver was felt to be hard and nodular. This, in addition to the history of hematemesis, indicated that control of the portal hypertension was necessary. In a patient with cirrhosis of the liver, venous hypertension would be expected in

(A) the hepatic vein
(B) the renal vein
(C) the short gastric veins
(D) the suprarenal vein
(E) none of the above

238. The incision was extended and the hepatic portal vein located. To relieve the portal hypertension, a side-to-side anastomosis was made between the portal vein and the inferior vena cava. The location of the inferior vena cava is

(A) across the epiploic foramen from the portal vein
(B) anterior and to the left of the portal vein
(C) immediately to the right of the portal vein
(D) posterior and to the right of the portal vein
(E) none of the above

(End of question set)

239. A posteriorly perforating ulcer in the pyloric antrum of the stomach is most likely to produce *initial* localized peritonitis or abscess formation in the

(A) greater sac
(B) left subhepatic and hepatorenal spaces (pouch of Morison)
(C) omental bursa
(D) right subphrenic space
(E) right subhepatic space

240. A patient is diagnosed as having intestinal angina (thrombotic occlusion of the superior mesenteric artery near its origin). If significant collateral circulation is not present or fails to develop, all the following parts of the intestinal tract may become gangrenous EXCEPT the

(A) ascending colon
(B) appendix
(C) descending colon
(D) ileum
(E) transverse colon

241. Mucosal necrosis of the rectum usually will not result from occlusion of the inferior mesenteric artery because

(A) a major arterial supply to the rectum is from anastomotic connections from the superior mesenteric artery
(B) a major arterial supply to the rectum is from the left colic artery with anastomoses occurring at Sudeck's point
(C) the inferior mesenteric artery does not supply the rectum
(D) a principal branch of the external iliac artery is a major supplier to the rectum
(E) the middle rectal artery, a branch of the internal iliac artery, is a major arterial supplier to the rectum

242. Pain associated with external hemorrhoids is mediated by

(A) the hypogastric nerves to the lumbar splanchnic nerves
(B) the pelvic splanchnic nerves (nervi erigentes)
(C) the pudendal nerve
(D) the sacral sympathetic chain
(E) none of the above

243. Sympathectomy may occasionally relieve intractable pain of visceral origin, inasmuch as visceral afferent pain fibers run along the sympathetic pathways in the abdomen. Autonomic control of peristalsis in the descending colon should not be affected by bilateral lumbar sympathectomy because

(A) the descending colon is controlled chiefly by parasympathetic innervation from the nervi erigentes
(B) the descending colon receives its parasympathetic innervation from the vagus nerve
(C) the descending colon receives its sympathetic innervation from thoracic splanchnic nerves
(D) lumbar splanchnics from L1, L2, and L3 only innervate the pelvic viscera via the hypogastric nerve
(E) only presynaptic sympathetic fibers have been severed

244. The false capsule of the kidney (renal or Gerota's fascia) separates paranephric and perinephric fat and prevents spread of renal infection to all the following locations EXCEPT the

(A) contralateral kidney
(B) deep pelvis
(C) infracolic compartment of the greater sac
(D) lesser sac
(E) supracolic compartment of the greater sac

Questions 245-248

A middle-aged woman describes flushing, severe headaches, and a feeling that her heart is "going to explode" when she gets excited. At the beginning of a physical examination her blood pressure (130/85) is not significantly above normal. However, upon palpation of her upper left quadrant the examining physician notices the onset of sympathetic signs. Her blood pressure (200/135) is abnormally high. A subsequent CT scan confirms the suspected tumor of the left adrenal gland. The patient is scheduled for surgery.

245. The symptoms that the patient correlated with the onset of excitement were due to nervous stimulation of the adrenal glands. The adrenal medulla receives its innervation from

(A) preganglionic sympathetic nerves
(B) postsynaptic sympathetic nerves
(C) preganglionic parasympathetic nerves
(D) postganglionic parasympathetic nerves
(E) somatic nerves

246. The surgeon decides to perform the left adrenalectomy via a posterior approach. In the process of making a deep posterior incision along the 12th rib, the surgeon notes that the blood seeping into the operative field has changed from bright red to dark, which indicates

(A) that the costodiaphragmatic recess has been entered
(B) that the liver has been incised
(C) that the peritoneal cavity has been opened
(D) that the renal capsule has been punctured
(E) none of the above

247. The adrenal gland is located and the venous drainage is ligated to prevent life-threatening quantities of adrenalin from entering the blood stream upon manipulation of the gland. Normally the left adrenal venous drainage is into the

(A) inferior vena cava
(B) left azygos vein
(C) left inferior phrenic vein
(D) left renal vein
(E) superior mesenteric vein

248. Once the adrenal vein has been ligated and sectioned, the arterial supply is identified and tied off. The left adrenal gland may receive arterial supply from all the following vessels EXCEPT

(A) the aorta
(B) the left inferior phrenic artery
(C) the left renal artery
(D) a superior polar artery
(E) the celiac artery

(End of question set)

Questions 249-257

While moving furniture, an 18-year-old man experiences excruciating pain in his right groin. A few hours later he also develops pain in the umbilical region, with accompanying nausea. At this point he seeks medical attention. Examination reveals a bulge midway between the midline and the anterior superior iliac spine, but superior to the inguinal ligament. On coughing or straining, the bulge increases and the inguinal pain intensifies. The bulge courses medially and inferiorly into the upper portion of the scrotum and cannot be reduced with the finger pressure of the examiner. It is decided that a medical emergency exists, and the patient is scheduled for immediate surgery.

249. An inguinal, rather than a femoral, hernia is suspected in this patient for all the following reasons EXCEPT

(A) the bulge begins superior to the inguinal ligament
(B) the bulge occurs midway between the symphysis pubis and anterior superior iliac spine
(C) femoral hernias occur only in females
(D) the hernia extends into the superior portion of the scrotal sac

250. Nausea and diffuse pain referred to the umbilical region in this patient most probably are due to

(A) compression of the genitofemoral nerve
(B) compression of the ilioinguinal nerve
(C) dilatation of the inguinal canal
(D) incarceration of a loop of small bowel
(E) ischemic necrosis of the cremaster muscle

251. With the patient under general anesthesia, an incision was made above and parallel to the inguinal ligament to the depth of the aponeurosis of the internal oblique muscle. The layers of abdominal wall incised include all the following EXCEPT the

(A) deep fascia
(B) fatty (superficial) layer of superficial fascia
(C) membranous (deep) layer of superficial fascia
(D) transversalis fascia

252. At this stage of surgery, one would expect to find which of the following arteries in the inguinal region?

(A) Aberrant obturator (if present)
(B) External iliac
(C) External pudendal
(D) Inferior epigastric
(E) Superficial circumflex iliac

253. The spermatic cord, which is observed exiting from the superficial inguinal ring, appears to be greatly distended. It is thus immediately apparent that the course taken by the herniation is correctly characterized by all the following statements EXCEPT

(A) it lies lateral to the inferior epigastric artery
(B) it lies superior to the inguinal ligament
(C) it occurs within the inguinal triangle (of Hesselbach)
(D) it passes through the deep inguinal ring
(E) it passes through the superficial inguinal ring

254. The external oblique aponeurosis is incised and the superficial ring opened. The inguinal canal is then opened by blunt dissection. Abdominal wall structures that usually contribute directly to the spermatic cord include which of the following?

(A) External oblique muscle
(B) Falx inguinalis
(C) Internal oblique muscle
(D) Rectus sheath
(E) Transversus abdominis muscle

255. At this point in the surgical procedure, it is noticed that a nerve has been inadvertently sectioned. This nerve exited through the superficial inguinal ring and was applied to the anterior aspect of the spermatic cord. As a result of this operative error, it is probable that the patient will

(A) be unable to produce spermatozoa in the right testis
(B) become impotent
(C) lose the cremasteric reflex on the right side
(D) lose the dartos response to cold
(E) lose sensation over portions of the base of the penis and anterior scrotum

256. In addition to the vas deferens, structures normally found within the spermatic cord include all the following EXCEPT the

(A) deferential artery
(B) efferent ductules
(C) pampiniform plexus of the testicular vein
(D) testicular artery
(E) testicular nerves

257. The hernial sac was incised and the intestine gently replaced into the peritoneal cavity. Reduction of the size of the internal inguinal ring by suturing resulted in reestablishment of the abdominal wall. In this repair, structures suitable for anchoring sutures include all the following EXCEPT the

(A) inguinal ligament (of Poupart)
(B) interfoveolar ligament
(C) lacunar ligament (of Gimbernat)
(D) pectineal ligament (of Cooper)
(E) rectus sheath

(End of question set)

258. The blood supply to the ureters is derived from all the following arteries EXCEPT the

(A) common iliac
(B) gonadal
(C) inferior mesenteric
(D) inferior vesical
(E) renal

259. Within the femoral triangle, the femoral vein and artery are encased in a fascial femoral sheath. The medial part of this sheath contains a small, vertical gap—the femoral ring—through which herniation may occur. The boundaries of the femoral ring include all the following EXCEPT the

(A) femoral nerve
(B) femoral vein
(C) inguinal ligament
(D) lacunar ligament (of Gimbernat)
(E) pectineal ligament (of Cooper)

260. The lymphatic drainage of the rectum is important because of the high incidence of rectal carcinoma. In the vicinity of the inferior rectal valve (of Houston), the pathways of lymphatic drainage can be to all the following EXCEPT the

(A) inferior mesenteric nodes
(B) inguinal nodes
(C) internal iliac nodes
(D) superior mesenteric nodes

DIRECTIONS: The group of questions below consists of four lettered headings followed by a set of numbered items. For each numbered item select

A	if the item is associated with	(A) **only**
B	if the item is associated with	(B) **only**
C	if the item is associated with	**both** (A) and (B)
D	if the item is associated with	**neither** (A) nor (B)

Each lettered heading may be used **once, more than once, or not at all.**

Questions 261-266

(A) Jejunum
(B) Ileum
(C) Both
(D) Neither

261. Thick wall due to numerous tall and feathery plicae circulares

262. Numerous aggregates of lymphoid tissue

263. Blood supply by the inferior mesenteric artery

264. Arterial supply characterized by few arcades and long terminal vessels

265. Location in the hypogastrium and deep pelvic cavity

266. Thick, fat-laden mesentery

DIRECTIONS: The group of questions below consists of lettered headings followed by a set of numbered items. For each numbered item select the **one** lettered heading with which it is **most** closely associated. Each lettered heading may be used **once, more than once, or not at all.**

Questions 267-270

Several major anatomic structures pass through hiatal openings in the diaphragm. Frequently, abdominal contents may herniate into the thorax, either through one of these hiatuses or through developmental defects in the diaphragm. For each of the following questions, select from the diagram below the lettered opening that is most appropriate.

267. The most common site for a diaphragmatic congenital hernia

268. Transmits the right phrenic nerve

269. Transmits a hiatal hernia of the stomach

270. Transmits the thoracic duct

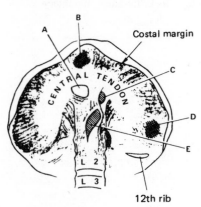

Diaphragm — Inferior Surface

Gross Anatomy: Abdomen

Answers

221. The answer is A. *(Hollinshead, ed 4. p 659.)* Visceral afferent pain fibers from the gallbladder travel through the celiac plexus, thence along the greater splanchnic nerves to levels T5-T9 of the spinal cord. Thus, pain originating from the gallbladder will be referred to (appear as if coming from) the dermatomes served by T5-T9, which include a band from the infrascapular region to the epigastrium.

222. The answer is B. *(Hollinshead, ed 4. pp 478, 592-593.)* When inflammatory processes in the gallbladder spread to the adjacent parietal peritoneum, somatic pain fibers of the abdominal extensions of the right intercostal nerves carry the sensation of abdominal wall pain to the spinal cord and the pain becomes localized to the right hypochondrium.

223. The answer is A. *(Hollinshead, ed 4. pp 585-588.)* The rectus sheath is formed by the aponeurotic tendons of the abdominal wall musculature. Between the costal margin and the umbilicus, the aponeurosis of the internal oblique muscle splits, one portion passing anterior and the other posterior to the rectus abdominis muscle. The aponeurosis of the external oblique muscle fuses with the anterior leaflet of the aponeurosis of the internal oblique muscle to form the anterior wall of the rectus sheath. The aponeurosis of the transversus abdominis muscle fuses with the posterior leaflet of the aponeurosis of the internal oblique muscle to form the posterior wall of the rectus sheath. Approximately midway between the umbilicus and symphysis pubis, the aponeuroses of the internal oblique and transversus abdominis muscles pass anterior to the rectus abdominis muscle to contribute to the anterior leaf of the rectus sheath. This abrupt transition results in a free edge to the posterior rectus sheath, known as the arcuate line (of Douglas). Between this line and the pubis, only the transversalis fascia separates the rectus abdominis muscle from the peritoneum. It is here where the inferior epigastric artery gains access to the rectus sheath that ventral lateral (Spigelian) herniation may occur.

224. The answer is B. *(Hollinshead, ed 4. p 593.)* Within the structure of the rectus abdominis muscle, the superior epigastric artery (a terminal branch of the internal thoracic artery) has profuse anastomotic connections with the inferior epigastric artery, a branch of the external iliac artery. These anastomotic connections assure an adequate blood supply to the entire rectus abdominis muscle in the event one or the other epigastric artery is ligated. Moreover, these anastomoses constitute an important collateral pathway to the lower regions of the body in the event of a gradual obstruction of the abdominal aorta.

225. The answer is C. *(Hollinshead, ed 4. pp 602-603.)* The epiploic foramen is bounded superiorly by the caudate lobe of the liver, inferiorly by the superior part of the duodenum, posteriorly by the inferior vena cava, and anteriorly by the hepatoduodenal ligament, which contains the common bile duct, hepatic artery proper, and portal vein. The hepatic vein(s) leave(s) the liver posterosuperiorly to join the inferior vena cava.

226. The answer is C. *(Hollinshead, ed 4. pp 653-654.)* Obstruction of any portion of the biliary tree will produce symptoms of gallbladder attack. If the common hepatic duct or common bile duct is occluded by stone or tumor, biliary stasis with accompanying jaundice occurs. In addition, blockage of the duodenal papilla (of Vater), distal to the juncture of the common bile duct with the pancreatic duct, can lead to complicating pancreatitis. If only the cystic duct is obstructed, jaundice will not occur because bile may flow freely from the liver to the duodenum. Common duct obstruction also may arise as a result of pressure exerted on the duct by an external mass, such as a tumor in the head of the pancreas.

227. The answer is E. *(April, ed 2. p 208.)* Compressing the hepatic pedicle, with its contained vascular structures, between the forefinger placed in the epiploic foramen (of Winslow) and the thumb placed anteriorly is a convenient way to stem extrahepatic hemorrhage until the source of bleeding can be located and ligated. The blood supply to the liver is variable; several potential anastomotic loops exist between branches of the extrahepatic arterial system. Thus, ligation of the *common* hepatic artery proximal to the gastroduodenal artery will enable arterial blood to reach the liver from branches of the splenic artery (via anastomotic left and right gastroepiploic arteries) and the superior mesenteric artery (via the anastomotic inferior and superior pancreaticoduodenal arteries). Ligation of the *proper* hepatic artery proximal to the origin of the right gastric artery will enable arterial blood to reach the liver from branches of the celiac artery (via anastomotic left and right gastric arteries). However, ligation *distal* to the juncture of the right gastric artery will terminate most of, if not all, the blood supply to the liver and incur a danger of ischemia, if not necrosis of hepatic tissue. Because accessory or aberrant hepatic arteries usually are not sources of collateral blood supply to the liver, they cannot be relied on to provide intrahepatic anastomotic connections.

228. The answer is B. *(April, ed 2. p 208.)* Because few intrahepatic arterial anastomoses exist, ligation of a left or right hepatic artery, or of an aberrant (accessory) hepatic artery, will result in ischemic necrosis of the region of the liver supplied by that vessel. The left hepatic artery supplies the left lobe and the quadrate lobe, as well as half the caudate lobe. The right hepatic artery supplies the right lobe and the other half of the caudate lobe; it also usually supplies the gallbladder through the cystic artery. No major extrahepatic anastomotic connections distal to the right gastric artery exist, and the hepatic portal vein has far too low a partial pressure of oxygen to supply the metabolic requirements of liver parenchyma.

229. The answer is C. *(Hollinshead, ed 4. p 607.)* The combined subhepatic and hepatorenal recesses are called the pouch of Morison, which represents the lowest part of the peritoneal cavity when a person is in a supine position. Since bile leakage subsequent to cholecystectomy or infection originating in the peritoneal cavity tends to drain to the pouch of Morison, this location is the most advantageous location for a drain.

230. The answer is B. *(Hollinshead, ed 4. pp 140, 588.)* The rectus abdominis muscle receives an abundant collateral blood supply. The nerve supply to the rectus abdominis muscle is derived from abdominal extensions of the lower seven intercostal nerves and from the iliohypogastric nerve. These nerves run between the internal oblique and transversus abdominis muscles to reach the lateral border of the rectus sheath, which they pierce to reach the rectus abdominis muscle. Consequently, a subcostal incision from the xiphisternal angle to the anterior axillary line is apt to sever three or four of these nerves, paralyzing a significant portion of the ipsilateral rectus abdominis muscle. An affected patient may be predisposed to subsequent abdominal herniation. Although the direction of an incision along the costal margin is perforce perpendicular to the dermal cleavage lines (of Langer) and thus may produce discomfort and healing with significant scarring, such an incision is justified by the required operative exposure that it provides.

231. The answer is C. *(Hollinshead, ed 4. pp 673-675.)* The umbilical region is innervated by the 10th intercostal nerve. The afferent nerve fibers from the jejunum and ileum as well as from the ascending colon and transverse colon travel through the superior mesenteric plexus and along the lesser splanchnic nerve to spinal nerves T10 and T11. Thus, pain originating from these portions of the gastrointestinal tract will refer pain to the umbilical region. The ascending colon and descending colon, being secondarily retroperitoneal, are unlikely to be involved in the umbilical herniation. The mobile transverse colon could be involved, but the referred pain would tend to be subumbilical, not periumbilical.

232. The answer is B. *(Hollinshead, ed 4. pp 657-658.)* In persons with liver damage, such as in alcohol abuse, the flow of blood through the liver is obstructed, which results in portal hypertension. The blood returning from the gastrointestinal tract must find other pathways to the systemic veins. One such pathway occurs between the portal vein tributaries of the falciform ligament and the paraumbilical veins of the anterior abdominal wall, which drain into the superior and inferior epigastric veins. Enlargement of these anastomoses radiating from the umbilicus produces the *caput medusae*. When present, enlarged paraumbilical veins may present surgical complications.

233. The answer is D. *(Hollinshead, ed 4. pp 657-658.)* Portosystemic venous shunts may develop in several areas. Typically, anastomoses occur between the veins of the falciform ligament and the superior and inferior epigastric veins, producing *caput medusae;* between the gastric veins and the esophageal veins, producing esophageal varices; between the superior hemorrhoidal vein and the middle as well as the inferior hemorrhoidal veins, producing hemorrhoids; and between veins of retroperitoneal structures and the body wall, the so-called veins of Retzius. The transverse colon is a peritoneal structure.

234. The answer is A. *(Hollinshead, ed 4. p 661.)* The ileal diverticulum (of Meckel) is a developmental remnant of the omphalomesenteric (vitelline) duct, or yolk stalk. It occurs in approximately 3 percent of the population, usually within 3 feet of the ileocecal junction on the antimesenteric side of the ileum, and averages about 3 inches in length. Because the mucosal lining of Meckel's diverticulum contains gastric mucosa with oxyntic cells that secrete acid, peptic ulceration may occur in the ileum adjacent to a persistent ileal diverticulum. In addition to being a source of obstructive inflammation, the anomaly may exhibit a persistent connective tissue or vascular connection to the umbilicus, about which intestinal volvulus with obstruction may occur.

235. The answer is E. *(Hollinshead, ed 4. p 667.)* The appendix, an undeveloped portion of the cecum, may be situated in the right paracolic gutter, in either ileocecal fossa, in the retrocecal fossa, or in the pelvis. Because all three teniae coli of the cecum converge to form a complete muscle layer about the appendix, it is best located by following the teniae coli of the ascending colon and cecum. The blood supply to the appendix is from the apicular artery, usually a branch of the ileocecal artery. The descending branch of the right colic artery supplies the ascending colon and distal cecum. The anterior and posterior cecal branches of the ileocecal artery supply the respective sides of the cecum.

236. The answer is D. *(Hollinshead, ed 4. pp 666-669.)* The jejunum and ileum receive principal blood supply from the superior mesenteric artery. A strong collateral circulation is derived from the superior pancreatic artery, a branch of the pancreaticoduodenal artery that arises from the hepatic branch of the celiac artery. The superior pancreatic artery anastomoses with the inferior pancreatic artery, the first branch of the superior mesenteric artery. The collateral circulation is weak between the right colic artery and the ileal branches. There are no possibilities for superior mesenteric anastomoses from the splenic, the descending branch of the left colic, or renal arteries.

237. The answer is C. *(Hollinshead, ed 4. pp 89, 656-658.)* The short gastric veins are branches of the splenic vein and therefore would experience the portal pressure. The short gastric veins also anastomose with the esophageal veins and produce esophageal varices. The hepatic vein, between the liver and inferior vena cava, drains the liver and is not part of the portal system. There are no communications between the portal system and the renal or suprarenal veins.

238. The answer is A. *(Hollinshead, ed 4. pp 652, 655-656.)* The boundaries of the epiploic foramen (of Winslow) are as follows: posteriorly, the inferior vena cava; superiorly, the caudate lobe of the liver; inferiorly, the first part of the duodenum; and anteriorly, the hepatic pedicle. The relationships with the hepatic pedicle are usually as follows: the hepatic portal vein lies posteriorly, the common bile duct anteriorly and to the right, and the hepatic artery anteriorly and to the left. A side-to-side portacaval anastomosis may be made across the epiploic foramen.

239. The answer is C. *(Hollinshead, ed 4. pp 626-628.)* The omental bursa (lesser sac) is the remnant of the right coelomic cavity, which, owing to rotation of the gut and differential growth of the liver, lies behind the stomach. A posterior gastric perforation or an inflamed pancreas could lead to abscess formation in the lesser sac. The right subhepatic space might become secondarily involved via communication through the epiploic foramen (of Winslow). The pouch of Morison, which is the combined right subhepatic and the hepatorenal spaces, may be the seat of abscess formation related to gallbladder disease or perforation of a duodenal ulcer. The right subphrenic space is between the liver and the diaphragm and communicates with the pouch of Morison. All these spaces are in communication with the greater sac of the peritoneal cavity.

240. The answer is C. *(Hollinshead, ed 4. p 668.)* The superior mesenteric artery supplies the terminal portion of the duodenum and head of the pancreas, the jejunum and ileum, appendix, ascending colon, and transverse colon. The inferior mesenteric artery supplies the descending colon, sigmoid colon, and proximal rectum. While there are usually profuse anastomoses between the superior pancreaticoduodenal branch of the gastroduodenal artery and the inferior pancreaticoduodenal branch of the superior mesenteric, there may be scant anastomoses between the left branch of the middle colic and the ascending branch of the left colic.

241. The answer is E. *(Hollinshead, ed 4. pp 761-762.)* The rectum receives blood from the superior rectal (hemorrhoidal) artery and from the paired middle and inferior rectal arteries. The superior rectal artery is a direct continuation of the inferior mesenteric artery, but the middle and inferior rectal arteries are branches of the internal iliac artery and continue to supply the distal rectum despite occlusion of the inferior mesenteric artery. It should be noted that Sudeck's point—between the last sigmoidal artery and the rectosigmoid artery—is an area of potentially weak arterial anastomoses.

242. The answer is C. *(Hollinshead, ed 4. pp 793, 810-811.)* External hemorrhoids, by definition, occur inferior to the pectinate line of the anal canal—the point of demarcation between visceral innervation and somatic innervation. The sharp and intense pain associated with external hemorrhoids is mediated through the inferior hemorrhoidal (rectal) branches of the pudendal nerve, which innervates the perineum. Internal hemorrhoids are not painful because most pain associated with the viscera is the result of severe distension. Distension of the proximal portion of the anal canal is transmitted along the pelvic splanchnic nerves to the midsacral levels of the spinal cord.

243. The answer is A. *(Hollinshead, ed 4. pp 672-673.)* Control of peristalsis is principally a function of the parasympathetic division of the autonomic nervous system. Although removal of the lumbar sympathetic chain (lumbar sympathectomy) does sever the sympathetic fibers innervating the descending colon as well as the pelvic viscera, the action of sympathetic fibers to the descending colon is apparently confined to vasoconstriction. Because the parasympathetic innervation to the descending colon is derived from the sacral outflow (S2-S4) through the nervi erigentes (pelvic splanchnic nerves), peristalsis will occur normally after lumbar sympathectomy.

244. The answer is B. *(Hollinshead, ed 4. pp 702-703.)* The condensation of transversalis fascia, forming the false capsule (of Gerota) about the kidney, limits the spread of renal abscess within the abdominal cavity. Since the capsule fuses about the renal vessels and does not communicate to the opposite side, the infection will not spread to a contralateral kidney. However, the infection may track inferiorly within Gerota's fascia along the ureters into the deep pelvis. This anatomic relationship is useful in diagnostic radiology—air, when injected through the rectal wall into the endopelvic fascia, will rise along the ureters within Gerota's fascia to outline the kidneys. In this way, renal morphology may be visualized in an ordinary abdominal radiograph.

245. The answer is A. *(Hollinshead, ed 4. p 708.)* The adrenal medulla is innervated from thoracic levels of the spinal cord mediated by preganglionic sympathetic nerve fibers traveling in the lesser and least splanchnic nerves, with some contribution from the greater splanchnic and lumbar splanchnic nerves. Since both the adrenal medulla and postganglionic sympathetic neurons are adrenergic and derived from neural crest tissue, the homology of the chromaffin cells and postganglionic sympathetic neurons is apparent. There appears to be no parasympathetic innervation to the adrenal medulla and no innervation whatever to the adrenal cortex.

246. The answer is A. *(Hollinshead, ed 4. p 484.)* The inferior borders of the pleural cavities run horizontally from the T12-L1 intervertebral disk to the 12th rib at midshaft. A deep posterior incision carried along the 12th rib has a high risk of entering the costodiaphragmatic recess of the pleural cavity with resultant pneumothorax and cyanosis owing to the decreased ventilation-to-perfusion ratio. The spleen on the left side also could be the source of venous blood; however, the liver is predominantly on the right and well away from the operative field in this case.

247. The answer is D. *(Hollinshead, ed 4. pp 705-706.)* The venous drainage from each adrenal gland tends to be through a single vein. The left adrenal gland usually drains into the left renal vein superior to the point where the gonadal vein enters the left renal vein. The left adrenal vein usually anastomoses with the hemiazygos vein and may provide an important route of collateral venous return. The right adrenal gland usually drains directly into the inferior vena cava.

248. The answer is E. *(Hollinshead, ed 4. p 705.)* There are usually three groups of vessels supplying the adrenal glands. The superior suprarenal arteries arise from the inferior phrenic artery (the first branches of the abdominal aorta), the middle suprarenal arteries arise directly from the abdominal aorta posterior to the inferior vena cava, and the inferior suprarenal arteries arise from the renal arteries. In addition, it is not uncommon for inferior suprarenal arteries to arise from a superior polar artery and occasionally from a gonadal artery. The celiac artery only supplies the foregut portion of the gastrointestinal tract.

249. The answer is C. *(Hollinshead, ed 4. pp 728-729.)* Although femoral hernias are more common in females than in males, they can occur in the male. Inguinal hernias present through the superficial inguinal ring, which lies superior to the inguinal ligament approximately midway between the symphysis pubis and the anterior superior iliac spine. An indirect inguinal hernia, as in the patient presented in the question, develops within the spermatic cord and therefore will be directed toward the scrotum. A femoral hernia appears as a bulge in the femoral triangle where the hernial sac, which gained access to the thigh by traversing the femoral ring, emerges from beneath the fascia lata via the fossa ovalis alongside the great saphenous vein.

250. The answer is D. *(Hollinshead, ed 4. pp 673-675.)* The diffuse central abdominal pain in the patient presented is probably referred pain from the loop of small bowel incarcerated within the herniated peritoneal sac. Compression of the bowel results in compromise of the blood supply and subsequent ischemic necrosis. The visceral afferent fibers from the distal small bowel travel along the blood vessels to reach the superior mesenteric plexus and lesser splanchnic nerves, which they follow to the T10-T11 levels of the spinal cord. The pain, therefore, is referred to (appears as if originating from) the T10-T11 dermatomes, which supply the umbilical region. Because the gut develops as a midline structure, visceral pain tends to be centrally located regardless of the adult location of any particular region of the gut. As a result of dilation of the inguinal canal by the hernial sac, however, the patient also experiences localized somatic pain mediated by the iliohypogastric, ilioinguinal, and genitofemoral nerves.

251. The answer is D. *(Hollinshead, ed 4. pp 581-582.)* The layers of fascia cut by an incision above and parallel to the inguinal ligament include the superficial (fatty) layer of the superficial fascia (Camper's fascia), the deep layer of the superficial fascia (Scarpa's fascia), and the deep (investing) fascia. The transversalis fascia is located between the transversus abdominis muscle and the peritoneum.

252. The answer is E. *(Hollinshead, ed 4. p 594.)* The superficial circumflex iliac, external pudendal, and superficial epigastric arteries are branches of the femoral artery that supply, respectively, the superficial pubic (hypogastric) region, the inguinal regions, and the anterior surfaces of the scrotum or labia majora. The inferior epigastric artery, a branch of the external iliac artery, courses superomedially beneath the aponeuroses of the abdominal wall to gain access to the rectus sheath by passing anterior to the arcuate line (of Douglas). An aberrant obturator artery (present in about 30 percent of the population) usually arises from the inferior epigastric artery and courses inferiorly deep to the pubic ramus to the obturator foramen.

253. The answer is C. *(Hollinshead, ed 4. p 727.)* A greatly distended spermatic cord implies that the associated hernia is within the spermatic cord, thus constituting an *indirect* inguinal hernia. This type of herniation enters the inguinal canal through the deep inguinal ring, which lies just lateral to the inferior epigastric artery and thus lateral to the inguinal triangle (of Hesselbach). In traversing the inguinal canal and the internal oblique muscle, the herniation comes to be enveloped by the cremaster muscle and then exits within the spermatic cord through the superficial inguinal ring in the direction of the scrotum. A *direct* inguinal hernia, however, passes directly through the inguinal triangle (of Hesselbach), medial to the inferior epigastric artery, and exits through the superficial inguinal ring adjacent to the spermatic cord, but does not (as in the case of indirect herniation) necessarily extend toward, or into, the scrotum.

254. The answer is C. *(Hollinshead, ed 4. pp 720-722.)* Several abdominal structures are involved in the formation of the spermatic cord. The deep fascia contributes the external spermatic fascia. Although some references include the external oblique muscle or aponeurosis, no contribution is derived from that layer owing to a hiatus in the aponeurosis. The cremaster muscle, a contribution of the internal oblique muscle, joins the spermatic cord as the inguinal canal passes through that layer. The transversus abdominis muscle, which usually terminates as the falx inguinalis just superior to the deep ring, contributes to the cremaster muscle in less than 5 percent of all males. The transversalis fascia contributes the internal spermatic fascia.

255. The answer is E. *(Hollinshead, ed 4. p 719.)* The ilioinguinal nerve exits the abdominal wall through the superficial inguinal ring, where it is applied to the anterior surface of the spermatic cord. Section of this nerve will result in paresthesia over the base of the penis and scrotum. The femoral branch of the genitofemoral nerve innervates the upper medial surface of the thigh, where it mediates the afferent limb of the cremasteric reflex. The efferent limb of this reflex is carried by the genital branch of the genitofemoral nerve, which lies within the cremaster layer. The dartos response is sympathetic, arising from the sacral sympathetic chain and reaching the pudendal nerve via gray rami communicantes.

256. The answer is B. *(Hollinshead, ed 4. p 719.)* Within the internal spermatic fascia of the spermatic cord lie the vas deferens, testicular artery, pampiniform plexus of the testicular vein, testicular nerve, and the processus vaginalis, which terminates as the tunica vaginalis testis. The pampiniform plexus, formed from the testicular vein, serves as a countercurrent heat exchanger, cooling the arterial blood and contributing to the maintenance of testicular temperature a few degrees cooler than body temperature. The pampiniform plexus on the left side is frequently varicose, the result of stasis in the testicular vein produced by the overlying sigmoid colon in the lower left quadrant of the abdomen. The efferent ductules empty into the epididymis from the hilum of the testis.

257. The answer is B. *(Hollinshead, ed 4. pp 729-730.)* The inguinal ligament and its extension through both the lacunar and pectineal ligaments along the pectin of the pubis provide good anchors for sutures in hernial repair. The lower margin of the rectus sheath also provides excellent anchoring for sutures. The interfoveolar ligament, a thin condensation of loose connective tissue (transversalis fascia) behind the inferior epigastric artery, is not suitable for sutures.

258. The answer is C. *(Hollinshead, ed 4. p 708.)* The blood supply to the ureters is variable and may be derived from numerous twigs off the renal, gonadal, common iliac, external iliac, internal iliac, and inferior vesical arteries. These twigs are so spaced that their anastomotic connections may be poor or absent. Generally, during abdominal surgery, surgeons stay well away from the ureters unless it is impossible to avoid them. When harvesting a kidney for renal transplant, care is taken to preserve an adequate blood supply from the ipsilateral renal artery to the upper portion of the ureter. The left ureter receives no blood supply from the overlying inferior mesenteric artery.

259. The answer is A. *(Hollinshead, ed 4. p 731.)* The femoral ring is a point of potential weakness in the abdominal wall, through which a femoral hernia may develop. Anteriorly, the femoral ring is bounded by the inguinal ligament (of Poupart). The medial border is formed by the sharp edge of the lacunar ligament (of Gimbernat). The posterior border is contributed by the pectineal ligament (of

Cooper). Just lateral to the femoral canal lies the femoral vein. The canal provides a lymphatic pathway from the lower extremity, as well as from the lower abdominal region, to the external iliac nodes. An invariable occupant of the femoral ring is a lymph node known as Cloquet's gland. The femoral nerve is located in the muscular compartment with the psoas muscle lateral to the femoral artery and vein.

260. The answer is D. *(Hollinshead, ed 4. pp 762-763.)* The lymphatic drainage from the middle portion of the rectum follows the three sources of arterial supply: along the superior rectal (hemorrhoidal) lymphatics to the inferior mesenteric nodes; along the middle rectal lymphatics to the internal iliac nodes; and along the inferior rectal lymphatics also to the internal iliac nodes. In addition, lymphatics from the rectum may anastomose with those of the anal canal, which drain along superficial lymphatic pathways to the superficial inguinal lymph nodes. An understanding of these lymphatic channels is clinically important because of the high incidence of rectal carcinoma.

261-266. The answers are: 261-A, 262-B, 263-D, 264-A, 265-B, 266-B. *(Hollinshead, ed 4. pp 657-658.)* Although the transition from jejunum to ileum is not sharp, gradual changes may be seen in the character of the bowel, its vasculature, the supporting mesentery, and even the general location.

The diameter of the jejunum is greater because the bulk of the chyme has not been reduced by absorption of fluids. The jejunal wall is also thicker owing to the taller and more numerous plicae circulares. Aggregates of lymphoid tissue (Peyer's patches) are more numerous in the ileum.

Blood is supplied to both the jejunum and ileum by the superior mesenteric artery. The jejunal arteries give rise to fewer long arcades that give off rather long terminal arteries (arteriae rectae); the ileal arteries give rise to numerous short arcades with short terminal arteries.

The jejunal and ileal portions of the small intestine are supported by mesenteries and are therefore mobile. However, the jejunum tends to lie in the umbilical and left lateral regions, whereas the ileum tends to occupy the hypogastrium and the deep pelvis. The ileal mesentery is thicker because it has a much greater concentration of fat between the vessels than has the jejunum.

267-270. The answers are: 267-D, 268-A, 269-C, 270-E. *(Hollinshead, ed 4. pp 681-685.)* The diaphragm possesses three principal hiatuses, shown in the diagram accompanying the question: the hiatus for the inferior vena cava (A), the esophageal hiatus (C), and the aortic hiatus (E). Potential diaphragmatic developmental defects include the foramen of Morgagni (B), just lateral to the xiphoid attachment of the diaphragm, and the pleuroperitoneal canal of Bochdalek (D), which is the most common site for congenital hernias. In the latter case, the pleuroperitoneal membranes fail to fuse to close the pleuroperitoneal canal—usually on the left side.

The inferior vena cava and, frequently, small branches of the right phrenic nerve pass through a hiatus (A) slightly to the right of the midline at the T8 level. The left phrenic nerve usually passes through the central tendon of the diaphragm on the left side to innervate the left hemidiaphragm from below.

The esophageal hiatus (C) just to the left of the midline at the T10 level transmits the esophagus, left and right vagus nerves, as well as the esophageal branches of the left gastric artery and vein. An acquired hiatus hernia usually is the consequence of a short esophagus or of a weakened esophageal hiatus. In such instances, a portion of the cardia and sometimes the fundus of the stomach slides upward through the diaphragm into the thorax. Radiographic examination will disclose a stomach that is constricted by the diaphragm, giving rise to the term "hour-glass stomach." Hiatus hernia may be complicated by gastric regurgitation, esophagitis, and dysphagia.

The two diaphragmatic crura are joined superiorly by the median arcuate ligament to form an opening (E) at the T12 level. The aortic hiatus transmits the aorta, thoracic duct, and a continuation of the azygos vein into the abdomen. The splanchnic nerves penetrate the crura on each side of the aortic hiatus to reach the abdomen.

Gross Anatomy: Pelvis

DIRECTIONS: Each question below contains four or five suggested responses. Select the **one best** response to each question.

271. The lesser sciatic foramen is associated with all the following structures EXCEPT the

(A) external pudendal artery and vein
(B) pudendal nerve
(C) sacrospinous ligament
(D) sacrotuberous ligament
(E) tendon of the obturator internus muscle

272. Which of the following is a characteristic of the female (as compared with the male) pelvis?

(A) A heart-shaped (as opposed to oval) pelvic inlet
(B) A relatively deep (as opposed to shallow) false pelvis with ilia that are more vertical
(C) A pelvic outlet of smaller diameter
(D) A narrow subpubic angle between the pubic rami
(E) None of the above

273. In addition to the vas deferens, structures normally found within the internal spermatic fascia of the spermatic cord include all the following EXCEPT the

(A) deferential artery
(B) ilioinguinal nerve
(C) pampiniform plexus
(D) testicular artery
(E) testicular nerve

274. The gubernaculum is a continuous mesenchymal condensation extending from the caudal pole of each testis through the inguinal canal to the scrotal swelling, inferiorly. In the female it becomes

(A) the canal of Nuck
(B) the ligament of the ovary
(C) the round ligament of the uterus
(D) the round ligament of the uterus and the ligament of the ovary
(E) none of the above

275. After iatrogenic rupture of the penile urethra, just distal to the urogenital diaphragm, the regions into which urine could extravasate beneath the deep layer of the superficial fascia include all the following EXCEPT the

(A) anterior abdominal wall
(B) ischioanal fossa
(C) penis
(D) scrotum
(E) superficial perineal pouch

276. The contents of the deep perineal pouch include all the following structures EXCEPT the

(A) bulbourethral glands in the male
(B) deep transverse perineal muscle
(C) external urethral sphincter
(D) membranous urethra in the male
(E) great vestibular glands in the female

277. Regions that drain to the inguinal lymph nodes include all the following EXCEPT the

(A) anal triangle
(B) lower abdominal wall
(C) lower extremity
(D) scrotum
(E) testis

278. The external urethral sphincter in the *female* is

(A) a modified portion of the pelvic diaphragm
(B) continuous completely around the urethra
(C) innervated by the pudendal nerve
(D) subject to involuntary control
(E) none of the above

279. All the following statements correctly characterize the pelvic diaphragm, which forms the floor of the abdominopelvic cavity, EXCEPT

(A) it comprises the levator ani and coccygeus muscles with their fascia
(B) it functions to support the pelvic organs
(C) it is innervated by twigs from the sacral plexus
(D) it lies in the same plane as the urogenital diaphragm
(E) it originates in part from a condensation of fascia across the obturator internis muscle

280. All the following statements apply to the uterine artery EXCEPT that it

(A) anastomoses with branches of the ovarian and internal pudendal arteries
(B) is the homologue of the artery of the vas deferens (deferential artery) in the male
(C) is a branch of the anterior trunk of the internal iliac artery
(D) passes immediately inferior to the ipsilateral ureter at one point
(E) runs in the transverse cervical ligament

Questions 281-291

A 24-year-old woman seeking assistance for apparent infertility has been unable to conceive in spite of repeated attempts in 5 years of marriage. She revealed that her husband had fathered a child in a prior marriage. Although the patient's menstrual periods are fairly regular, they are accompanied by extreme low back pain.

281. The low back pain during menstruation experienced by the woman described probably is referred from the pelvic region. The pathways that convey this pain sensation to the central nervous system involve

(A) the hypogastric nerve to L1-L2
(B) the lumbosacral trunk to L4-L5
(C) the nervi erigentes (pelvic nerve) to S2-S4
(D) the pudendal nerve to S2-S4
(E) none of the above

282. On digital examination of the apical region of the vagina, the structure presented first to the examining finger is the posterior lip of the cervix. This observation precludes which of the following uterine postures?

(A) Anteflexion
(B) Anteversion
(C) Retroflexion
(D) Retroversion
(E) None of the above

283. The ovaries are palpable and appear normal on pelvic examination. Other structures that could be palpated on pelvic examination include all the following EXCEPT the

(A) aorta
(B) coccyx
(C) ischial spines
(D) sacral promontory
(E) sacrospinous ligament

284. The uterus is indirectly supported by all the following pelvic structures EXCEPT the

(A) obturator internus muscle
(B) pubovaginalis and puborectalis portions of the levator ani muscle
(C) rectum
(D) urinary bladder
(E) vagina

285. Structures that contribute to the direct support of the uterus include all the following EXCEPT the

(A) lateral or transverse cervical ligaments
(B) uteropubic ligaments
(C) round ligaments of the uterus
(D) suspensory ligaments
(E) uterosacral ligaments

286. Which of the following would be found immediately inferior to the cardinal (lateral cervical) ligaments?

(A) Ovarian neurovascular bundle
(B) Oviduct
(C) Round ligaments of the uterus
(D) Ureter
(E) Uterine arteries and veins

287. The patient is scheduled for a hysterosalpingogram, in which radiopaque material is injected into the uterus and oviducts. Examination of subsequent radiographs discloses spillage of the contrast medium into the peritoneal cavity, an indication that

(A) the mesonephric ducts failed to form properly
(B) the oviduct is normal
(C) the paramesonephric ducts failed to form properly
(D) there is a rectouterine fistula
(E) there is a vesicovaginal fistula

288. After receiving counseling as to both the best time in the ovulatory cycle and the most favorable coital position for conception, the patient becomes pregnant. She is observed closely throughout the pregnancy. At delivery, caudal analgesia is induced by administration of anesthetic into the epidural space in the sacral region. The needle is introduced via the

(A) anterior sacral foramina
(B) dural sac
(C) intervertebral foramina
(D) posterior sacral foramina
(E) sacral hiatus

289. Properly administered caudal analgesia accomplishes all the following EXCEPT

(A) blockage of pain fibers arising from the cervix
(B) blockage of pain fibers arising from the perineum
(C) elimination of uterine contraction
(D) paralysis of perineal musculature

290. As delivery begins, a midline episiotomy is performed to the external anal sphincter. An incision that is precise will sever all the following structures EXCEPT the

(A) central tendon of the perineum
(B) fourchette or frenulum of the labia
(C) posterior vaginal wall
(D) superficial transverse perineal muscle

291. The delivery, which is a difficult one requiring extensive use of forceps, produces tearing of the external anal sphincter and anal canal. A normal boy is delivered. Both the sphincteric tear and episiotomy incision are sutured. In retrospect, a posterolateral (mediolateral) episiotomy may have been preferable to a midline incision in this case. A posterolateral episiotomy would involve sectioning all the following structures EXCEPT the

(A) central tendon of the perineum
(B) deep transverse perineal muscle
(C) perineal branches of the internal pudendal artery
(D) perineal branches of the pudendal nerve
(E) superficial transverse perineal muscle

(End of question set)

292. Bilateral lumbar sympathectomy does not affect autonomic control of the descending colon because

(A) the descending colon receives its parasympathetic innervation from the pelvic splanchnics
(B) the descending colon receives its parasympathetic innervation from the vagus nerve
(C) the descending colon receives its sympathetic innervation from thoracic splanchnic nerves
(D) lumbar splanchnics innervate the pelvic viscera via the hypogastric nerve
(E) only presynaptic sympathetic fibers have been severed

293. Sympathetic and parasympathetic nerves reach the pelvic plexus by different pathways. During surgical resection of the rectum, the sympathetic nerves had to be excised bilaterally, leading to which of the following complications?

(A) A dilated and neurogenic bladder
(B) Loss of control of the external urethral sphincter
(C) Impotence (inability to obtain erection)
(D) Inability to ejaculate
(E) None of the above

294. The following pelvic structures are correctly linked to the somatic regions to which they refer pain EXCEPT

(A) the cervix to the perineum, leg, and foot
(B) the epididymis to the lumbar and umbilical regions
(C) the mid-ureter to the inguinal region, pubic region, and medial thigh
(D) the ovary to the umbilical region, lumbar region, and medial thigh
(E) the uterine body to the inguinal region, hypogastric region, and medial thigh

DIRECTIONS: Each group of questions below consists of four lettered headings followed by a set of numbered items. For each numbered item select

A	if the item is associated with	(A) **only**
B	if the item is associated with	(B) **only**
C	if the item is associated with	**both** (A) and (B)
D	if the item is associated with	**neither** (A) nor (B)

Each lettered heading may be used **once, more than once, or not at all.**

Questions 295-298

(A) Mesosalpinx
(B) Suspensory ligament
(C) Both
(D) Neither

295. Continuous with the broad ligament

296. Suspends the oviduct

297. Contains the gonadal neurovascular bundle

298. Contains the proper ligament of the ovary

Questions 299-302

(A) Prostate gland
(B) Seminal vesicle
(C) Both
(D) Neither

299. Direct emptying into the prostatic urethra

300. Storage of spermatozoa prior to ejaculation

301. Secretion of fructose as a component of seminal fluid

302. Palpation via the rectum

DIRECTIONS: Each group of questions below consists of lettered headings followed by a set of numbered items. For each numbered item select the **one** lettered heading with which it is **most** closely associated. Each lettered heading may be used **once, more than once, or not at all.**

Questions 303-306

The diagram below represents a frontal section through the bladder and prostate gland. For each description that follows, select the lettered structure with which it is most closely associated.

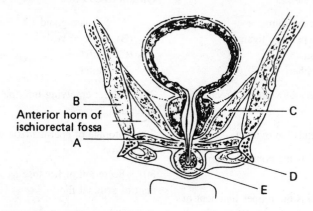

303. Contributes to anal continence
304. Reinforces the urogenital hiatus of the levator ani muscle
305. Forms the external urinary sphincter
306. Functions in part to expel residual urine from the penile urethra

Questions 307-310

For each female pelvic structure, select the appropriate male homologue.

(A) Corpus spongiosum
(B) Scrotum
(C) Scrotal raphe
(D) Penile (cavernous) urethra
(E) None of the above

307. Labia majora

308. Vestibule

309. Vestibular bulbs

310. Glans clitoris

Gross Anatomy:
Pelvis
Answers

271. The answer is A. *(Hollinshead, ed 4. pp 354, 364-365, 808, 809.)* The sacrotuberous ligament, extending from the ischial tuberosity to the lateromedial aspect of the sacrum and coccyx, forms, in conjunction with the sciatic notch of the innominate bone, the sciatic foramen. The sacrospinous ligament, running from the ischial spine to the lateromedial aspect of the sacrum and coccyx, divides the sciatic foramen into greater and lesser sciatic foramina and forms the superior border of the lesser sciatic foramen. The tendon of the obturator internus muscle, which originates on the internal surface of the pelvis, passes through the lesser sciatic foramen to reach its insertion into the medial surface of the greater trochanter of the femur. Together with the internal pudendal artery and vein, the pudendal nerve leaves the deep pelvis through the infrapiriformis recess of the greater sciatic foramen and enters the perineum by passing through the lesser sciatic foramen. The external pudendal vessels, which are branches of the femoral artery and vein, are associated with the anterosuperior aspects of the penis and scrotum, or labia majora, as the case may be.

272. The answer is E. *(April, ed 2. p 288. Hollinshead, ed 4. pp 739-740.)* The male pelvis is generally heavier than the female pelvis, with stronger bone structure and more definitive muscle markings reflecting the larger male musculature and generally heavier male build. The generally wider and shallower female pelvis is more suited to childbearing. In the female the false pelvis tends to be shallower with flared ilia, the pelvic inlet more oval, and the pelvic outlet larger than in the male. Also, the subpubic angle between inferior pubic rami is significantly greater in the female than in the male.

273. The answer is B. *(Hollinshead, ed 4. pp 719-721.)* The internal spermatic fascia of the spermatic cord lies within the confines of the cremaster layer. It contains the vas deferens, the deferential artery, the testicular artery and nerve, and the pampiniform venous plexus. The ilioinguinal nerve is found on the posterior aspect of the spermatic cord between the external spermatic fascia and cremaster muscle. This nerve then passes through the external spermatic fascia into the superficial fascia to innervate the skin over the root of the penis or mons and the anterior aspect of the scrotum or labia majora.

274.   The answer is D. *(Hollinshead, ed 4. pp 727, 783.)* The gubernaculum, which runs from the gonadal anlage to the sexually undifferentiated labioscrotal fold, guides the descent of the testes into the scrotum in the male and the descent of the ovary into the deep pelvis in the female. In the female, the developing uterus grows into the gubernacular tract and divides it into the proper ligament of the ovary and the round ligament of the uterus. Thus, the proper ligament of the ovary runs within the broad ligament from the medial pole of each ovary to the uterus. It then continues within the broad ligament as the round ligament of the uterus into the deep inguinal ring, thereby gaining access to the canal of Nuck (the female homologue of the inguinal canal) to insert into the major labial folds.

275.   The answer is B. *(Hollinshead, ed 4. pp 798-800.)* Perforation of the urethra below the deep transverse perineal muscle of the urogenital diaphragm will result in extravasation of urine within the superficial perineal pouch. Since the deep (Colle's) layer of the superficial perineal fascia is continuous with that of the scrotum (dartos) and penis, as well as that of the abdominal wall (Scarpa's), urine may extravasate widely beneath this continuous layer. However, because this layer does not extend into the anal triangle and because this layer also inserts onto the fascia lata of the thigh, urine will not extravasate into the ischioanal fossa or the lower extremity.

276.   The answer is E. *(Hollinshead, ed 4. pp 797-798.)* The deep perineal pouch consists of the urogenital diaphragm, that is, the deep transverse perineal muscle and its associated inferior and superior fascial layers. The external urethral sphincter is a modification of the deep transverse perineal muscle around the membranous urethra. In the male, the bulbourethral glands are contained within the deep pouch, but in the female the vestibular glands are within the superficial pouch. The membranous urethra, the continuation of the prostatic portion, passes through the deep pouch before becoming the penile urethra.

277.   The answer is E. *(Hollinshead, ed 4. p 725.)* Lymphatic fluid from the lower abdominal wall and inferior part of the anal canal as well as most of the perineum (including the scrotum and vulva) and the lower extremities drains into the inguinal lymph nodes. Lymph from the erectile tissue of the penis drains along the deep veins of the penis into the pelvic lymph nodes. The testes develop high in the abdominal cavity and descend with their neurovascular supply into the scrotum. Thus, the testes drain directly to the paraaortic lymph nodes in the vicinity of the renal vessels.

278.   The answer is C. *(Hollinshead, ed 4. pp 769, 796.)* The external urethral sphincter, partially surrounding the membranous portion of the urethra in the female, is a modified portion of the deep transverse perineal muscle of the urogenital diaphragm. Somatically innervated by the deep perineal branches of the pudendal nerve, the sphincter, in addition to contracting with the musculature of the pelvic and urogenital diaphragms on coughing or sneezing, can be voluntarily contracted to maintain urinary continence once the desire to micturate is experienced. However, the effectiveness of this muscle is greater in the male where it completely surrounds the membranous urethra.

279. The answer is D. *(Hollinshead, ed 4. pp 741-743.)* The pelvic diaphragm, comprising the levator ani and coccygeus muscles and their associated fascia, is shaped like an inverted cone and forms the floor of the abdominopelvic cavity. It functions to suspend and support pelvic organs as well as to provide the principal component for fecal continence. The urogenital hiatus, a midline gap in the pelvic diaphragm and a weak area, is reinforced by the urogenital diaphragm, which comprises the deep transverse perineal muscle and the associated superior and inferior fascial layers. The urogenital diaphragm, unlike the pelvic diaphragm, lies in a horizontal plane; it is inferior to the pelvic diaphragm. Finally, the pelvic diaphragm is innervated by twigs from the sacral plexus; the urogenital diaphragm is innervated on its perineal surface by twigs from the pudendal nerve.

280. The answer is D. *(Hollinshead, ed 4. pp 785-786.)* The uterine artery, a branch of the anterior trunk of the internal iliac artery, runs in the transverse cervical (cardinal, Mackenrodt's) ligament at the base of the broad ligament. While coursing in the transverse cervical ligament to the uterus, it lies immediately superior to the ureter. It is at this point that the ureter is in jeopardy of being ligated and sectioned as part of the procedure for hysterectomy. In addition to supplying the uterus, a tubal branch supplies the oviducts and anastomoses with the ovarian artery. A vaginal branch supplies the vagina and anastomoses with the perineal branches of the internal pudendal artery. The uterine artery is the homologue of the deferential artery in the male.

281. The answer is A. *(April, ed 2. pp 234-235, 335-336.)* The visceral afferent fibers that mediate sensation from the fundus and body of the uterus, as well as from the oviducts, tend to travel along the sympathetic nerve pathways (via the hypogastric nerve and lumbar splanchnics) to reach the upper lumbar levels (L1-L2) of the spinal cord. Thus, uterine pain will be referred to (appear as if originating from) the upper lumbar dermatomes, producing apparent backache. The visceral afferent fibers that mediate sensation from the cervical neck of the uterus travel along the parasympathetic pathways (via the pelvic splanchnic nerves [nervi erigentes]) to the midsacral levels (S2-S4) of the spinal cord. In this instance, pain originating from the cervix will be referred to the midsacral dermatomes, producing pain that appears to arise from the perineum, gluteal region, and legs.

282. The answer is B. *(Hollinshead, ed 4. p 782.)* The normal posture of the uterus is anteverted and anteflexed. If the anterior lip of the cervix is palpated first during vaginal examination, the cervix is in an anteverted position. If the cervix is retroverted, either the cervical os or the posterior lip of the cervix is the first structure to be palpated. In either case, the uterine fundus may be anteflexed or retroflexed; bimanual examination will disclose which.

283. The answer is A. *(April, ed 2. pp 287-288, 336-338.)* Several bony landmarks that are palpable on pelvic examination are used in pelvimetry. The distance between the promontory of the sacrum and the posteroinferior margin of the symphysis pubis—the diagonal conjugate—provides a good indication of the size of the pelvic *inlet*. The distance between the ischial spines provides the midplane transverse diameter of the pelvic *outlet*. Other internally palpable structures include the coccyx and the sacrotuberous ligaments. Besides the ovaries, other soft-tissue structures that are internally palpable include the urethra, urinary bladder when distended, the ureters, and (bimanually) the uterus and uterine tubes. The aortic bifurcation is well out of reach from the 3-inch-long vagina.

284. The answer is A. *(Hollinshead, ed 4. pp 742-743, 782-784.)* The pelvic diaphragm and uterine ligaments constitute the major support of the uterus. Considerable support also is provided by the urinary bladder and, to a lesser extent, by the rectum, both of which, in turn, are supported by the pelvic diaphragm. In its normal antiverted (angle between cervical and vaginal planes) and antiflexed (angle between uterine neck and body) position, the uterus is supported by the bladder. In the retroverted position, the uterus is borne completely by the uterine ligaments and vagina, a situation that predisposes to uterine prolapse. The urogenital diaphragm (deep transverse perineal muscle and associated fascial layers surrounding the lower third of the vagina) and the obturator internis muscle are not in positions to provide uterine support.

285. The answer is D. *(Hollinshead, ed 4. pp 744-745, 782-784.)* Except for the round ligament of the uterus and its continuation as proper ligament of the ovary as well as the broad ligament, ligaments supporting the uterus are formed by condensations of endopelvic fascia in the region of the uterine cervix. The uterosacral ligaments, which pass around the rectum between cervix and sacrum, provide support to the uterus and assist in maintaining its anteverted posture. Although the cardinal ligaments (also known as lateral cervical ligaments of Mackenrodt) contribute support from the lateral pelvic walls, it is the uterine vessels conveyed by these ligaments that appear to provide the major lateral support to the uterus. The round ligament of the uterus (the remnant of the gubernaculum in the female), which runs within the broad ligament from the anterolateral wall of the uterus to the deep inguinal ring, tends to keep the uterus in an anteverted and anteflexed posture so that it may derive maximum support from the underlying urinary bladder. The uteropubic ligaments (puboprostatic in the male) extend from the cervix to the tendinous arch of the pelvic fascia and provide anterior support for the uterus. The suspensory ligaments, containing the ovarian neurovascular bundle, provide support for ovaries.

286. The answer is D. *(Hollinshead, ed 4. pp 767-768.)* The ureter, lying just medial to the internal iliac artery in the deep pelvis, passes from posterior to anterior immediately inferior to the lateral cervical ligament. This ligament contains the uterine artery and vein to which the ureters pass inferior approximately midway along their course between internal iliac artery and uterus. The ureter continues inferior to the anterior portion of the lateral cervical ligament (where it can sometimes be palpated through the walls of the vagina at the lateral fornices) to gain access to the base of the urinary bladder. The close association between uterine vessels and ureter is of major importance during surgical procedures in the female pelvis.

287. The answer is B. *(Hollinshead, ed 4. pp 777-778.)* The uterus is formed by fusion of the paired paramesonephric ducts. The uterine tubes are the unfused portions of these ducts. Oviduct patency may be ascertained by hysterosalpingography, wherein radiopaque material is injected into the uterine cavity and oviducts through a catheter inserted into the external cervical os. Radiographs delineate the cavity of the body of the uterus and the oviducts. Spillage of the contrast material through the abdominal ostia into the peritoneal cavity demonstrates normal patency of the oviducts. The abdominal ostia of the oviducts permit passage of infection, air, and spermatozoa into the female peritoneal cavity. The rare rectouterine fistula would result in the appearance of contrast media in the rectum. A vesicovaginal fistula between the vagina and urethra or bladder would not be evident on a hysterosalpingogram.

288. The answer is E. *(Hollinshead, ed 4. pp 322-323.)* Caudal analgesia can be induced by injection of anesthetic through the sacral hiatus into the sacral epidural space of the vertebral canal well caudal to the termination of the dural sac. The sacral hiatus, representing the absence of a complete neural arch of the fifth sacral vertebra, is bounded by the sacral cornua, representing the rudiments of the pedicles of the fifth sacral vertebra. The four anterior and posterior sacral foramina on either side of the midline join the intervertebral foramen and provide egress for the anterior and posterior primary rami of the sacral spinal nerves. The level to which the anesthesia blocks the spinal nerves is a function of the amount delivered.

289. The answer is C. *(April, ed 2. p 276.)* Sacral or caudal analgesia blocks visceral pain fibers (arising from the cervical region of the uterus and deep vagina) that travel along the nervi erigentes (pelvic splanchnics) to the second through fourth sacral levels. Somatic pain fibers arising from the perineum, which travel along the pudendal nerve to the second through fourth sacral levels, also are blocked, along with the motor nerves to the perineal and pelvic musculature, thus providing muscular relaxation. In addition, portions of the lower extremities are anesthetized by this procedure. The visceral motor nerves that originate in the upper lumbar levels and that course to the pelvis through the hypogastric plexus and pelvic plexus to mediate uterine contraction are unaffected by properly administered sacral analgesia. Also unaffected are the somatic motor nerves that arise from the lower thoracic and upper lumbar levels and that control abdominal contraction.

290. The answer is D. *(Hollinshead, ed 4. pp 796-797.)* Episiotomy frequently is performed to prevent perineal tearing during parturition. The midline episiotomy involves incising the posterior vaginal mucosa, the epithelium of the fossa navicularis, and the fourchette or frenulum of the labia through the central tendon of the perineum to the deep fibers of the external anal sphincter. A midline incision transects neither the superficial transverse perineal nor the bulbospongiosus muscles because these muscles essentially do not cross the midline. Midline incisions that do not transect the transverse perineal neurovascular bundle, which accompanies the superficial transverse muscle, are relatively bloodless, require only local anesthesia, and are easy to close.

291. The answer is A. *(April, ed 2. p 313.)* In addition to the posterior vaginal mucosa and the epithelium of the fossa navicularis, a posterolateral episiotomy incises the following structures: the skin over the ischioanal fossa, the bulbospongiosus muscle, the superficial transverse perineal muscle and associated transverse perineal neurovascular bundle, a portion of the deep transverse perineal muscle and associated fascial layers (urogenital diaphragm), and, frequently, the medial fibers of the pubovaginalis and puborectalis portions of the levator ani. A posterolateral episiotomy provides greater enlargement of the birth canal than is possible with a midline approach, but reapproximation of the various structural layers is considerably more difficult.

292. The answer is A. *(Hollinshead, ed 4. pp 755, 772-773.)* Parasympathetic nerves arising from sacral levels S2-S4 run along the pelvic splanchnic nerves (nervi erigentes) to the lateral pelvic plexus located along the wall of the rectum. From there some parasympathetic nerves pass in retrograde fashion along the inferior and superior hypogastric plexuses and the aortic plexus to reach the inferior mesenteric plexus. This plexus innervates the descending and sigmoid colons. Because peristalsis is largely a parasympathetic function, lumbar sympathectomy does not affect autonomic control of the descending colon. The parasympathetic fibers from the vagus nerve innervate the proximal portion of the gastrointestinal tract as far as the splenic flexure of the colon.

293. The answer is D. *(Hollinshead, ed 4. pp 773-774.)* Loss of sympathetic innervation to the pelvic plexus results in an inability to ejaculate. Parasympathetic innervation in this region mediates penile erection, without which ejaculation probably cannot occur. The afferent and efferent limbs of the detrussor reflex, which controls reflex emptying of the bladder, also travel in the nervi erigentes with the parasympathetics. Thus injury to this pathway would result in a dilated bladder. Voluntary control of the external anal sphincter and levator ani muscles is mediated through branches of the pudendal nerve.

294. The answer is B. *(April, ed 2. pp 235, 316, 325-326, 332, 336.)* Afferent nerves from the epididymis travel along the pelvic splanchnic nerves (nervi erigentes) to reach spinal segments S2 through S4. As such, pain originating in the epididymis is referred to (appears as if originating from) dermatomes S2 through S4, which include the perineum, leg, and foot. The visceral afferents from the cervix take the same pathway and refer pain to the same areas. Afferent nerves from the mid-ureters as well as the uterine body travel along the lumbar splanchnic nerves and the hypogastric plexus, respectively, to reach spinal segments L1 and L2, thereby referring pain to the inguinal and pubic regions as well as to the anterior scrotum or labia and the medial thigh. Afferent nerves from the testes and ovaries follow the gonadal nerves to spinal segments T12 and L1, thereby referring pain to the lumbar and inguinal regions.

295-298. The answers are: 295-C, 296-A, 297-B, 298-D. *(Hollinshead, ed 4. pp 776-777.)* The mesosalpinx, mesovarium, and suspensory ligament are all continuous with the broad ligament, which is a reflection of peritoneum over the female reproductive organs. The mesovarium attaches the ovary to the broad ligament.

The mesosalpinx supports the uterine tube and contains the tubal branch of the uterine artery. Also contained within the mesosalpinx are developmental remnants such as the epoophoron and paroophoron in which cysts may develop.

The suspensory ligament of the ovary runs from the pelvic brim to the lateral pole of the ovary. It contains the ovarian artery, ovarian vein, ovarian lymphatics, and ovarian nerves. Volvulus of the ovary (usually associated with an ovarian tumor) may constrict the neurovascular bundle with ovarian infarct and pain referred to the inguinal and hypogastric regions.

The proper ligament of the ovary (ovarian ligament), the remnant of the gubernaculum, courses within the broad ligament from the medial pole of the ovary to the uterus. At the uterus, it continues as the round ligament of the uterus, which runs laterally within the broad ligament to the deep inguinal ring and along the inguinal canal to the labia majora.

299-302. The answers are: 299-A, 300-D, 301-B, 302-C. *(Hollinshead, ed 4. pp 770-771, 774.)* Each seminal vesicle lies inferior to the ampulla of a vas deferens, which it joins to form the ejaculatory duct. The ejaculatory duct subsequently empties into the prostatic urethra on either side of the colliculus seminalis. Although the seminal vesicles contribute a substantial volume of secretion with a high fructose content, they do not store sperm prior to ejaculation.

The prostate gland contributes substantially to the volume of seminal fluid. The prostatic secretions contain high concentrations of citric acid, acid phosphatase, prostaglandins, and fibrinogen. The gland is composed of five lobes that empty into the prostatic urethra by numerous ductules.

Both the prostate gland and the seminal vesicles can be palpated via the rectum. This is an especially important consideration in the diagnosis of prostatic hypertrophy and malignancy.

303-306. The answers are: 303-C, 304-A, 305-A, 306-E. *(Hollinshead, ed 4. pp 742, 796, 803.)* The primary factor in control of anal continence is the rectal sling, which is the puborectalis portion of the levator ani muscle (C in the diagram accompanying the question). Tension in this portion of the pelvic diaphragm, when the rectum contains feces, draws the lower portion of the rectum anteriorly, effectively obstructing the rectal canal. Contraction of the external anal sphincters for 30-second periods is just sufficient to counteract a peristaltic wave. Although the obturator internis muscle (B), a lateral rotator of the thigh, does not contribute to the support of the pelvic viscera, the tendinous arch of the obturator *fascia* provides an origin for the levator ani muscle.

The deep perineal pouch is formed by the deep transverse perineal muscle (A). This muscle, along with its inferior and superior fascial layers, forms the urogenital diaphragm. Extending from the ischiopubic ramus to meet its counterpart of the opposite side in a midline raphe, the deep transverse perineal muscle reinforces the urogenital hiatus of the pelvic diaphragm formed by the central defect in the levator ani muscle (C).

The anterior portion of the deep transverse perineal muscle (A) is closely associated with the urethra and forms the external urethral sphincter. Voluntary control of this muscle is mediated by the pudendal nerve. The muscles of the superficial pouch generally are associated with the penis or clitoris.

The bulbospongiosus muscle (E), overlying the erectile tissue of the corpus spongiosus urethrae, functions to compress the penile urethra to expel residual urine. The ischiocavernosus muscles (D), overlying the corpora cavernosa, along with the bulbospongiosus muscle, may assist in maintenance of erection by retarding venous return from the erectile tissue.

307-310. The answers are: 307-B, 308-D, 309-A, 310-A. *(April, ed 2. pp 295-296. Hollinshead, ed 4. p 126.)* The labia majora and the scrotum both develop from the labial-scrotal folds of the undifferentiated external genitalia. In the male the scrotal folds fuse along the scrotal raphe to form the scrotum.

The vestibule of the vulva, lying within the labia minora, represents the persistent urogenital sinus of the undifferentiated external genitalia. In the developing male, the urethral folds (homologous to the labia minora) fuse over the urogenital sinus to form the penile urethra. Therefore the vestibule and the penile urethra are homologous.

The vestibular bulbs, underlying the urethral folds, are homologous to the male corpus spongiosum. Fusion of the urethral folds in the male results in the fusion of the underlying erectile tissue into the single bulb of the penis, through which the penile urethra passes.

The glans clitoris is formed by the conjoined anterior terminal portions of the left and right vestibular bulbs. It is thus homologous to the glans penis, which is the terminal portion of the male corpus spongiosum.

Gross Anatomy: Head and Neck

DIRECTIONS: Each question below contains four or five suggested responses. Select the **one best** response to each question.

311. The carotid sheath and its contents may be safely retracted as a unit during surgical procedures on the neck. The contents of the carotid sheath include all the following structures EXCEPT the

(A) common carotid artery
(B) external carotid artery
(C) internal jugular vein
(D) sympathetic chain
(E) vagus nerve

312. A man who has a deep laceration of the scalp with profuse bleeding is seen in the emergency room. His epicranial aponeurosis (galea aponeurotica) is penetrated, resulting in severe gaping of the wound. The structure underlying the epicranial aponeurosis is

(A) a layer containing blood vessels
(B) bone
(C) the dura mater
(D) the periosteum (pericranium)
(E) the tendon of the epicranial muscles (occipitofrontalis)

Questions 313-318

A 53-year-old woman has a paralysis of the right side of her face that produces an expressionless and drooping appearance. She is unable to close her right eye, has difficulty chewing and drinking, perceives sounds as annoyingly intense in her right ear, and experiences some pain in her right external auditory meatus. Physical examination reveals loss of blink reflex in the right eye upon stimulation of either cornea and loss of taste from the anterior two-thirds of the tongue on the right side. Lacrimation appears normal in the right eye, the jaw-jerk reflex is normal, and there appears to be no problem with balance.

313. The inability to close the right eye is the result of involvement of

(A) the buccal branch of the facial nerve
(B) the buccal branch of the trigeminal nerve
(C) the levator palpebrae superioris muscle
(D) the superior tarsal muscle (of Müller)
(E) none of the above

151

314. The difficulty with mastication is the result of paralysis of

(A) the right buccinator muscle
(B) the right lateral pterygoid muscle
(C) the right masseter muscle
(D) the right zygomaticus major muscle
(E) none of the above

315. The pain in the external auditory meatus is due to involvement of sensory neurons that have their cell bodies in the

(A) facial nucleus
(B) geniculate ganglion
(C) pterygopalatine ganglion
(D) spinal nucleus of cranial nerve V
(E) trigeminal ganglion

316. The hyperacusia associated with the right ear results from involvement of

(A) the auditory nerve
(B) the chorda tympani nerve
(C) the stapedius muscle
(D) the tensor tympani muscle
(E) the tympanic nerve of Jacobson

317. The branch of the facial nerve that conveys secretomotor neurons involved in lacrimation is the

(A) chorda tympani
(B) deep petrosal nerve
(C) greater superficial petrosal nerve
(D) lacrimal nerve
(E) lesser superficial petrosal nerve

318. To produce the described signs and symptoms, a lesion involving the facial (CN VII) nerve would be located

(A) in the internal auditory meatus
(B) at the geniculate ganglion
(C) in the facial canal just distal to the geniculate ganglion
(D) at the stylomastoid foramen
(E) within the parenchyma of the parotid gland

(**End of question set**)

319. Which of the following statements concerning the lacrimal apparatus is correct?

(A) The lacrimal gland lies in the medial portion of the orbit
(B) Lacrimal fluid is secreted at the puncta in the medial edges of both upper and lower lids
(C) The nasolacrimal duct has a blind-ending lacrimal sac at its upper portion
(D) The nasolacrimal duct ends in the middle meatus of the nose
(E) None of the above

320. A small tumor of the orbit that involves the orbital foramen will produce which of the following signs and symptoms?

(A) Blindness in one eye
(B) Dilated pupil with loss of the pupillary reflex and accommodation
(C) Paralysis of the superior rectus, inferior rectus, medial rectus, inferior oblique, and levator palpebrae superioris muscles
(D) Venous engorgement of the retina
(E) None of the above

321. All the following signs could result from infection within the right cavernous sinus EXCEPT

(A) constricted pupil in response to light
(B) engorgement of the retinal veins upon fundoscopic examination
(C) loss of corneal blink reflex upon touching right conjunctiva
(D) ptosis (drooping) of the right eyelid
(E) right ophthalmoplegia (loss of all voluntary movement of an eye)

322. Reflexes that protect the inner ear from excessive noise involve the contraction of the tensor tympani and stapedius muscles. Correct statements about the tensor tympani muscle include all the following EXCEPT

(A) it inserts onto the malleus
(B) it is derived from the first branchial arch
(C) it is innervated by the chorda tympani nerve
(D) it lies parallel to the auditory tube

323. In addition to hearing loss and balance disturbances, a tumor in the internal acoustic meatus may be responsible for all the following signs and symptoms EXCEPT

(A) dry eye from loss of secretion of the lacrimal gland
(B) loss of secretion of the parotid gland on one side
(C) loss of secretion of the submandibular and sublingual glands on one side
(D) dry nasal mucosa from loss of secretion of the nasal glands on one side
(E) facial paralysis

324. A cranial fracture through the foramen rotundum that compresses the enclosed nerve results in

(A) inability to clench the jaw firmly
(B) paralysis of the inferior oblique muscle of the orbit
(C) regurgitation of fluids into the nasopharynx during swallowing
(D) uncontrolled drooling from the mouth
(E) none of the above

325. In dislocation of the jaw, displacement of the articular disk beyond the articular tubercle of the temporomandibular joint results from spasm or excessive contraction of which of the following muscles?

(A) Buccinator
(B) Lateral pterygoid
(C) Medial pterygoid
(D) Masseter
(E) Temporalis

326. Infection of the angular vein may result in venous thrombosis in which of the following intracranial vessels?

(A) Cavernous sinus
(B) Inferior petrosal sinus
(C) Sagittal sinus
(D) Sigmoid sinus
(E) Sphenoid sinus

327. Infection may spread from the nasal cavity to the meninges along the olfactory nerves. Olfactory fibers pass from the mucosa of the nasal cavity to the olfactory bulb via

(A) the anterior and posterior ethmoidal foramina
(B) the hiatus semilunaris
(C) the sphenopalatine foramen
(D) the nasociliary nerves
(E) none of the above

328. The blood supply to the vestibular region of the nasal cavity is from branches of all the following vessels EXCEPT the

(A) anterior ethmoidal branch of the ophthalmic artery
(B) incisive branch of the descending palatine artery
(C) posterior ethmoidal branch of the ophthalmic artery
(D) sphenopalatine artery
(E) superior labial branch of the facial artery

329. Although the ciliary action of the mucosa facilitates drainage of the paranasal sinuses, body position is paramount. Paranasal sinuses that drain by gravity with the body in the erect position include all the following EXCEPT the

(A) frontal
(B) inferior ethmoidal
(C) middle ethmoidal
(D) maxillary
(E) superior ethmoidal

330. Injury to the motor root of the mandibular division of the trigeminal nerve (CN V_3) would incur paralysis of all the following EXCEPT the

(A) anterior belly of the digastric muscle
(B) buccinator muscle
(C) mylohyoid muscle
(D) tensor tympani muscle
(E) tensor veli palatini muscle

331. The pterygomandibular raphe is a useful landmark in the oral cavity. This tendinous tissue marks the juncture of two muscles that are innervated by which of the following cranial nerves?

(A) Maxillary (CN V_2) and mandibular (CN V_3)
(B) Mandibular (CN V_3) and glossopharyngeal (CN IX)
(C) Mandibular (CN V_3) and vagus (CN X)
(D) Facial (CN VII) and glossopharyngeal (CN IX)
(E) Facial (CN VII) and vagus (CN X)

332. In the course of administering a local anesthetic, a needle that is placed too far into the greater palatine canal may paralyze an autonomic ganglion. In addition to dry nasal mucosa from loss of nasal gland secretion, loss of function at this ganglion would result in

(A) dry eye from loss of lacrimal gland secretion
(B) dry mouth from loss of parotid gland secretion
(C) dry mouth from loss of submandibular and sublingual gland secretions
(D) pupillary constriction
(E) none of the above

333. The palatine tonsils are located between the anterior and posterior faucial folds. The muscles that form these folds are, respectively, the

(A) levator veli palatini and tensor veli palatini
(B) palatoglossus and palatopharyngeus
(C) palatopharyngeus and salpingopharyngeus
(D) styloglossus and stylopharyngeus
(E) superior constrictor and middle constrictor

334. During anesthesia-induced muscle relaxation, obstruction of the respiratory passage is prevented by forward traction on the mandible. Normally, the tongue is prevented from falling backward and obstructing respiration by the

(A) genioglossus muscle
(B) hyoglossus muscle
(C) mylohyoid muscle
(D) palatoglossus muscle
(E) styloglossus muscle

335. The muscles originating from the styloid process are innervated by all the following nerves EXCEPT the

(A) facial nerve
(B) glossopharyngeal nerve
(C) hypoglossal nerve
(D) mylohyoid nerve

336. The superior laryngeal branch of the vagus nerve provides sensory innervation to the mucosa of all the following EXCEPT the

(A) epiglottic taste buds
(B) inferior surface of the epiglottis
(C) larynx inferior to the vocal folds
(D) larynx superior to the vocal folds

Questions 337-339

A person is attacked with a baseball bat and sustains a cranial fracture that extends through the jugular foramen and injures the enclosed nerves. The patient is hoarse and complains of having difficulty swallowing.

337. When the interior of the mouth is examined and the patient asked to say AH-H-H-H, the palate is observed to deviate to the normal side and there is loss of the gag reflex on the injured side. From these observations, it can be determined that all the following muscles are paralyzed on the injured side EXCEPT the

(A) levator veli palatini
(B) palatopharyngeus
(C) stylohyoid
(D) stylopharyngeus
(E) superior pharyngeal constrictor

338. Hoarseness is due to paralysis of the laryngeal muscles and adduction of the vocal fold on the involved side. Which of the following muscles normally abducts the vocal folds?

(A) Cricothyroid muscle
(B) Interarytenoid muscle
(C) Lateral cricoarytenoid muscle
(D) Posterior cricoarytenoid muscle
(E) Thyroarytenoid muscle

339. Other signs that might be compatible with this injury include all the following EXCEPT

(A) inability to induce a slowing of the pulse rate by pressure applied to the affected side of the neck
(B) inability to shrug the shoulder on the affected side
(C) inability to strongly turn the head away from the affected side
(D) loss of secretion from the parotid gland on the affected side
(E) paralysis of the occipital muscle

(End of question set)

340. Like all endocrine glands, the thyroid is highly vascular. The thyroid gland receives its blood supply in part from branches of the

(A) internal carotid artery
(B) lingual artery
(C) subclavian artery
(D) transverse cervical artery

341. The internal carotid arteries have significant anastomotic connections with tributaries of all the following arteries EXCEPT the

(A) facial
(B) internal maxillary
(C) lingual
(D) superficial temporal
(E) vertebral

DIRECTIONS: The group of questions below consists of four lettered headings followed by a set of numbered items. For each numbered item select

A	if the item is associated with	(A) **only**
B	if the item is associated with	(B) **only**
C	if the item is associated with	**both** (A) and (B)
D	if the item is associated with	**neither** (A) nor (B)

Each lettered heading may be used **once, more than once, or not at all.**

Questions 342-345

(A) Temporalis muscle
(B) Medial pterygoid muscle
(C) Both
(D) Neither

342. Protrusion of the jaw

343. Retraction of the jaw

344. Elevation of the jaw

345. Depression (opening) of the jaw

DIRECTIONS: Each group of questions below consists of lettered headings followed by a set of numbered items. For each numbered item select the **one** lettered heading with which it is **most** closely associated. Each lettered heading may be used **once, more than once, or not at all.**

Questions 346-349

For the reflex described in each of the following questions, select the appropriate nerve.

(A) Facial nerve (CN VII)
(B) Glossopharyngeal nerve (CN IX)
(C) Mandibular nerve (CN V₃)
(D) Maxillary nerve (CN V₂)
(E) Vagus nerve (CN X)

346. Efferent limb of the blink reflex

347. Afferent limb of the sneeze reflex

348. Efferent limb of the jaw-jerk reflex

349. Afferent limb of the cough reflex

Questions 350-353

A patient is suspected of having a basal skull fracture. During examination of the oropharynx, she is asked to stick out her tongue and say "ah." Indirect laryngoscopy is then performed by inserting a mirror into the oropharynx. For each physical finding described, select the nerve with whose injury such a finding is most likely to be associated.

(A) Left lingual nerve
(B) Right glossopharyngeal nerve
(C) Left glossopharyngeal nerve
(D) Right vagus nerve
(E) Right hypoglossal nerve

350. Deviation of the tongue to the right side

351. Deviation of the uvula to the left side

352. Loss of the gag reflex on the right side

353. Adduction of the true vocal fold on the right side

Questions 354-357

Certain neurons supplying the head and neck region have their cell bodies located in ganglia. For each of the neurons described, select the ganglion with which its cell bodies are associated.

(A) Geniculate ganglion
(B) Pterygopalatine ganglion
(C) Otic ganglion
(D) Superior cervical ganglion
(E) None of the above

354. Postganglionic fibers of the autonomic nervous system that bring about constriction of the pupil

355. Postganglionic parasympathetic secretomotor fibers that regulate lacrimal gland secretion

356. Parasympathetic secretomotor fibers that supply the parotid gland

357. Sensory fibers that convey taste from the anterior two-thirds of the tongue

Questions 358-360

A patient is brought into the emergency room with an attack of paroxysmal tachycardia. The resident physician restores the heart to normal sinus rhythm by simple massage of the region superficial to the carotid sinus. For each description, select the nerves that are most closely matched.

(A) Cardiac nerves arising from the cervical sympathetic chain
(B) Glossopharyngeal nerves
(C) Vagus nerves
(D) Hypoglossal nerves
(E) Inferior roots of the ansa cervicalis

358. The nerve that primarily contains the afferent component of the cardiac reflex responsible for slowing the heart

359. The nerve whose branch constitutes the efferent component of the cardiac reflex that slows the heart

360. The nerve whose excessive activity may contribute to tachycardia

Questions 361-365

For each muscle described, from the diagram below choose the lettered anatomic structure with which it is most closely associated.

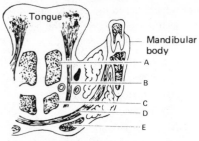

Floor of the mouth —
coronal section

361. The muscle that is innervated by the motor root of the trigeminal nerve and elevates the tongue

362. The muscle that is innervated by the motor root of the trigeminal nerve and assists in lowering the jaw

363. The muscle that is innervated by the hypoglossal nerve and protrudes the tongue

364. The muscle that is innervated by the hypoglossal nerve and retracts and depresses the tongue

365. The muscle that is innervated by the superior ramus of the ansa cervicalis (C1 to C2) and assists in lowering the jaw

Gross Anatomy:
Head and Neck
Answers

311. The answer is D. *(Hollinshead, ed 4. pp 826-827, 830, 850.)* The carotid sheath is a condensation of the deep fascia from the base of the skull to the mediastinum. It contains the carotid arteries, the internal jugular vein, and the vagus nerve. Within the sheath the common carotid artery bifurcates to form the external carotid artery and the internal carotid artery. The internal jugular vein lies immediately posterolaterally to the carotid arteries and the vagus nerve lies posteriorly. The cervical sympathetic chain lies in the retropharyngeal space posterior to the carotid sheath and anterior to the prevertebral fascia.

312. The answer is A. *(Hollinshead, ed 4. pp 876-878.)* A mnemonic device for remembering the order in which the soft tissues overlie the cranium is *SCALP:* Skin, Connective tissue, Aponeurosis, Loose connective tissue, and Periosteum. The scalp proper is composed of the outer three layers, of which the connective tissue contains one of the richest cutaneous blood supplies of the body. The occipitofrontal muscle complex inserts into the epicranial aponeurosis, which forms the intermediate tendon of this digastric muscle. This structure, along with the underlying layer of loose connective tissue, accounts for the high degree of mobility of the scalp over the pericranium. If the aponeurosis is lacerated transversely, traction from the muscle bellies will cause considerable gaping of the wound. Secondary to trauma or infection, blood or pus may accumulate subjacent to the epicranial aponeurosis.

313. The answer is E. *(Hollinshead, ed 4. pp 880, 883-884.)* The palpebral portion of the orbicularis oculi muscle (innervated by the facial nerve) produces the blink. The buccal branch of the facial nerve innervates muscles of facial expression (including the buccinator muscle) between the eye and the mouth, while the buccal branch of the trigeminal nerve is sensory. The levator palpebrae superioris muscle, which elevates the upper eyelid, is innervated by the oculomotor nerve, while the involuntary superior tarsal muscle is supplied by sympathetic nerves.

314. The answer is A. *(Hollinshead, ed 4. pp 878-879.)* The buccinator muscle draws the cheek against the teeth during mastication and with the tongue serves to keep food on the grinding surface of the molars. The buccinator is innervated by the buccal branch of the facial nerve (CN VII) and paralysis of this muscle results in accumulation of food in the cheek so that mastication becomes awkward and difficult.

161

Because the orbicularis oris muscle is also paralyzed, the patient tends to drool and to have difficulty drinking.

315. The answer is B. *(Hollinshead, ed 4. pp 935-936.)* The auricular branch of the facial nerve (CN VII) innervates a variable portion of the external auditory meatus. These sensory neurons have their cell bodies in the geniculate ganglion and synapse in the brain stem with neurons in the spinal nucleus of cranial nerve V. The geniculate ganglion also contains the cell bodies for the taste fibers from the anterior two-thirds of the tongue, which course in the chorda tympani.

316. The answer is C. *(Hollinshead, ed 4. pp 936, 949-950.)* The stapedius muscle is innervated by a branch of the facial nerve (CN VII) given off within the facial canal. Paralysis of this muscle results in loss of a reflex that dampens movement of the stapes—as a result normal sounds are perceived as annoyingly loud. The tensor tympani muscle is innervated by a twig from the mandibular division of the trigeminal nerve (CN V_3). The chorda tympani conveys taste from the anterior two-thirds of the tongue and secretomotor neurons for the submandibular and sublingual glands. The tympanic nerve of Jacobson, a branch of the glossopharyngeal nerve (CN IX), conveys secretomotor neurons to the parotid gland.

317. The answer is C. *(Hollinshead, ed 4. pp 936, 950-951.)* The greater superficial petrosal nerve leaves the facial nerve (CN VII) at the geniculate ganglion. It carries secretomotor neurons from the superior salivatory nucleus to the pterygopalatine ganglion, joining along the way with the sympathetic deep petrosal nerve to become the nerve of the pterygoid canal.

318. The answer is C. *(April, ed 2. pp 498-500.)* The facial nerve conveys special visceral efferent (branchiomotor) neurons to the muscles of facial expression and, in the facial canal, gives off a branch to the stapedius muscle. In addition, it carries general visceral efferent (secretomotor) neurons to the salivary glands and special visceral afferent (taste) fibers from the anterior two-thirds of the tongue via the chorda tympani. It also carries general visceral efferent (secretomotor) neurons to the lacrimal gland via the greater superficial petrosal nerve, and general somatic afferent neurons from the region of the external ear. Because lacrimation and balance are unaffected and the patient complains of hyperacusia, the lesion must be located in the facial canal between the geniculate ganglion and the origin of the nerve to the stapedius muscle. A lesion at the stylomastoid foramen or within the parotid gland would produce facial paralysis only. A lesion in the internal auditory meatus would affect lacrimation and might also involve the acousticovestibular nerve (CN VIII).

319. The answer is C. *(Hollinshead, ed 4. pp 959-962, 980.)* The lacrimal gland lies in the upper lateral portion of the orbit. Normally, lacrimal fluid flows across the cornea to enter puncta in the medial edges of both upper and lower lids. From the puncta, canaliculi run to enlarged ampullae. The nasolacrimal duct has a blind-ending lacrimal sac at its upper portion that is squeezed like a bulb syringe by the opening and closing of the eyelids, thereby aspirating the lacrimal fluid. The nasolacrimal duct ends in the inferior meatus of the nose.

320. The answer is A. (*Hollinshead, ed 4. pp 964-968.*) A small tumor of the orbit that involves the orbital foramen will compromise the optic nerve and the ophthalmic artery, producing ischemia and blindness in the affected eye. Because the oculomotor, trochlear, and abducens nerves pass through the superior orbital fissure, there may be no loss of voluntary ocular movement or of the ocular reflexes. Similarly, the ophthalmic veins drain by way of the superior and inferior orbital fissures; therefore, venous congestion would not occur.

321. The answer is A. (*Hollinshead, ed 4. pp 888-889, 925, 971-972, 974-975.*) Infection within the cavernous sinus, along with thrombus formation and venous stasis leading to edema and local anoxia, will affect the contained nerves. Loss of function of the oculomotor (CN III), trochlear (CN IV), and abducens (CN VI) nerves will produce ophthalmoplegia (ocular paralysis). Since the oculomotor nerve also innervates the levator palpebrae superioris muscle, there will be ptosis of the eyelid. Because the oculomotor nerve also contains the parasympathetic nerves that innervate the iridal constrictors, there is loss of this function and the pupil will remain dilated on the affected side. Because the ophthalmic and maxillary portions of the trigeminal nerve (CN V) also pass through the cavernous sinus, involvement will lead to loss of the blink reflex when the eye of the affected side is touched. The retinal veins drain into the cavernous sinus; therefore, septic thrombosis of this sinus will obstruct blood return with venous congestion of the retina and the optic nerve with resultant visual changes or blindness.

322. The answer is C. (*Hollinshead, ed 4. p 949.*) The tensor tympani muscle, a derivative of the first branchial arch and therefore innervated by a twig from the motor root of the trigeminal nerve (CN V_3), arises from the walls of a canal lying superior to the auditory tube; it inserts onto the manubrium (handle) of the malleus. Reflex contraction of this muscle in response to loud noise tends to dampen movement of the tympanic membrane to which the handle of the malleus is attached along its length. The stapedius muscle, a derivative of the second branchial arch and therefore innervated by a twig from the facial nerve (CN VII), arises from the posterior wall of the middle ear and inserts onto the neck of the stapes. Reflex contraction of this muscle attenuates sound transmission through the ossicles by dampening the range and movement of the stapes. Damage to the motor nerves of these muscles results in hyperacusia.

323. The answer is B. (*Hollinshead, ed 4. pp 935-936, 939-941.*) The internal acoustic meatus contains the acousticovestibular nerve (CN VIII) and the facial nerve

(CN VII), both of which may be affected by an acoustic neuroma. The parasympathetic component of the facial nerve, the nervus intermedius, provides neurons that travel along the greater superficial petrosal nerve and synapse in the pterygopalatine ganglion as well as neurons that travel along the chorda tympani nerve and synapse in the submandibular ganglion. The secretomotor neurons of the pterygopalatine ganglion innervate the lacrimal gland, the glands of the nasal mucosa, and the glands of the palate. The secretomotor neurons of the submandibular ganglion innervate the submandibular gland, the sublingual gland, and the glands of the anterior part of the tongue. The parotid gland is innervated by the glossopharyngeal nerve (CN IX) via its tympanic branch and the lesser superficial petrosal nerve to the otic ganglion.

324. The answer is E. *(Hollinshead, ed 4. pp 933-934.)* The maxillary division of the trigeminal nerve (CN V₂), which passes through the foramen rotundum, is entirely sensory. Damage to this nerve results in sensory deprivation over the maxillary region of the face and loss of the sneeze reflex. The mandibular division of the trigeminal nerve, which passes through the foramen ovale, innervates the masticatory muscles responsible for clenching the jaw as well as the tensor palatini muscle, which assists in the establishment of the velopharyngeal seal. The other muscles of the soft palate are innervated by the pharyngeal branch of the vagus nerve (CN X), which transits the jugular foramen. The orbicularis oris and buccinator muscles are innervated by the facial nerve (CN VII), which transits the stylomastoid foramen. The inferior oblique muscle of the eye is innervated by the inferior branch of the oculomotor nerve, which enters the orbit through the superior orbital fissure.

325. The answer is B. *(Hollinshead, ed 4. p 898.)* The temporalis, masseter, and medial and lateral pterygoid muscles attach to the mandible and are the major muscles involved in movements of the jaw. The buccinator muscle, which controls the contents of the mouth during mastication, is innervated by the seventh cranial nerve and constitutes the chief muscle of facial expression. The lateral pterygoid muscles, acting bilaterally, protract the jaw and, acting unilaterally, rotate the jaw during chewing. Since the fibers of the superior head of the lateral pterygoid muscle insert onto the anterior aspect of the articular disk of the temporomandibular joint as well as onto the head of the mandible, spasm of this muscle, such as in a yawn, can result in dislocation of the mandible by pulling the disk anterior to the articular tubercle. Reduction is accomplished by pushing the mandible downward and back, so that the head of the mandible reenters the mandibular fossa. The temporalis, medial pterygoid, and masseter muscles primarily elevate the jaw in molar occlusion.

326. The answer is A. *(Hollinshead, ed 4. pp 886, 925-926, 971-972.)* The angular veins anastomose with the superficial branches of the ophthalmic veins. Therefore an infection in the angular vein or in the face sufficiently close to the angular vein to block normal drainage into the submandibular vein may cause retrograde flow into the ophthalmic vein. Because the ophthalmic veins drain into the cavernous sinus, the infection may spread into this intracranial vessel with resultant venous thrombosis.

327. The answer is E. *(Hollinshead, ed 4. pp 931-932.)* The olfactory neurons pass from the olfactory mucosa to the olfactory bulb via the olfactory foramina of the cribriform plate of the ethmoid bone. The anterior ethmoidal foramen contains the nasal branch of the nasociliary nerve and the anterior ethmoidal artery; the posterior ethmoidal foramen contains the posterior ethmoidal artery. The hiatus semilunaris is the space in the middle meatus into which the frontal, anterior ethmoidal, and maxillary sinuses drain. The sphenopalatine foramen connects the nasal cavity with the pterygopalatine fossa and transmits the sphenopalatine artery and nerve.

328. The answer is C. *(Hollinshead, ed 4. p 982.)* The nasal cavity is supplied by the anterior and posterior ethmoidal branches of the ophthalmic artery, the lateral and septal posterior nasal branches of the sphenopalatine artery, the incisive branch of the descending palatine artery, and branches from the superior labial branch of the facial artery. All but the posterior ethmoidal branch anastomose freely in the region of the nasal vestibule. Intractable epistaxis may require ligation of these vessels or of the external carotid.

329. The answer is D. *(Hollinshead, ed 4. p 985.)* Because the openings of the maxillary and sphenoidal sinuses normally are located high on the sinus walls, with the head in the erect position gravity drainage is precluded. The frontal sinuses and ethmoidal air cells normally have good drainage. Nasal infections may spread to the paranasal sinuses producing sinusitis and causing pain that is referred to those regions innervated by branches of the same nerve that innervates the sinus mucosa. Sinusitis of the maxillary sinus, for instance, may affect the branches of the maxillary nerve to produce pain, often severe, referred to the maxillary teeth.

330. The answer is B. *(Hollinshead, ed 4. pp 933-934, 949, 995.)* All muscles of mastication (medial and lateral pterygoids, temporalis, and masseter), as well as the anterior belly of the digastric, mylohyoid, tensor tympani, and tensor veli palatini are innervated by the motor root of the trigeminal nerve. The buccinator muscle and posterior belly of the digastric muscle as well as the muscles of facial expression, which are second branchial arch derivatives, are innervated by the facial nerve (CN VII).

331. The answer is E. *(Hollinshead, ed 4. pp 879, 883, 988-989.)* The pterygomandibular raphe extends from the hamulus of the medial pterygoid plate to the mandible and marks the junction of the buccinator and the superior constrictor muscles. The buccinator, a muscle of facial expression, is innervated by the facial nerve (CN VII). The superior constrictor is innervated by the pharyngeal branch of the vagus nerve (CN X).

332. The answer is A. *(Hollinshead, ed 4. pp 939-940.)* The sphenopalatine (pterygopalatine) ganglion is the site of the postsynaptic autonomic neurons that control lacrimation and nasal and palatine secretion. This ganglion lies high in the pterygopalatine fossa, the bottom of which gains access to the oral cavity via the greater palatine canal. The postsynaptic autonomic neurons that control parotid secretion are in the otic ganglion, which is located adjacent to the motor root of the trigeminal nerve. The ganglionic neurons associated with submandibular and sublingual secretion are located in the submandibular ganglion, which is suspended from the lingual nerve. While sympathetic nerves pass through the pterygopalatine fossa, they do not reach the pupil by this route.

333. The answer is B. *(Hollinshead, ed 4. pp 992-993.)* The anterior faucial pillar, or palatoglossal arch, is formed by the mucosa overlying the palatoglossus muscle. The posterior faucial pillar, or palatopharyngeal arch, likewise is formed by the palatopharyngeus muscle. The palatoglossus and palatopharyngeus muscles insert into the tongue and pharynx, respectively, and both are innervated by the pharyngeal branch of the vagus nerve (CN X). The levator veli palatini and tensor veli palatini, arising from opposite sides of the cartilaginous portion of the auditory tube and base of the skull, insert into the soft palate. They are innervated by the pharyngeal branch of the vagus nerve. The salpingopharyngeus, also innervated by the pharyngeal branch of the vagus nerve, arises from the torus tubarius at the opening of the auditory tube and inserts into the pharyngeal musculature. The styloglossus and stylopharyngeus originate on the styloid process and insert into the tongue and onto the lesser horn of the hyoid bone, respectively. The superior and middle constrictors, likewise, are innervated by the pharyngeal branch of the vagus nerve.

334. The answer is A. *(Hollinshead, ed 4. p 907.)* The attachment of the genioglossus to the genial tubercles on the inner surface of the symphysis of the mandible makes protrusion of the tongue possible. This action also prevents the tongue from falling back and obstructing respiration. The mylohyoid elevates the anterior portion of the tongue; the styloglossus and palatoglossus elevate the posterior portion of the tongue during deglutition. The hyoglossus depresses the tongue.

335. The answer is D. *(April, ed 2. pp 513-514, 528, 534. Hollinshead, ed 4. pp 904, 907, 909.)* The stylohyoid muscle, running from the styloid process to the lesser horn of the hyoid bone, is innervated by the facial nerve. The stylopharyngeus is the only muscle innervated by the glossopharyngeal nerve. The styloglossus muscle is innervated by the hypoglossal nerve. The mylohyoid nerve and the facial nerve innervate the anterior and posterior bellies of the digastric muscle, respectively.

336. The answer is C. *(Hollinshead, ed 4. p 1004.)* The superior laryngeal nerves arise from the vagus nerves. The internal branch of the superior laryngeal nerve distributes sensory branches to the laryngeal mucous membranes superior to the vocal folds, to the surface of the epiglottis (including the epiglottic taste buds), and to the arytenoepiglottic folds. The vagus nerve provides the afferent limb of the cough reflex. The cricothyroid muscle is supplied by the external branch of the superior laryngeal nerve. The region of the larynx inferior to the vocal folds as well as the trachea is supplied by the inferior (recurrent) laryngeal nerve.

337. The answer is C. *(Hollinshead, ed 4. pp 990, 993, 996.)* The glossopharyngeal and vagus nerves pass through the jugular foramen. Inability to evoke a gag reflex on the injured side indicates involvement of the glossopharyngeal nerve (CN IX). The stylopharyngeus, the only muscle innervated by the glossopharyngeal nerve, can be assumed to be paralyzed. The uvulae, levator veli palatini, palatoglossus, palatopharyngeus, salpingopharyngeus, and middle and inferior pharyngeal constrictors are all innervated by the pharyngeal branch of the vagus nerve. Paralysis of these muscles makes deglutition difficult; paralysis of the levator veli palatini results in unbalanced lifting of the palate toward the normal side upon phonation. The stylohyoid muscle is innervated by the facial nerve (CN VII).

338. The answer is D. *(Hollinshead, ed 4. pp 1004-1005.)* The posterior cricoarytenoid muscle, innervated by the recurrent laryngeal nerve, is the sole abductor of the true vocal folds. This muscle, originating from the posterior lamina of the cricoid cartilage and inserting onto the muscular process of the arytenoid cartilage, acts to rotate the arytenoid laterally and thereby abduct the vocal folds and open the glottis. Both the lateral cricoarytenoid and interarytenoid muscles are adductors that close the glottis. The thyroarytenoid (vocalis) muscle is a tensor. All three are innervated by the recurrent laryngeal branch of the vagus. The superior laryngeal branch of the vagus nerve innervates the cricothyroid muscle, which selectively tenses regions of the vocal cords.

339. The answer is E. *(Hollinshead, ed 4. pp 936-937.)* The occipital belly of the frontooccipital muscle, a muscle of facial expression, is innervated from the auricular branch of the facial nerve (CN VII), which leaves the skull via the stylomastoid foramen. In addition to the vagus nerve, the glossopharyngeal (CN IX) and spinal accessory nerves (CN XI) pass through the jugular foramen. The tympanic (Jacobson's) branch of the glossopharyngeal nerve passes through the middle ear and exits into the middle cranial fossa as the lesser superficial petrosal nerve, which carries presynaptic parasympathetic neurons to the otic ganglion for parotid secretion. The carotid branch of the glossopharyngeal nerve supplies the afferent limb of the carotid reflex, which controls the pulse rate. The spinal accessory nerve innervates the sternocleidomastoid muscle, which turns the head to the opposite side, as well as the trapezius muscle, which acts upon the scapula.

340. The answer is C. *(Hollinshead, ed 4. pp 839-840.)* The inferior thyroid artery arises from the thyrocervical trunk, a branch of the subclavian artery. The superior thyroid artery arises from the external carotid artery. An inconsistent thyroid ima artery, when present, may arise from the aortic arch, the innominate artery, or the common carotid artery. There are no branches of the internal carotid artery and infrequent branches of the common carotid artery in the neck. The transverse cervical artery supplies the posterior triangle of the neck.

341.   The answer is C. *(Hollinshead, ed 4. pp 926-930.)* The posterior communicating branches of the internal carotid arteries, forming a part of the anastomotic cerebral arterial circle (of Willis), connect with the basilar artery, which arises by the fusion of the paired vertebral arteries. The ophthalmic arteries, which arise from the internal carotids, anastomose with the facial, the superficial temporal, and the internal maxillary branches of the external carotid artery in the vicinity of the eye. The internal carotids also anastomose with the internal maxillary artery via the artery of the pterygoid canal and the middle meningeal artery.

342-345.   The answers are: 342-D, 343-A, 344-C, 345-D. *(Hollinshead, ed 4. pp 895-898, 903-904.)* The lateral pterygoid muscles run from the lateral side of the lateral pterygoid plate and from the infratemporal fossa to the head of the mandible and to the articular disk of the temporomandibular joint. Contraction of the lateral pterygoid muscles, bilaterally, protrudes the jaw. Unilateral contraction swings the jaw toward the opposite side.

The posterior muscle bundles of the temporalis muscle function as jaw retractors. These fibers originate over the temporal region and run nearly horizontally to the coronoid process of the mandible.

The muscle bundles of the anterior portion of the temporalis muscle run nearly vertically into the coronoid process so that this portion of the muscle is an elevator (closer) of the jaw. In addition, the medial pterygoid muscle, originating from the medial side of the lateral pterygoid plate, and masseter muscle, originating from the zygomatic arch, pass medially and laterally to the ramus of the mandible and form a sling about the ramus of the mandible. These muscles are powerful elevators.

The submental muscles, assisted by gravity, are the primary depressors of the jaw. These include the geniohyoid and mylohyoid muscles as well as the anterior belly of the digastric muscle, all of which function in conjunction with the infrahyoid strap muscles.

346-349.   The answers are: 346-A, 347-D, 348-C, 349-E. *(Hollinshead, ed 4. pp 936-937, 1004.)* The facial nerve is the efferent limb of the blink reflex; the ophthalmic and a small portion of the maxillary nerves innervate the conjunctiva and thus provide the afferent limb of this reflex. Because the blink reflex is consensual, i.e., both eyes blink to a unilateral stimulus, it is possible to determine whether the afferent or efferent limb is injured by the response pattern.

The maxillary nerve provides the afferent limb of the sneeze reflex. A cotton swab providing light stimulation just at the entrance of the external nares will produce a withdrawal response, if not the urge to sneeze. The mandibular nerve contains both the afferent and efferent limbs of the jaw-jerk reflex. This reflex is elicited by tapping the slack jaw at the chin. The sudden stretch of the gamma receptors causes a sharp reflex closing of the jaw. The superior and inferior laryngeal branches of the vagus nerve provide the afferent limb of the cough reflex. The action of the efferent limb of the vagus nerve in the pharynx is noted by observing whether the uvula remains in the midline when the patient says "AH-H-H."

350-353. The answers are: 350-E, 351-D, 352-B, 353-D. *(April, ed 2. pp 529, 533-534, 539.)* The lingual branches of the mandibular nerves (CN V₃) are sensory to the anterior two-thirds of the tongue; the glossopharyngeal nerves (CN IX) are sensory to the posterior third of the tongue and part of the pharynx. Protrusion of the tongue is accomplished by the genioglossus muscles, which are innervated by the hypoglossal nerve (CN XII). Paralysis of the left genioglossus muscle by injury to the left hypoglossal nerve results in protrusion of the tongue with deviation toward the side of injury because the muscle on the normal side is unopposed.

With the exception of the tensor veli palatini muscle (innervated by the mandibular nerve, CN V₃), all muscles of the soft palate are innervated through the pharyngeal plexus. Motor fibers to the pharyngeal plexus are derived from the vagus nerve (CN X) with a possible contribution from the cranial root of the accessory nerve (CN XI), which joins the vagus nerve in the jugular canal. One or more pharyngeal branches of the vagus nerve also contribute to the pharyngeal plexus. Paralysis of the palatal musculature on one side will result in deviation of the uvula toward the *normal* side. As a result, the nasopharyngeal seal loses competence and nasal speech results.

The pharyngeal plexus also contains sensory fibers derived from the pharyngeal branches of the glossopharyngeal nerve (CN IX). Damage to this nerve will, on the injured side, abolish the pharyngeal gag reflex, taste to the posterior third of the tongue, and the carotid reflex. In addition, since the glossopharyngeal nerve usually provides motor innervation of the middle pharyngeal constrictor, constriction of the posterior pharyngeal wall will not occur when saying "ah."

The recurrent laryngeal nerve, another branch of the vagus, supplies the muscles of the larynx other than the cricothyroid, which is supplied by the superior laryngeal branch of the vagus. Unilateral dysfunction of the vagus nerve, which produces inability to abduct the ipsilateral vocal cord, results in assumption of a closed or adducted position by the cord and, as a consequence, hoarseness of speech. The vagus also is sensory to the glottis and larynx, providing the afferent limb of the cough reflex and taste to the region of the epiglottis.

354-357. The answers are: 354-E, 355-B, 356-C, 357-A. *(Hollinshead, ed 4. pp 937, 939-940, 950.)* Constriction of the pupil is a function of the parasympathetic division of the autonomic nervous system. Parasympathetic secretomotor fibers, originating from the nucleus of Edinger-Westphal adjacent to the motor nucleus of CN III in the midbrain, leave the central nervous system via the oculomotor nerve (CN III), which enters the orbit through the superior orbital fissure. The parasympathetic fibers leave the major part of the oculomotor nerve in the inferior branch and, through the short oculomotor root, enter and synapse with neurons of the ciliary ganglion. From the ciliary ganglion, the postsynaptic fibers reach the eyeball by means of the short ciliary nerves, which innervate the pupillary sphincter muscle of the iris. Other postganglionic neuronal processes, taking the same pathway, terminate in the ciliary muscle, contraction of which thickens the lens and brings the focal point nearer. Postsynaptic sympathetic fibers from the superior cervical ganglion run with the arterial supply to reach the orbit and innervate the pupillary dilator muscle.

Lacrimation is principally a function of the parasympathetic division of the autonomic nervous system. Parasympathetic secretomotor fibers, originating in the superior salivatory nucleus of the brain stem, leave the central nervous system in the nervus intermedius of the facial nerve (CN VII), which traverses the internal auditory meatus to gain access to the facial canal. At the genu of the facial canal, the fibers of the nervus intermedius divide into two branches carrying the parasympathetic fibers, one to the pterygopalatine ganglion via the greater superficial petrosal nerve and the other to the submandibular ganglion via the chorda tympani. The greater superficial petrosal nerve carries the secretomotor fibers through the hiatus of the facial canal into the middle cranial fossa, the pterygoid canal, and finally the pterygopalatine fossa to reach the pterygopalatine ganglion. The postsynaptic parasympathetic fibers for lacrimation, in company with the infraorbital branch of the maxillary nerve (CN V_2), leave the pterygopalatine ganglion and then pass in the zygomaticotemporal branch of CN V_2 along the lateral wall of the orbit to reach the lacrimal branch of the ophthalmic nerve (CN V_1), which they follow to the lacrimal gland. From the pterygopalatine ganglion, postsynaptic parasympathetic secretomotor fibers also pass through the pterygopalatine foramen as well as down the greater palatine canal, innervating, respectively, the mucous glands of the nasal mucosa and the mucous glands of the palate.

Parotid secretion is principally a function of the parasympathetic division of the autonomic nervous system. The parasympathetic preganglionic fibers arise from the inferior salivatory nucleus of the brain stem and leave the central nervous system in the glossopharyngeal nerve (CN IX). Within the jugular canal, the tympanic nerve (of Jacobson) leaves the glossopharyngeal nerve and courses anteriorly through the temporal bone, gaining access to the medial wall of the middle ear and continuing across the tympanic bulla to form the tympanic plexus. From this plexus, the secretomotor fibers unite to form the lesser superficial petrosal nerve, which gains access to the middle cranial fossa just below the facial hiatus and terminates in the otic ganglion. The otic ganglion lies just medial to the mandibular nerve (CN V_3) as it passes through the foramen ovale from the middle cranial fossa to the infratemporal region. Postsynaptic secretomotor fibers from the otic ganglion travel along the mandibular nerve to its auriculotemporal branches, which they follow to the parotid gland. Taste is a special afferent function. Taste fibers from the *anterior two-thirds* of the tongue travel along the lingual nerve to the chorda tympani. The chorda tympani, which also conveys the parasympathetic presynaptic secretomotor fibers from the facial nerve to the submandibular ganglion, enters the petrotympanic fissure to gain access to the middle ear, where it lies directly behind the tympanic membrane and malleus. The chorda tympani passes posteriorly through the temporal bone to reach the facial nerve (CN VII), along which the taste fibers travel to the nucleus solitarius of the brain stem. The cell bodies of these taste fibers are located in the geniculate ganglion, which is a cranial equivalent of a dorsal root ganglion for the facial nerve.

Taste fibers from the *posterior third* of the tongue and vallate papillae are carried by special afferent fibers in the lingual branches of the glossopharyngeal nerve (CN IX). The cell bodies of these fibers are located in the inferior glossopharyngeal ganglion, and the central processes also terminate in the nucleus solitarius of the brain stem. Taste from the area of the epiglottis is conveyed in the special afferent fibers of the vagus nerve (CN X). These fibers have their cell bodies in the inferior vagal ganglion and likewise terminate in the nucleus solitarius of the brain stem.

358-360.   The answers are: 358-B, 359-C, 360-A. *(Hollinshead, ed 4. pp 538-539, 835.)* The carotid sinus and carotid body, located at the bifurcation of the common carotid artery, are innervated by the carotid branch (of Hering) of the glossopharyngeal nerve (CN IX) and function to regulate cardiac output. The carotid body acts as a *chemo*receptor, responding to changes in the partial pressure of oxygen in the circulating blood. The carotid sinus acts as a *baro*receptor, responding to either elevated blood pressure or pressure applied to the anterolateral surface of the neck. Afferent volleys from these specialized receptors travel along the glosso-pharyngeal nerve, which has its afferent cell bodies located in the inferior petrosal ganglion, to the excitatory and inhibitory areas of the vasomotor center of the medulla and the adjacent dorsal motor nucleus of the vagus nerve.

From the dorsal motor nucleus of the vagus nerve (CN X), efferent volleys travel along the vagus nerve and through the cardiac plexus to terminate in ganglia associated with the heart, especially in the atrial region. Short postganglionic para-sympathetic fibers continue to the sinoatrial and atrioventricular nodes as well as to the atrial musculature. The inhibitory action of acetylcholine reduces both cardiac rate and stroke volume. Stimulation of the sinus nerve by carotid massage may return a bounding heart rate to normal (as in the patient who is the subject of this question), but in older persons the reflex arc involved may well be hypersensitive, and brady-cardia or even syncope (carotid sinus syndrome) may result. In addition, carotid massage may dislodge an atherosclerotic plaque from the internal carotid, producing cerebrovascular embolism.

Increased cardiac activity of the sort exhibited in the patient discussed may in part be due to increased sympathetic stimulation of the heart. The lateral portion of the vasomotor center of the medulla transmits excitatory volleys through the sympathetic pathways to the heart. The cardiac accelerator nerves, which arise from the superior, middle, and inferior cervical ganglia as well as directly from T1 through T4, pass through the cardiac plexus to reach the heart. Sympathetic stimulation increases both heart rate and stroke volume.

361-365. The answers are: 361-D, 362-E, 363-A, 364-B, 365-C. *(Hollinshead, ed 4. pp 904, 907.)* The mylohyoid muscle (D in the diagram accompanying the question) is innervated by the mylohyoid branch of the inferior alveolar nerve from CN V$_3$. This muscle arises from the internal surface of the mandible anteriorly and laterally, fuses anteriorly with its contralateral counterpart in a midline raphe, and inserts posteriorly onto the hyoid bone. Functioning as a diaphragm that forms the floor of the oral cavity, the mylohyoid muscle supports and elevates the tongue during deglutition; it also serves as a barrier to spread of infection from the oral cavity to the submandibular region. The sublingual gland and submandibular duct lie superior to and the submandibular gland for the most part lies inferior to the mylohyoid muscle.

The anterior belly of the digastric muscle (E), lying immediately inferior to the mylohyoid muscle, is innervated by the mylohyoid branch of the inferior alveolar nerve from CN V$_3$. Inserting at one end onto the inferior border of the mandible just lateral to the mandibular symphysis, it is continuous at the other end with the *posterior* belly of the digastric muscle (innervated by CN VII) through an intermediate tendon that attaches to the greater horn of the hyoid bone by a fascial sling. The anterior belly of the digastric acts to open the mouth by pulling the mandible downward and backward.

The genioglossus muscle (A), lying superior to the geniohyoid muscle, is innervated by the hypoglossal nerve (CN XII). It originates from the superior genial tubercle on the internal aspect of the mandible just lateral to the mandibular symphysis and inserts into the body of the tongue by decussating with the intrinsic musculature of the tongue. The genioglossus acts to protrude the tongue and, during deglutition, to depress it. The lingual artery passes lateral to the genioglossus muscle and medial to the hyoglossus muscle.

The hyoglossus muscle (B), a flat quadrangular muscle running perpendicular to the lateral aspect of the tongue, is innervated by the hypoglossal nerve (CN XII). Originating from the sides of the hyoid bone, it inserts into the body of the tongue by decussating with the more lateral intrinsic lingual musculature. The hyoglossus acts to retract the tongue and, during deglutition, to depress it. The submandibular duct, lingual nerve, and submandibular ganglion lie just lateral to the hyoglossus muscle.

The geniohyoid muscle (C), lying immediately superior to the mylohyoid, is innervated by the descendens hypoglossi (C1 to C2 of the ansa cervicalis). It is attached at one end to the inferior genial tubercle on the internal aspect of the mandible just lateral to the mandibular symphysis, and at the other end to the anterior aspect of the hyoid bone. The geniohyoid acts to lower the jaw and, during deglutition, to protrude the hyoid bone.

Other extrinsic muscles of the tongue include the palatoglossus, innervated by the vagus nerve (CN X) through the pharyngeal plexus. The palatoglossus arises from the posterior lateral edge of the hard palate and inserts into the lateral and dorsal intrinsic musculature of the tongue. The styloglossus muscle, innervated by the hypoglossal nerve (CN XII), extends from the styloid process and inserts into the sides and body of the tongue. Both muscles function to elevate the posterior aspect of the tongue and retract the tongue during deglutition.

Gross Anatomy: Extremities and Back

DIRECTIONS: Each question below contains four or five suggested responses. Select the **one best** response to each question.

366. Injury to the posterior cord of the brachial plexus involves all the following nerves EXCEPT the

(A) axillary nerve
(B) long thoracic nerve
(C) radial nerve
(D) subscapular nerves
(E) thoracodorsal nerve

367. Injury to the upper trunk or lateral cord of the brachial plexus is fairly common and usually produces all the following signs EXCEPT

(A) absence of the biceps brachii tendon reflex
(B) diminished flexor tendon reflexes on the ulnar side of the wrist
(C) loss of sensation along the lateral aspect of the forearm
(D) paralysis of the clavicular head of the pectoralis major muscle
(E) severe weakness of elbow flexion

368. All the following statements correctly pertain to the median nerve EXCEPT

(A) it contains segmental contributions from roots C6, C7, and C8.
(B) it innervates no muscles in the brachium
(C) it is formed by contributions from both the lateral and medial cords
(D) it passes posterior to the axillary artery
(E) it receives contributions only from the anterior divisions of the brachial plexus

Questions 369-377

A 52-year-old man is brought to the emergency room after being found in the park where apparently he had lain overnight after a fall. He complains of severe pain in the left arm. Physical examination suggests that he has a broken humerus, which is confirmed radiologically. The patient can extend the forearm at the elbow, but supination appears to be somewhat weak; the hand grasp is very weak when compared with the uninjured arm. Neurologic examination reveals an inability to extend the wrist ("wrist drop"). Since these findings point to apparent nerve damage, the patient is scheduled for a surgical reduction of the fracture.

369. The observation that extension at the elbow appears normal, but supination of the forearm weak, warrants localization of the nerve lesion to the

(A) posterior cord of the brachial plexus in the axilla
(B) posterior division of the brachial plexus
(C) radial nerve at the distal third of the humerus
(D) radial nerve in the midforearm
(E) radial nerve in the vicinity of the head of the radius

370. The patient exhibits marked weakness of supination when the elbow joint is fully extended, but there is little weakness of supination evident when the elbow is partially flexed. The reason for this observation is

(A) the biceps brachii muscle is a powerful supinator
(B) the brachialis muscle is functional
(C) the pronator teres is functional
(D) the supinator muscle is not paralyzed
(E) none of the above

371. "Wrist drop" results in a hand grasp that is very weak. The strength of the grasp is greatest with the wrist in the extended position because the

(A) flexor digitorum superficialis and profundis muscles are stretched when the wrist and metacarpophalangeal joints are extended
(B) lever arms of the interossei are longer when the metacarpophalangeal joints are extended
(C) lever arms of the lumbrical muscles are longer when the metacarpophalangeal joints are extended
(D) line of action of the extensor digitorum muscle is most direct in full extension
(E) radial half of the flexor digitorum profundis muscle is paralyzed because it is innervated by the radial nerve

372. The patient suffers weakness of flexion at the elbow with the arm in a neutral (thumb up) position because of functional paralysis of the

(A) brachioradialis
(B) coracobrachialis
(C) extensor carpi radialis
(D) extensor carpi ulnaris
(E) triceps brachii

373. The thumb action that is totally affected by radial nerve trauma is

(A) abduction
(B) adduction
(C) extension
(D) flexion
(E) opposition

374. On examination of muscle function at the metacarpophalangeal (MP), proximal interphalangeal (PIP), and distal interphalangeal (DIP) joints, the findings expected in the presence of radial nerve palsy would include which of the following?

(A) Inability to abduct the digits at the MP joint
(B) Inability to adduct the digits at the MP joint
(C) Inability to extend the MP joint only
(D) Inability to extend the MP, PIP, and DIP joints
(E) Inability to extend the PIP and DIP joints

375. Flexion and extension of the fingers depend on a unique relationship among several flexor and extensor tendons. All the following statements concerning these relationships are true EXCEPT the

(A) dorsal and palmar interossei arise from the sides and fronts of the metacarpals in such a way that the dorsal interossei abduct and the palmar interossei adduct the fingers
(B) extensor tendons all insert into the dorsal or extensor hood of each finger
(C) flexor digitorum profundus tendons insert into the bases of the four distal phalanges
(D) flexor digitorum superficialis pierces the tendon of the flexor digitorum profundus before inserting into the bases of the four proximal phalanges
(E) lumbricals arise from the deep flexor tendons and flex the metacarpophalangeal joints as well as extend the interphalangeal joints

376. At surgery the fracture field disclosed a large hematoma resulting from a tear in a large artery by a bone fragment. The apparent nerve paralysis was the result of pressure on the nerve by the hematoma. The artery most likely to be involved in this fracture is the

(A) axillary
(B) brachial
(C) deep brachial
(D) radial
(E) ulnar

377. In the dorsal view of the hand shown below, the lettered areas refer to cutaneous nerve distribution. Trauma to the radial nerve in the arm (brachium) or axilla will most likely result in loss of sensation over which area?

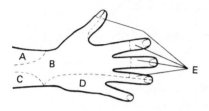

(A) A
(B) B
(C) C
(D) D
(E) E

(End of question set)

378. The patterns for both containment and spread of infection within the palmar anatomic spaces of the hand are explained by all the following relationships EXCEPT

(A) the synovial sheath of the flexor pollicis longus (radial bursa) extends through the palm to the distal phalanx of the thumb
(B) the common tendon sheath (bursa), containing the flexor tendons of the second, third, and fourth digits, extends through the palm to the distal phalanges
(C) the synovial sheath of the flexor tendons of the fifth digit (ulnar bursa) extends through the palm to the distal phalanx
(D) the radial, ulnar, and common bursas extend beneath the flexor retinaculum into the wrist
(E) the radial and ulnar bursas may communicate with the common tendon sheath

Questions 379-382

A workman accidentally lacerated his wrist as shown in the accompanying diagram. Upon exploration of the wound, a vessel and nerve are found to have been severed, but no muscle tendons were damaged.

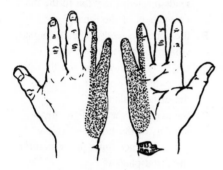

379. From the indicated location of the laceration, the involved nerve is

(A) the median nerve
(B) the recurrent branch of the median nerve
(C) the superficial branch of the radial nerve
(D) the ulnar nerve
(E) none of the above

380. Motor changes would include all the following losses of function EXCEPT

(A) abduction of the fifth digit
(B) adduction of the index finger
(C) adduction of the ring finger
(D) adduction of the fifth digit
(E) flexion of the distal phalanges of the fourth and fifth fingers

381. Which of the following thumb movements would be abolished?

(A) Abduction
(B) Adduction
(C) Extension
(D) Opposition
(E) None of the above

382. The vessel involved in the laceration is likely to be

(A) the anterior interosseus artery
(B) the cephalic vein
(C) the deep palmar artery
(D) the radial artery
(E) none of the above

(End of question set)

383. In children, the head of the femur is supplied by all the following arteries EXCEPT the

(A) artery of the ligamentum teres
(B) lateral femoral circumflex artery
(C) medial circumflex artery
(D) nutrient artery
(E) obturator artery

384. The type of femoral fracture most likely to result in avascular necrosis of the femoral head in adults is

(A) acetabular
(B) cervical
(C) intertrochanteric (between the trochanters)
(D) subtrochanteric
(E) midhumeral shaft

385. Muscles of the anterior compartment of the leg, which act as dorsiflexors of the foot, include all the following EXCEPT the

(A) extensor digitorum longus
(B) extensor hallucis longus
(C) peroneus longus
(D) peroneus tertius
(E) tibialis anterior

386. Injury to the sciatic nerve by intramuscular injection can be avoided if the needle is inserted into the upper lateral quadrant of the buttock. This is because the sciatic nerve has all the following relationships EXCEPT

(A) it emerges through the lesser sciatic foramen inferior to the piriformis muscle
(B) it is located midway between the ischial tuberosity and the posterior superior iliac spine
(C) it lies deep to the gluteus medius and minimus muscles
(D) it lies deep to the gluteus maximus muscle
(E) it passes into the thigh between the greater trochanter and the ischial tuberosity

387. The posterior femoral muscles innervated by the tibial division of the sciatic nerve are referred to as the "hamstring group." Muscles belonging to this group include all the following EXCEPT the

(A) long head of the biceps femoris
(B) semimembranosus
(C) semitendinosus
(D) short head of the biceps femoris

388. In the extended position, the knee becomes rigid and stable because the medial femoral condyle rides posteriorly and on the tibial plateau, rotating the femur medially or the tibia laterally and achieving a configuration that effectively "locks" the knee. The process of "unlocking" the knee in preparation for flexion requires initial contraction of the

(A) gastrocnemius, soleus, and plantaris muscles
(B) hamstring muscles
(C) popliteus muscle
(D) quadriceps femoris muscle
(E) sartorius muscle and short head of the biceps femoris muscle

Questions 389-394

A 57-year-old man comes to a hospital clinic complaining of pain in the left calf after walking five to six blocks. Cramping occurs if walking is continued, but is relieved by resting. This problem has begun to interfere with his employment. Over the past 10 years he has noticed a gradual loss of hair on the left leg, thickening of the toenails, and a general coolness over the lower extremity. In the last year or so he has noticed that small cuts or abrasions heal slowly and occasionally ulcerate. The patient admits to smoking three packs of cigarettes a day for many years. Physical examination reveals a cool, slightly cyanotic left leg with evidence of ulcer scars and an active ulceration on the anterior surface of the ankle. The inguinal lymph nodes on the left side are swollen.

389. Swollen lymph nodes frequently result from inflammation within the region draining to the involved nodes. The regions of the body that drain to the superficial (as opposed to the deep) inguinal lymph nodes include all the following EXCEPT the

(A) anal canal
(B) anterior abdominal wall inferior to the umbilicus
(C) external genitalia
(D) gluteal region
(E) sole of the foot and posterior aspect of the leg

390. On his affected side, the patient is found to have a normal femoral pulse within the femoral triangle. The boundaries of the femoral triangle include all the following EXCEPT the

(A) adductor longus muscle
(B) iliotibial tract
(C) inguinal ligament
(D) sartorius muscle

391. The patient is found to have diminished pulses distally within the affected leg, which provides evidence of vascular disease. This is consistent with the long history of heavy smoking. Locations where arterial pulsations are readily palpable in the lower extremity include all the following EXCEPT

(A) halfway between the anterior superior iliac spine and symphysis pubis
(B) deep in the popliteal fossa when the knee is flexed
(C) behind the lateral malleolus
(D) between the tendons of the extensor hallucis longus and the extensor digitorum longus muscles

392. Angiography reveals arteriosclerotic and thrombotic occlusion of the femoral artery in the femoral (adductor) canal (of Hunter), where it becomes the popliteal artery. All the following statements correctly pertain to the popliteal artery in the popliteal fossa EXCEPT

(A) it is covered superficially by the popliteal vein
(B) it is situated deep to the tibial nerve
(C) it lies superficial to the popliteus muscle
(D) it seldom contributes branches to the collateral circulation about the knee
(E) it gives rise to the anterior and posterior tibial arteries

393. Femoral-popliteal bypass is a common surgical procedure for patients with arteriosclerotic disease of the distal femoral artery. Operative dissection of the popliteal fossa reveals its boundaries to include all the following muscles EXCEPT the

(A) biceps femoris, superolaterally
(B) semimembranosus, superomedially
(C) gastrocnemius, inferomedially
(D) popliteus, inferolaterally

394. A section of long saphenous vein was removed from the right thigh for graft purposes. The long saphenous vein, which is relatively consistent in its anatomic position, is correctly characterized by all the following statements EXCEPT

(A) it has no valves
(B) it originates along the medial border of the foot
(C) it passes anterior to the medial malleolus
(D) it runs along the medial side of the calf and thigh
(E) it terminates by joining the femoral vein in the femoral triangle

(End of question set)

395. The muscles of the anterior compartment of the leg are innervated primarily by which of the following nerves?

(A) Deep peroneal
(B) Lateral sural cutaneous
(C) Saphenous
(D) Superficial peroneal
(E) Sural

396. Articulation of the talus with the malleoli and lower tibia forms the ankle, or talocrural, joint. Factors that contribute to the stability of this joint include all the following EXCEPT the

(A) calcaneonavicular ("spring") ligament
(B) deltoid ligament
(C) lateral ligament
(D) posterior tibiofibular ligament
(E) trapezoidal shape of the talar articular surface (wider anteriorly than posteriorly)

397. The vertebral arteries are correctly characterized by which of the following statements?

(A) They arise from the common carotid arteries

(B) They enter the cranium through the anterior condylar canals

(C) They enter the cranium through the posterior condylar canals

(D) They pass through the transverse foramina of several cervical vertebrae

(E) None of the above

398. The odontoid process (dens) is correctly described by which of the following statements?

(A) It articulates with the occipital portion of the skull

(B) It is separated from the atlas by an intervertebral disk

(C) It projects from the inferior surface of the atlas

(D) It represents the vertebral body of the first cervical vertebra

(E) None of the above

399. The spinous process of which vertebra is most easily palpated with assurance and functions as a landmark?

(A) C1
(B) C7
(C) T4
(D) L1
(E) S5

400. Lumbar vertebrae are characterized by all the following EXCEPT

(A) a large and heavy body

(B) articular surfaces that permit little rotation

(C) deep intervertebral notches in the inferior surfaces of the pedicles

(D) greater thickness anteriorly than posteriorly to provide the lumbar curvature

(E) short, broad, horizontal spinous processes

401. The rotators, as the name implies, are the principal muscles responsible for rotation of the vertebral column. True statements concerning these muscles include all the following EXCEPT

(A) arising from the vertebral transverse process, the short rotators insert into the base of the spinous process of the vertebra immediately above

(B) arising from the transverse process of one vertebra, the long rotators insert into the base of the spinous process of the second vertebra above

(C) branches from the ventral primary rami of the spinal nerves innervate the rotator muscles

(D) the long and short rotators are part of the transversospinalis group

(E) the rotators lie deep to the multifidus muscles

402. In performing a spinal tap in the lower lumbar region, which of the following is a valid consideration?

(A) The conus medullaris is protected by the filum terminale
(B) The lumbar spinous processes are nearly horizontal when the vertebral column is flexed
(C) The nerve roots of the cauda equina are protected by the denticulate ligaments
(D) The spinal cord, very thin between L2 and S2, is protected by the coccygeal ligament
(E) None of the above

403. Landmarks useful in determining the proper location for a spinal tap include

(A) the hiatus of the sacral canal
(B) the iliac crests
(C) the posterior superior iliac spines
(D) the vertebra prominens
(E) none of the above

404. If a needle used to sample CSF is placed precisely in the midline between the L4 and L5 vertebrae, all the following structures will be penetrated EXCEPT the

(A) arachnoid layer
(B) dura mater
(C) interspinous ligament
(D) posterior longitudinal ligament
(E) supraspinous ligament

405. Intervertebral disks have a tendency to herniate into the intervertebral foramen because the

(A) annulus fibrosus is attenuated in the posterolateral regions
(B) interspinous ligament reinforces the disks anteriorly and anterolaterally
(C) ligamentum flavum reinforces the intervertebral disks posteriorly
(D) lumbar intervertebral disks are thicker posteriorly than anteriorly
(E) posterior longitudinal ligament is stronger and more complete posteriorly than posterolaterally

406. Knowledge of the segmental cutaneous innervation of the skin of the lower extremity is important in determining the level of intervertebral disk disease. Thus, S1 nerve root irritation will result in pain located along the

(A) anterior aspect of the thigh
(B) medial aspect of the thigh
(C) anteromedial aspect of the leg
(D) medial side of the foot
(E) lateral side of the foot

DIRECTIONS: Each group of questions below consists of four lettered headings followed by a set of numbered items. For each numbered item select

A	if the item is associated with	(A) **only**
B	if the item is associated with	(B) **only**
C	if the item is associated with	**both** (A) and (B)
D	if the item is associated with	**neither** (A) nor (B)

Each lettered heading may be used **once, more than once, or not at all.**

Questions 407-411

(A) Median nerve
(B) Ulnar nerve
(C) Both
(D) Neither

407. Abductor pollicis longus muscle

408. Dorsal interossei muscles

409. Flexor digitorum profundus muscle

410. Lumbrical muscles

411. Flexor pollicis brevis muscle

Questions 412-415

(A) Epidural space
(B) Subarachnoid space
(C) Both
(D) Neither

412. Site of the ascending and descending spinal arteries

413. Site of the cauda equina

414. Site of the vertebral venous plexus

415. Site of infusion with anesthetic to block the spinal nerves

DIRECTIONS: Each group of questions below consists of lettered choices followed by a set of numbered items. For each numbered item select the **one** lettered choice with which it is **most** closely associated. Each lettered choice may be used **once, more than once, or not at all.**

Questions 416-420

For each clinical description of an injury involving the brachial plexus that follows, select the lettered location in the diagram below that most closely corresponds to the site of such injury.

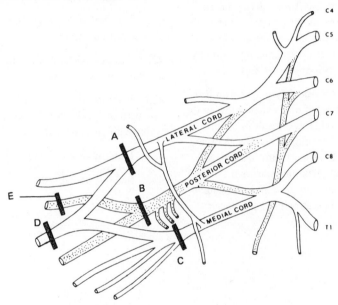

416. A man who had long used a crutch for walking developed "wrist drop," weakness of the deltoid muscle, and sensory denervation of the dorsum of the hand

417. A newborn infant who experienced a difficult delivery is found to have a complete claw-hand, adduction and weakness of the thumb, loss of sensation on the ulnar side of the palm of the hand, and loss of sensation on the dorsal surface of the ulnar side of the hand

418. In the course of a barroom disagreement, an unruly person was subdued and suffered an anterior glenohumeral dislocation. Among other symptoms, he experienced partial loss of cutaneous sensory innervation to the lateral forearm and weakness of the biceps brachii muscles

419. A young swimmer who slipped while jumping from a diving board caught her armpit on one corner of the board. In due course she developed, among other related findings, atrophy of the dorsal interossei muscles

420. An ice-hockey player who had been subjected to a violent blow in the anterior axilla as a result of "high sticking" developed anesthesia on the radial side of the palm, inability to completely flex the index and middle fingers, inability to oppose the thumb, and eventual atrophy of the thenar eminence

Questions 421-425

For each clinical finding of paralysis below, select the nerve with which it would be most closely associated.

(A) Femoral nerve
(B) Tibial nerve
(C) Common peroneal nerve
(D) Obturator nerve
(E) Superior gluteal nerve

421. Inability to stand on the toes and loss of Achilles tendon reflex

422. Atrophy of the flexor muscles of the thigh and loss of knee-jerk reflex

423. Inability to maintain a level pelvis, with the result that the person walks with an "abductor lurch"

424. Inability to stand on the heels

425. Inability to evert the foot

Gross Anatomy:
Extremities and Back
Answers

366. The answer is B. *(Hollinshead, ed 4. pp 185-186.)* Nerve roots C5 through T1 give rise to the brachial plexus. The long thoracic nerve (of Bell) to the serratus anterior muscle is derived from nerve roots C5 through C7. Injury to this nerve results in winged scapulas. Roots C5 and C6 form the upper trunk, C7 continues as the middle trunk, and C8 and T1 form the lower trunk. The trunks separate into anterior and posterior divisions, which link up to form three cords named according to their position in relation to the axillary artery. The posterior cord of the brachial plexus supplies the skin of the postaxial surface and the muscles of the extensor side of the upper extremity. The major branches of the posterior cord include the upper subscapular nerve to the subscapularis, the thoracodorsal nerve to the latissimus dorsi muscle, the lower subscapular nerve to the subscapularis and teres major muscles, the axillary nerve to the deltoid and teres minor muscles, and the radial nerve to the extensors of the forearm, wrist, and proximal phalanges. Injury to the posterior cord results in extensor paralysis of the shoulder, arm, and wrist (''wrist drop'').

367. The answer is B. *(Hollinshead, ed 4. pp 185-186.)* The anterior divisions of the upper and middle trunks of the brachial plexus unite to form the lateral cord. The lateral cord of the brachial plexus gives off the lateral pectoral nerve to the clavicular head of the pectoralis major with paralysis indicated by the inability to strongly bring one's hand to the opposite ear. The lateral cord divides to form the musculocutaneous nerve and a strong contribution to the median nerve. The musculocutaneous nerve innervates the major flexors of the elbow joint, tested by the biceps tendon reflex, before continuing as the lateral antebrachial cutaneous nerve in the preaxial forearm. The ulnar nerve, derived from the medial cord, is the principal innervation of the flexors on the ulnar side of the wrist.

368. The answer is D. *(Hollinshead, ed 4. pp 185, 212.)* The anterior division of the lower trunk gives rise to the medial cord, which gives rise to the medial pectoral nerve—innervating the sternal head of the pectoralis major muscle—and gives off the medial contribution (root) to the medial nerve. The medial cord continues as the ulnar nerve and also gives off the medial antebrachial cutaneous and medial bracheal cutaneous nerves. The median nerve, lying anterior to the axillary artery, only contains contributions from the anterior divisions of the brachial plexus. Even though the median nerve is formed from both lateral and medial cords, contributions from

C5 are seldom included and contributions from T1 are frequently absent. The median nerve generally innervates flexor musculature on the lateral aspects of the forearm and hand.

369. The answer is C. *(Hollinshead, ed 4. pp 213, 217, 245.)* The clinical signs and findings in the patient presented in the question indicate radial nerve damage. The evidence that extension at the elbow appeared normal while supination appeared weak can be used to localize the lesion. The innervation to the medial and long heads of the triceps brachii, principal extensor of the arm, arises from the radial nerve (in the axilla) as the medial muscular branches; the innervation to the lateral head, and to a smaller portion of the medial head, arises from the radial nerve as it passes along the musculospiral groove at midhumerus. The supinator muscle is innervated by muscular twigs from the deep branch of the radial nerve in the forearm, just before the radial nerve reaches the supinator muscle. Thus, paralysis of the supinator muscle, but not of the triceps brachii, localizes the fracture to the distal third of the humeral shaft between the elbow and musculospiral groove.

370. The answer is A. *(Hollinshead, ed 4. p 211.)* Even though the supinator muscle acts to supinate the forearm, the biceps brachii muscle (which inserts on the medial aspect of the radius) is the strongest supinator of the forearm. However, the arm must be flexed at the elbow (brachialis and brachioradialis muscles) and stabilized (triceps brachii muscle) in order for the biceps to perform this action with optimum mechanical advantage. This explains why it is easier to use a screwdriver in the right hand to drive a screw (supination) than to back the screw out (pronation) or drive it with the left hand (also pronation). With the supinator muscle paralyzed by radial nerve palsy, supination will be weak with the arm extended but almost normal with the arm flexed. Neither the pronator teres muscle, innervated by the median nerve, nor the brachialis muscle, innervated by the musculocutaneous nerve, has a role in supination.

371. The answer is A. *(Hollinshead, ed 4. pp 97, 245.)* Muscles are most powerful (disregarding leverage factors) when stretched by extension of the joint(s) over which they pass, since this places the sarcomeres at the optimum tension-producing length in the length-tension relationship. Thus, hand grasp is strongest when wrist joint and metacarpophalangeal joints are extended, thereby stretching the digitorum superficialis and profundus flexors to their optimum tension-producing position in the length-tension relationship. Paralysis of the radial nerve with subsequent "wrist drop" will weaken hand grasp because the extrinsic flexor muscles are compelled to operate in a nonoptimum region of the length-tension relationship. The lever arms of the lumbricals and interossei are greatest when the metacarpophalangeal joints are flexed, a consideration that does not apply to the patient presented in the question. The radial side of the flexor digitorum profundis is innervated by the median nerve.

372. The answer is A. *(Hollinshead, ed 4. p 241.)* Radial nerve palsy in the arm will produce weakness of flexion at the elbow with the forearm in the neutral (thumb up) position owing to functional loss of the brachioradialis muscle. The brachioradialis muscle, the only flexor of the forearm innervated by the radial nerve, receives twigs from the lateral muscular branch of the radial nerve in the vicinity of the elbow.

373. The answer is C. *(Hollinshead, ed 4. pp 244, 245.)* The thumb may be used to test motor integrity of all major nerves of the forearm. Thus, the ability to *extend* the thumb tests radial nerve function because this nerve innervates both the extensors pollicis longus and brevis. The ability to *oppose* the thumb tests median nerve function, and the ability to *adduct* the thumb tests ulnar nerve function. Flexion and *ab*duction, on the other hand, cannot be used as discrete diagnostic tests. Abduction is a function of the abductor pollicis longus muscle, innervated by the radial nerve, and the abductor pollicis brevis muscle, innervated by the median nerve. Likewise, flexion is a function of the flexor pollicis longus muscle, innervated by the median nerve, and flexor pollicis brevis muscle, innervated variably by the median and ulnar nerves.

374. The answer is C. *(Hollinshead, ed 4. p 245.)* Radial nerve palsy produces an inability to extend the metacarpophalangeal joints owing to paralysis of the extensor digitorum communis muscle. However, the lumbrical and interossei muscles, which are served by the median and ulnar nerves and insert into the dorsal expansions (extensor hoods) of the proximal phalanges, are able simultaneously to flex the metacarpophalangeal joints *and* to extend the interphalangeal joints. Also, abduction of the digits, a function of the dorsal interossei, and adduction, a function of the palmar interossei, are both mediated by the ulnar nerve and, therefore, unaffected.

375. The answer is D. *(Hollinshead, ed 4. pp 250-253, 261-262.)* The tendons of the flexor digitorum superficialis split at the level of the proximal phalanges to insert into the sides of the middle phalanges of the four digits. The principal action of this muscle is to flex the middle phalanges at the proximal interphalangeal joints. The tendons of the flexor digitorum *profundus* pierce the superficialis tendons over the proximal phalanges to reach the insertions at the bases of the distal phalanges. The principal action of the flexor digitorum profundus is to flex the *distal* phalanges at the distal interphalangeal joints. Working together, the flexors digitorum profundus and superficialis also act to flex both the metacarpophalangeal and wrist joints.

376. The answer is C. *(Hollinshead, ed 4. p 214.)* The deep brachial artery (profunda brachii) courses around the lateral side of the humerus with the radial nerve in the musculospiral groove. In this location the neurovascular bundle is especially vulnerable to trauma associated with a humeral fracture. The artery may be torn by the sharp edges of bone, and the nerve, even if intact (as in the patient presented in the question), may be subject to pressure from the resultant hematoma.

377. The answer is B. *(Hollinshead, ed 4. pp 232-234, 244.)* The dorsal antebrachial cutaneous nerve innervates the dorsum of the forearm and wrist, whereas the superficial radial nerve (of the hand) innervates the radial side of the dorsum of the hand (area B in the diagram accompanying the question). Because of considerable sensory overlap, a patient with radial nerve palsy usually experiences paresthesia in this region. However, a small area in the web space of the thumb, supplied exclusively by the radial nerve, provides a useful site for testing radial nerve sensory function. The dorsal branch of the ulnar nerve supplies the dorsum of the ulnar side of the hand (area D in the diagram) and the medial antebrachial cutaneous nerve the lateral aspect of the forearm to the wrist (area C in the diagram). The lateral antebrachial cutaneous nerve (the extension of the musculocutaneous nerve into the forearm) supplies the lateral aspect of the forearm to the wrist (area A in the diagram). The dorsum of the tips of the index and middle fingers and a variable portion of the ring finger are supplied by the median nerve (area E in the diagram).

378. The answer is B. *(Hollinshead, ed 4. pp 251-253, 260, 262-263.)* Infection of the second, third, and fourth tendon sheaths within the digits usually is confined to the digit involved because the synovial sheaths of the flexor tendons of the second, third, and fourth fingers do not extend proximal to the metacarpal heads. Infection within the *fifth* digit tendon sheath, however, may spread widely within the palm because the synovial sheath of the flexor tendons of the fifth digit continues into the palm as the ulnar bursa, where it becomes the common flexor sheath for the superficial and deep flexor tendons. Infection within the radial or ulnar bursa can extend proximally into the palm and through the carpal tunnel into the wrist and distal forearm. Infection may also pass between the ulnar and radial bursas through occasional cross communications. Swelling and edema from such infection may result in carpal tunnel syndrome.

379. The answer is D. *(Hollinshead, ed 4. pp 259-260.)* The ulnar nerve descends along the postaxial (ulnar) side of the forearm. It passes lateral to the pisiform bone and under the carpal volar ligament, but superficial to the transverse carpal ligament. In the hand it divides into superficial and deep branches. The median nerve lies deep to the transverse carpal ligament where it is protected from superficial lacerations. Emerging from the carpal tunnel, it gives off the vulnerable recurrent branch to the thenar eminence. The superficial branch of the radial nerve supplies the dorsolateral aspects of the wrist and hand.

380. The answer is E. *(Hollinshead, ed 4. pp 253, 261, 271.)* The ulnar nerve innervates the dorsal interosseous muscles, which produce abduction of digits two through five, as well as the palmar interossei muscles, which produce adduction of digits two, four, and five. The ulnar nerve also innervates the lumbricals associated with the fourth and fifth digits. Flexion of the fifth phalanx of the fourth and fifth digits is accomplished by that portion of the flexor digitorum profundus innervated by the ulnar nerve. However, this muscle receives its innervation in the forearm, well above the level of the laceration, so that all fingers would flex normally.

381. The answer is B. *(Hollinshead, ed 4. pp 264-266.)* The ulnar nerve innervates two of the intrinsic thenar muscles: the adductor pollicis and frequently the deep head of the flexor pollicis brevis. Because of the actions of the flexor pollicis longus and the superficial head of the flexor pollicis brevis, there would probably be no noticeable deficit in flexion. However, the ability to adduct the thumb would be lost.

382. The answer is E. *(Hollinshead, ed 4. pp 161, 246-247, 268-269.)* The ulnar artery is vulnerable in a superficial laceration of the anteromedial aspect of the wrist. It does not usually give off the deep palmar branch until it reaches the base of the fifth metacarpal. The radial artery lies deep within the carpal tunnel, where it is protected from superficial laceration. The anterior interosseus is also very deep and at the wrist terminates by anastomosing with the carpal rete. The cephalic vein lies on the radial side of the dorsum of the wrist; the basilic vein could be involved, depending on how far the laceration extended to the dorsal side of the ulnar aspect.

383. The answer is D. *(Hollinshead, ed 4. pp 295-297.)* In children, the blood supply to the portion of the femoral head proximal to the epiphyseal plate is by the artery of the ligamentum teres, a branch of the obturator artery. The trochanters, the neck, and the portion of the head distal to the epiphyseal plate are supplied by the cruciate anastomosis, which comprises the lateral and medial femoral circumflex arteries and supplies the retinacular arteries. The nutrient artery supplies the femoral shaft.

384. The answer is B. *(Hollinshead, ed 4. p 360.)* Fractures of the femoral neck will completely interrupt the blood supply to the femoral head in adults. If the capsular retinaculum also is torn, avascular necrosis of the head will certainly occur because the only remaining blood supply to the head (through the ligamentum teres) is inadequate to sustain it. The nearer the fracture to the femoral head, the more likely will the retinacular blood supply be disrupted.

385. The answer is C. *(Hollinshead, ed 4. pp 420, 423.)* The peroneus longus muscle, located in the lateral compartment of the leg, acts to evert and abduct the foot as well as to assist in plantar flexion. The muscles of the anterior compartment of the leg, especially the tibialis anterior, dorsiflex the foot at the ankle. This action of the tibialis anterior acts to draw the tibia forward when the foot is planted, as in walking. The peroneus tertius muscle assists in dorsiflexion of the foot, but operates in eversion, not inversion. The extensor hallucis longus dorsiflexes the great toe, and the extensor digitorum longus dorsiflexes the proximal and distal phalanges of the lateral four toes.

386. The answer is C. *(Hollinshead, ed 4. pp 368, 392.)* The sciatic nerve emerges from the greater sciatic foramen through the infrapiriformis recess. This occurs midway between the posterior superior iliac spine and the ischial tuberosity deep to the gluteus maximus muscle. The sciatic nerve passes into the posterior thigh about midway between the greater trochanter and the ischial tuberosity. It passes deep to the hamstring muscles to enter the popliteal fossa, where it bifurcates into the common peroneal nerve and the tibial nerve. The sciatic nerve may arise as separate tibial and common peroneal nerves, or it may divide into these components at any point within the posterior thigh.

387. The answer is D. *(Hollinshead, ed 4. pp 389-391.)* The hamstring muscle group, composed of the semimembranosus and semitendinosus muscles together with the long head of the biceps femoris, arises from the ischial tuberosity and is innervated by the tibial division of the sciatic nerve. The major action of the hamstring muscles is to flex the leg at the knee and extend the thigh at the hip. The *short* head of the biceps femoris muscle, however, arises from the midfemoral shaft and is innervated by the common peroneal portion of the sciatic nerve. Because of its origin and innervation and the fact that it does not extend the thigh at the hip, the short head of the biceps femoris cannot be considered a part of the hamstring group.

388. The answer is C. *(Hollinshead, ed 4. pp 431, 438.)* To "unscrew" a knee from its locked and slightly hyperextended position, the popliteus muscle contracts and causes medial rotation of the tibia or, if the foot is planted, lateral rotation of the femur. This movement frees the medial femoral condyle from its posterior position on the tibial condylar surface. The quadriceps femoris then relaxes and knee flexion occurs by contraction of the hamstring muscles, assisted by the short head of the biceps femoris, sartorius, gracilis, and gastrocnemius muscles.

389. The answer is E. *(Hollinshead, ed 4. pp 345-347, 371-372, 434.)* The superficial lymphatic drainage from the sole of the foot, as well as from the posterior and lateral aspects of the leg, parallels the lesser (short) saphenous vein. These lymphatic vessels drain into the popliteal lymph nodes, which in turn drain along the femoral vessels to the *deep* inguinal lymph nodes in the femoral canal. The remaining superficial lymphatics from the dorsum of the foot, anterior aspect of the leg, and the complete thigh, as well as the lymphatics of the gluteal region, external genitalia, and lower abdominal wall, all drain into the *superficial* inguinal lymph nodes. In the patient presented in the question, active ulceration on the anterior surface of the ankle would explain the palpable superficial inguinal lymph nodes.

390. The answer is B. *(Hollinshead, ed 4. pp 373-374.)* The boundaries of the femoral triangle include the inguinal ligament, the medial border of the adductor longus muscle, and the medial border of the sartorius muscle. The floor of the triangle is formed by the iliopsoas, pectineus, and adductor longus muscles; the fascia lata provides the covering. The contents of the femoral triangle, beginning laterally, include the femoral nerve and the femoral sheath, which contains the femoral artery, femoral vein, and deep inguinal lymph nodes.

391. The answer is C. *(Hollinshead, ed 4. pp 386, 395, 424-425, 432-434.)* The femoral pulse is palpable high in the femoral triangle at the midinguinal point, which is approximately halfway between the anterior superior iliac spine and the symphysis pubis. At this point, the femoral artery lies anterior to the head of the femur. The popliteal pulse is most easily palpated deep in the popliteal fossa when the knee is flexed and the muscles relaxed. The dorsalis pedis pulse is palpable between the tendons of the extensor hallucis longus and the extensor digitorum longus on the anterior aspect of the ankle. However, the dorsalis pedis artery may be absent in 14 percent of the population. The posterior tibial artery is located approximately one finger breadth below and behind the medial malleolus. This artery may be absent in 5 percent of the population.

392. The answer is D. *(Hollinshead, ed 4. pp 343, 395, 432-433.)* Over a period of time, the tendon of the adductor magnus muscle may damage the femoral artery at the adductor hiatus and predispose the artery to arteriosclerotic or thrombotic occlusion, especially in a person who is a heavy smoker. In addition to the femoral artery, the adductor hiatus contains the femoral vein and saphenous nerve. The popliteal artery, which is the continuation of the femoral artery from the adductor hiatus through the popliteal fossa, lies deep to the femoral vein and tibial nerve, and superficial to the femur and popliteus muscle. The popliteal artery gives off several muscular (sural) branches and five geniculate branches before bifurcating into the anterior tibial artery and the posterior tibial artery; the posterior tibial artery, in turn, gives rise to the peroneal artery. The medial and lateral superior geniculate—and the medial and lateral inferior geniculate—arteries form anastomoses about the knee joint.

393. The answer is D. *(Hollinshead, ed 4. p 392.)* The long head of the biceps femoris muscle contributes to the superolateral boundary of the popliteal fossa, whereas the semimembranosus muscle tendon contributes to the superomedial boundary. The lateral and medial heads of the gastrocnemius muscle constitute the inferolateral and inferomedial borders of the popliteal fossa. The popliteus muscle forms a portion of only the *floor* of the fossa.

394. The answer is A. *(Hollinshead, ed 4. pp 345, 371.)* The great (long) saphenous vein originates on the medial border of the foot, passes anterior to the medial malleolus (where it is conveniently located for venipuncture), and runs proximally along the medial side of the leg. Passing over the medial epicondyle of the femur and continuing along the medial aspect of the thigh, the long saphenous vein terminates in the femoral triangle, where it pierces the fascia lata to enter the femoral vein several centimeters below the inguinal ligament. Venipuncture may be accomplished just medial to the femoral pulse. The lesser (short) saphenous vein, beginning along the *lateral* margin of the foot, passes proximally along the posterior aspect of the calf to enter the popliteal fossa and join the femoral vein. Defective valves along the saphenous veins, as well as between the saphenous and deep veins, result in varicosities.

395. The answer is A. *(Hollinshead, ed 4. pp 420-423.)* The common peroneal nerve bifurcates into superficial and deep branches. The deep peroneal nerve innervates all muscles of the anterior compartment of the leg. The superficial peroneal nerve emerges from the deep fascia and descends in the lateral compartment, where it innervates the peroneus longus and brevis muscles before dividing into median dorsal cutaneous and intermediate dorsal cutaneous nerves, which supply the distal third of the leg, dorsum of the foot, and all the toes. The saphenous nerve (the terminal branch of the common femoral nerve) distributes cutaneous branches to the anterior and medial aspects of the leg as well as to the posterodorsal and posteromedial aspects of the foot. The sural nerve follows the course of the lesser saphenous vein, becoming the lateral sural cutaneous nerve to supply the anterolateral aspect of the foot.

396. The answer is A. *(Hollinshead, ed 4. p 456.)* The calcaneonavicular ("spring") ligament between the two tarsal bones is instrumental in maintaining the longitudinal arch of the foot. The lateral collateral ligaments are composed of the anterior talofibular and posterior talofibular ligaments and a calcaneofibular ligament. These ligaments, especially the anterior talofibular, are usually torn during an inversion ankle "sprain." The medial collateral (deltoid) ligament consists of the anterior and posterior tibiotalar ligaments with the tibionavicular ligament between them and the tibiocalcaneal ligament. The anterior and posterior tibiofibular ligaments maintain the tibiofibular joint capsule for the talocrural articulation. The ankle is most stable in the position of dorsiflexion owing to the trapezoidal or wedge shape (wider anteriorly than posteriorly) of the talar articular surface, which completely fills the subtibial fossa during dorsiflexion.

397. The answer is D. *(Hollinshead, ed 4. pp 845-846, 873, 927-928.)* The vertebral arteries arise from the subclavian arteries and pass through the transverse foramina of the sixth through the first cervical vertebrae, but not the seventh. The paired vertebral arteries enter the cranium by passing through the foramen magnum, after which they join to form the basilar artery. The condylar canals lie at the base of the skull at the occipital condyles. The hypoglossal nerve (CN XII) leaves the cranium via the anterior condylar (hypoglossal) canal, while the posterior condylar canal transmits an emissary vein.

398. The answer is D. *(Hollinshead, ed 4. pp 287-289.)* The odontoid process (dens) of the axis, the second cervical vertebra, is the remnant of the body of the first cervical vertebra. Developing from a separate ossification center, it fused to the body of the atlas. The fact that there is no intervertebral disk between the atlas and axis probably facilitated the fusion. The dens, projecting from the superior surface of the axis, provides a pivot about which rotation occurs at the atlantoaxial joint. Fracture and posterior dislocation of the dens may crush the spinal cord with fatal results.

399. The answer is B. *(Hollinshead, ed 4. pp 287-291.)* The spinous process of the seventh cervical vertebra—the vertebra prominens—is the most prominent of the vertebral column and serves as a useful landmark for the cervical and upper thoracic regions. The atlas (C1) and the fourth and fifth sacral vertebrae have no spinous processes, and the last also lacks lamina—the S5 pedicles are the palpable sacral cornua that define the sacral hiatus. The thoracic and lumbar spinous processes, while palpable for the most part, are rather indistinguishable from one another.

400. The answer is D. *(Hollinshead, ed 4. pp 290-291.)* The lumbar vertebrae are relatively large and heavy. The horizontal projection of the short, broad spinous processes offers ready access to the lumbar vertebral canal for cerebrospinal fluid puncture. Because the superior and inferior articular surfaces are on nearly para-sagittal planes, rotation is restricted to approximately 5 degrees for the whole lumbar region. The deep intervertebral notches in the inferior surfaces of the pedicles allow the corresponding spinal nerve to exit the vertebral canal without passing adjacent to the intervertebral disk. Thus, a posterolateral herniation of a disk will involve the nerve of the next vertebral level below. Finally, secondary spinal curvatures are the result of shape differences of the intervertebral disks, not of the vertebrae.

401. The answer is C. *(Hollinshead, ed 4. pp 315-316, 318.)* With the exception of the intertransverse muscles and the anterior group of muscles, the deep back muscles are supplied by the dorsal primary rami of the spinal nerves. The more oblique or horizontal the course of a muscle of the vertebral column, the more it functions in rotation. The more a muscle bundle parallels the vertebral column, the more it is concerned with extension, lateral flexion, or control of lateral flexion against gravity. The rotators, which fall into the first category, lie under the multi-fidus layer.

402. The answer is B. *(Hollinshead, ed 4. pp 320-324.)* Spinal taps (lumbar puncture) are performed in the lumbar region for several reasons. Because the lumbar vertebral spines are nearly horizontal and because the lumbar vertebrae allow con-siderable flexion of the lumbar spine, the space between the spinous processes of adjacent lumbar vertebrae allows greater access. But, most important, because spinal cord usually terminates by the level of the L1-L2 intervertebral disk, the possibility of incurring a nonregenerating upper-motor-neuron injury to the spinal cord is avoided. The filum terminale, an extension of the pia mater, runs from the conus medullaris to the termination of the dural sac at level S2 and then continues to the coccyx. The denticulate ligaments, lateral condensations of pia that pass through the subarachnoid space to the dura, suspend the spinal cord in the center of the meningeal cavity in the cervical and thoracic regions.

403. The answer is B. *(April, ed 2. p 276.)* The most superior extent of the iliac crests defines the level of the fourth lumbar vertebra. Thus, the spinous process felt beneath a line connecting the left and right iliac crests must be L4. The preferred location for a spinal tap or introduction of spinal or epidural anesthesia is at the level of the L4-L5 interspace for two reasons: The spinal cord usually ends by the L2 level, except in some newborn infants, eliminating the possibility of spinal cord injury; and the horizontal orientation of the L4 spinous process provides ample access to the dural sac. The posterior inferior iliac spines and the coccyx provide landmarks for the location of the hiatus of the sacral canal.

404. The answer is D. *(Hollinshead, ed 4. pp 295-296, 320-322.)* During lumbar (spinal) puncture, a needle inserted perpendicularly in the midline between the spinous processes of the fourth and fifth lumbar vertebrae successively pierces skin, subcutaneous tissue, supraspinous ligament, and interspinous ligament. The epidural space will be entered at a depth of approximately 4 to 6 cm. (If the needle penetrates slightly off the midline, the ligamentum flavum will be pierced and the resistance offered by this structure will be apparent.) The needle then passes through the epidural fat, the dura mater (which also offers noticeable resistance), and the arachnoid layer into the subarachnoid space. The posterior longitudinal ligament is located along the posterior surface of the vertebral bodies and intervertebral disks.

405. The answer is E. *(Hollinshead, ed 4. pp 295-297.)* Intervertebral disks are strongly reinforced ventrally and laterally by the anterior longitudinal ligaments. The posterior longitudinal ligament, while it is denticulate and attenuated laterally, reinforces the posterior aspect of the intervertebral disk. Because the posterolateral region of the disk is supported least by ligamentous structures, a nucleus pulposus that is herniated through the annulus fibrosus of the intervertebral disk will take the line of least resistance and move posterolaterally into the intervertebral canal. In so doing, the herniation is apt to impinge on a spinal nerve of the next lower vertebral level.

406. The answer is E. *(Hollinshead, ed 4. pp 53-55, 334-335.)* Roots L1, L2, and L3 supply the medial, anterior, and lateral aspects of the thigh through the femoral, obturator, and lateral femoral cutaneous nerves, respectively. The frontomedial aspect of the leg is innervated by L4 through the saphenous branch of the femoral nerve. The frontolateral aspect of the leg and the dorsum of the foot are supplied by the common peroneal and superficial peroneal nerves. The medial side of the foot is innervated by L5 via the tibial nerve. The posterior thigh and leg, as well as the sole and lateral side of the foot, are supplied by S1 via the tibial nerve.

The buttock and posterior perineal region are supplied by S3 and S4 via the superior and inferior cluneal nerves and the pudendal nerve; the anterior regions of the external genitalia are supplied by L1 via the ilioinguinal nerve.

407-411. The answers are: 407-D, 408-B, 409-C, 410-C, 411-C. *(Hollinshead, ed 4. pp 263, 266, 271.)* The abductor pollicis longus muscle is innervated by the radial nerve, while the abductor pollicis brevis, opponens pollicis, and the superficial head of the flexor pollicis brevis muscles are innervated by the recurrent branch of the median nerve.

The flexor digitorum profundus has a dual innervation. The two heads on the radial side of the arm are innervated by the median nerve; the two heads on the ulnar side of the arm are innervated by the ulnar nerve. The only other muscle of the forearm innervated by the ulnar nerve is the flexor carpi ulnaris. The flexor digitorum superficialis is innervated solely by the median nerve.

The lumbrical muscles originate from the tendons of the flexor digitorum profundus muscle, so it follows that the innervation should be similar. The two lumbricals on the radial side of the hand are innervated by the median nerve, whereas the two lumbricals on the ulnar side of the hand are innervated by the ulnar nerve.

The ulnar nerve supplies the remaining intrinsic muscles of the hand, including the palmar and dorsal interossei muscles as well as the adductor pollicis muscle and the deep head of the flexor pollicis brevis muscle.

412-415. The answers are: 412-D, 413-B, 414-A, 415-C. *(Hollinshead, ed 4. pp 319-323.)* Spinal branches from the vertebral, deep cervical, intercostal, and lumbar arteries penetrate the dura and subarachnoid spaces to reach the pia mater, in which they bifurcate into ascending and descending spinal arteries. There is a single dorsal spinal artery and paired ventral spinal arteries.

The subarachnoid space lies between the pial and subarachnoid layers. The space is traversed by the arachnoid trabeculae and provides for the circulation of cerebrospinal fluid. Below the conus terminalis at L2, it is termed the *dural sac* and contains a large amount of cerebrospinal fluid in which the cauda equina is suspended. The lumbar puncture samples the cerebrospinal fluid in the dural sac.

The dura mater, the outer meningeal layer, defines an epidural space and a subdural space. The epidural space contains the vertebral venous plexus embedded in a layer of fat. This plexus receives the venous drainage from the spinal cord and drains into the vertebral veins. It has extensive anastomotic connections with the venous plexuses of the deep pelvis and with the venous sinuses of the cranium, which are of considerable importance in the venous spread of metastatic carcinoma.

Lumbar epidural anesthesia involves infusing the anesthetic agent into the epidural space in the lumbar region to block the lumbar nerves as they exit through the dura. Caudal epidural anesthesia is similar except that the needle is inserted into the epidural space of the sacral vertebral canal via the sacral hiatus between the sacral cornua. Conversely, spinal anesthesia requires that the needle penetrate the dura

mater in the lumbar region to infuse the anesthetic agent into the subarachnoid space
(dural sac) in order to block all the lumbar and sacral nerves of the cauda equina.

416-420. The answers are: 416-B, 417-C, 418-A, 419-C, 420-D. *(April, ed 2. pp
59, 85, 99.)* The posterior cord of the brachial plexus is located posterior to the
axillary artery and is the most vulnerable of the three cords to "crutch injury" or
"Saturday night palsy." The resulting injury (B) produces significant motor, but
only minor sensory, denervation along the course of the radial nerve. Radial nerve
palsy results in loss of elbow and wrist extension ("wrist drop") and inability to
extend the metacarpophalangeal joints of the hand. Loss of radial nerve sensory
innervation would involve the dorsum of the wrist and hand; axillary nerve involvement would result in deltoid paralysis and loss of cutaneous sensation over the deltoid
region.

Injury to the medial cord of the brachial plexus (Klumpke paralysis) may result
from difficult parturition, in which a baby presenting in a breech position has the
arm delivered last, along with the head. This type of injury (C) affects the ulnar
nerve and the component of the median nerve derived from roots C8 and T1. The
ulnar nerve supplies the ulnar half of the flexor digitorum profundus as well as the
intrinsic muscles of the hand, the hypothenar muscles, and the adductor of the thumb.
It also mediates sensory innervation from the ulnar side of the palm. The median
nerve contributions (when present) from C8 to T1 supply a portion of the flexor
digitorum superficialis, the flexor digitorum profundus, the thenar muscles, and the
first two lumbricals. The median nerve also carries sensation from the radial side of
the palm. Injury to the medial brachial cutaneous and medial antebrachial cutaneous
nerves would result in loss of sensory innervation to the medial surfaces of the arm
and forearm.

Injury to the lateral cord of the brachial plexus (similar to Erb-Duchenne paralysis of the upper trunk, but sparing the posterior division) frequently is a consequence of anterior (medial) dislocation of the humerus. In this type of injury (A),
the musculocutaneous nerve and the component of the median nerve derived from
roots C5 (if present), C6, and C7 are involved. The musculocutaneous nerve innervates the coracobrachialis, biceps brachii, and brachialis muscles before innervating
the lateral aspect of the forearm (as the lateral antebrachial cutaneous nerve). This
portion of the median nerve usually innervates the flexor carpi radialis, palmaris
longus, flexor pollicis longus, and some of the hypothenar muscles as well as providing sensory innervation to the thenar region.

Atrophy of the dorsal interossei muscles is a sign of ulnar nerve or medial cord
injury. The dorsal interossei muscles and all the intrinsic muscles of the hand, with
the exception of the first two lumbricals, opponens pollicis, abductor pollicis, and a
portion of the flexor pollicis brevis muscles, are innervated by the ulnar nerve. The
radial nerve does not innervate any intrinsic hand muscles.

Laceration of the median nerve just distal to the brachial plexus (D) will result
in abduction and extension of the thumb owing to the unopposed action of the

extensor pollicis longus and abductor pollicis longus because the thenar muscles (opponens pollicis and flexor pollicis longus and most of the flexor pollicis brevis) are paralyzed. Paralysis of the flexor digitorum superficialis, the radial half of the flexor digitorum profundus, and the first two lumbricals results in the loss of flexion of the first two digits. There will be accompanying anesthesia or at least paresthesia over the radial side of the palm, the palmar aspect of the thumb, and usually two and one-half digits.

421-425. The answers are: 421-B, 422-A, 423-E, 424-C, 425-C. *(April, ed 2. pp 363, 393, 402.)* The Achilles tendon is the tendon of insertion of the triceps surae (gastrocnemius and soleus muscles) into the calcaneus. These muscles, strong plantar flexors of the foot, are innervated by the tibial nerve. A lesion of the tibial nerve would result in loss of the Achilles tendon reflex as well as inability to stand on the toes.

The flexor muscles of the thigh, including the rectus femoris, iliopsoas, and sartorius muscles are innervated by the femoral nerve. Atrophy of the flexor muscles of the anterior aspect of the thigh is a sign of injury to the femoral nerve. Inasmuch as the femoral nerve also innervates all the heads of the quadriceps femoris muscle (rectus femoris, vastus lateralis, intermedius, and medialis), there would be loss of the knee-jerk reflex.

The principal abductors of the thigh are the gluteus medius and gluteus minimus muscles, which are innervated by the superior gluteal nerve. Paralysis of this nerve results in the inability to abduct the thigh and, more importantly, to stabilize the pelvis when the opposite leg is raised from the ground. Persons with such a lesion usually throw their center of gravity over the affected femoral head in order to take a step without falling—"abductor lurch."

The muscles of the anterior compartment of the leg (tibialis anterior, flexor hallucis longus, and flexor digitorum longus) are strong dorsiflexors of the foot. These muscles, innervated by the deep peroneal branch of the common peroneal nerve, enable one to pick up the foot when walking and prevent it from slapping down when the weight is transferred to the calcaneus. Paralysis of these anterior compartment muscles results in "foot drop" or "foot slap" and inability to stand on the heels.

The muscles of the lateral compartment of the leg are the major evertors of the foot. The tendon of the peroneus longus muscle passes under the cuboid bone on the lateral border of the foot, to insert on the first metatarsal deep within the foot. These muscles are innervated by the superficial peroneal branch of the common peroneal nerve. Paralysis of this nerve results in weakness of dorsiflexion and the inability to evert the foot.

Neuroanatomy

DIRECTIONS: Each question below contains five suggested responses. Select the **one best** response to each question.

426. Impulses originating from the contralateral side of the body are mediated by all the following tracts EXCEPT the

(A) anterior spinocerebellar tract
(B) anterior spinothalamic tract *light touch pain*
(C) lateral spinothalamic tract *temp*
(D) medial lemniscus
(E) posterior spinocerebellar tract

Contra-lateral

Ipsi lateral

427. Excitation of a gamma motor neuron directly causes

(A) increased tonus in the intrafusal fibers
(B) reflex movement
(C) stimulation of the reticular substance in the medulla
(D) stimulation of the alpha motor neurons
(E) voluntary movement

428. Transection of a peripheral nerve fiber results in processes that include all the following EXCEPT

(A) the axon regenerates at a rate of 1 to 2 mm per month *1-4 mm/day*
(B) the disconnected axon loses its myelin sheath
(C) the nerve cell body swells
(D) the Nissl bodies of the cell undergo chromatolysis
(E) some cells recover, with restoration of Nissl substance

429. The accompanying diagram is most characteristic of which of the following levels of the spinal cord?

(A) C1
(B) C8
(C) T2
(D) T12
(E) L4

430. True statements regarding the pyramidal tract include all the following EXCEPT

(A) it is a one-neuron pathway
(B) it is a 90 percent *un*crossed system
(C) it originates in Betz cells of the motor cortex
(D) it passes through the internal capsule and the pyramid of the medulla
(E) it terminates on spinal cord lower motor neurons

431. After several weeks or months, an upper motor neuron lesion affecting an arm probably would produce which of the following clinical findings?

(A) Flail-like movements
(B) Hypoactive tendon reflexes
(C) Muscle bundle fasciculations
(D) Muscle fiber fibrillation
(E) Postural flexion

432. A patient with a history of syphilis is found to have sensory loss in the lower extremities, as well as impairment of position sense and vibratory sensation. In addition, the patient has radicular (root) pain and paresthesia. There is marked ataxia and difficulty walking with reduction of the deep tendon reflexes, particularly in the lower extremities. The lesion is most probably located in the

(A) anterior commissure
(B) anterior funiculus
(C) intermediate gray area
(D) lateral funiculus
(E) posterior funiculus

433. An extramedullary spinal cord tumor produces loss of pain and temperature sense on the left side of the body inferior to the lesion site, followed by spastic paralysis on the right side. This tumor is located

(A) inferiorly between the right and left ventral horns
(B) laterally on the left side
(C) laterally on the right side
(D) posteromedially on the left side
(E) posteromedially on the right side

434. As a result of automotive trauma, a person sustains a complete crush-injury of the right half of the spinal cord (Brown-Séquard's syndrome) at the T12 level. Findings at neurologic examination include

(A) contralateral flaccid paralysis at the level of the lesion
(B) contralateral loss of position sense and two-point discrimination below the lesion
(C) contralateral loss of light touch below the lesion
(D) ipsilateral loss of pain and temperature below the lesion
(E) ipsilateral motor paralysis with spasticity below the lesion

Questions 435-438

A woman comes to the emergency room after sustaining a severe burn on her left hand. She was unaware of the injury until the burn area was observed. Neurologic examination reveals a bilateral dissociated sensory loss (absence or impairment of pain and temperature sense with nearly normal tactile pressure and position sense) over most of the left and right upper extremities and first thoracic dermatome of the chest. Above and below a shawl-like region about the shoulders, all sensory modalities are normal.

[handwritten margin: 6 pts / Syringo- myelia]

435. In the patient presented, the lesion most probably involves the
(A) anterior white commissure *(i.e. Spinothalamic)*
(B) dorsal horn
(C) dorsal nucleus (of Clarke)
(D) dorsolateral funiculus
(E) posterior funiculus

436. Unfortunately, this patient's disease is progressive. In due course, weakness of the left lower arm muscles and flaccid atrophic paralysis of intrinsic muscles of the left hand appear. These signs are explained by extension of the lesion to the
(A) anterior gray horn
(B) lateral gray cell column
(C) medial longitudinal fasciculus
(D) posterior gray horn
(E) substantia gelatinosa

437. Later, the patient develops enophthalmia and pseudoptosis of the left eyelid as well as miosis of the left pupil. Also, the skin and fingernails of the left hand exhibit trophic changes. These findings indicate that the cavitation process has involved the
(A) anterior gray horn
(B) cerebrospinal tracts
(C) lateral gray cell column *i.e. Sympatho Blockade of the Lower Cervical + top thora cic = Horner's*
(D) posterior gray horn
(E) substantia gelatinosa
C7-T1

438. In the patient described, the level of the lesion may be localized to
(A) the lower medulla
(B) C1-C3
(C) C4-C6
(D) C7-T1
(E) T2-T4

(End of question set)

439. Afferent neurons that synapse in the nucleus of the solitary tract provide the afferent limb for all the following reflexes EXCEPT the *touch-PV5-D6 ACK 7 → Blink*
(A) blink reflex 5
(B) carotid body reflex ? v-CN 9
(C) carotid sinus reflex 3
(D) cough reflex V-10
(E) gag reflex v CN 9 - to Nuc Ambiguous

440. The glossopharyngeal nerve receives *efferent* fibers from which of the following nuclei?
(A) Petrosal ganglion
(B) Solitary nucleus
(C) Spinal nucleus of CN V
(D) Superior salivatory nucleus
(E) None of the above
Nuc aMbiguus

Questions 441-444

A patient reveals loss of sensation of pain and temperature on the entire left side of the body, except for the face, where the loss of these modalities is on the right side. Touch on the right side of the face is normal. There is difficulty in swallowing, difficulty in phonation with drawing of the palate toward the left, inability to initiate a gag reflex from the right side of the pharynx, and hoarseness caused by paralysis of the vocal cords on the right side.

441. A symptom complex of dysphagia, dysphonia with deviation of the palate to the left, and hoarseness caused by adduction of the right vocal cords is due to involvement of which of the following nerves?

(A) Left glossopharyngeal nerve
(B) Left vagus nerve
(C) Left vagus AND left glossopharyngeal nerves
(D) Right glossopharyngeal nerve
(E) Right vagus nerve

442. Loss of sensation of pain and temperature on the left side of the body in the patient described is best explained by involvement of the

(A) crossed spinothalamic tract on the right
(B) crossed spinothalamic tract on the left
(C) mesencephalic nucleus of the trigeminal nerve
(D) principal sensory nucleus of the trigeminal nerve
(E) spinal trigeminal nucleus and tract

443. The observation that touch modality on the right side of the face appears normal in the patient described may best be explained by the different pathways taken by the touch fibers. These fibers are associated with which of the following pathways?

(A) Crossed spinothalamic tract on the right
(B) Crossed spinothalamic tract on the left
(C) Mesencephalic nucleus and tract of the trigeminal nerve
(D) Right principal sensory nucleus and tract of the trigeminal nerve
(E) Spinal trigeminal nucleus and tract

444. The brain lesion in the patient described must be located in the

(A) basal region of the midbrain
(B) posterolateral region of the mid-pons
(C) medial region of the caudal pons
(D) posterolateral region of the medulla
(E) medial region of the medulla

(End of question set)

Questions 445-447

A patient is observed to suffer from an alternating hypoglossal hemiplegia. There is atrophy of the tongue on one side and deviation of the tongue toward the right on protrusion. In addition, the patient exhibits upper motor neuron paralysis of the left side of the body.

445. Deviation of the tongue toward the right involves the

(A) left nucleus ambiguus
(B) left pyramidal tract caudal to the decussation
(C) right hypoglossal nerve
(D) right nucleus ambiguus
(E) right pyramidal tract rostral to the decussation

446. The contralateral hemiplegia of the left side of the body in the patient described is a result of involvement of the

(A) corticobulbar projections on the right
(B) lateral lemniscus on the right
(C) left pyramidal tract rostral to the decussation
(D) medial lemniscus on the right
(E) right pyramidal tract rostral to the decussation

447. A lesion that produces alternating hypoglossal hemiplegia as well as upper motor neuron paralysis of the left side of the body must be located in the

(A) caudal region of the midbrain
(B) medial region of the caudal pons
(C) medial region of the upper medulla
(D) posterolateral region of the caudal medulla
(E) posterolateral region of the midpons

(End of question set)

Questions 448-451

A patient is found to have internal (medially directed) strabismus of the left eye, paralysis of the muscles of facial expression on the left side, hyperacusis (louder perception of sounds) of the left ear, and loss of taste from the anterior two-thirds of the tongue on the left. The mouth is somewhat drier than normal. In addition, in the left eye there is a lack of tearing, and a blink reflex cannot be elicited from the stimulation of either the right or the left cornea. There is accompanying upper motor neuron paralysis of the right side of the body.

448. In this patient, paralysis of the left facial nerve accounts for all the following EXCEPT

(A) hyperacusis on the left side
(B) loss of the corneal blink reflex
(C) loss of left lacrimal gland secretion
(D) loss of left parotid gland secretion
(E) loss of taste from the left anterior two-thirds of the tongue

449. Internal strabismus (deviation of the eye medially) results from paralysis of which of the following cranial nerves?

(A) Cranial nerve II
(B) Cranial nerve III
(C) Cranial nerve IV
(D) Cranial nerve V
(E) Cranial nerve VI

450. A lesion producing the alternating hemiplegia with facial nerve involvement in the patient described must be located in which of the following regions of the brain?

(A) Basal region of the midbrain
(B) Medial region of the caudal pons
(C) Medial region of the medulla
(D) Posterolateral region of the medulla
(E) Posterolateral region of the midpons

451. If the lesion described in the preceding question had extended rostrally and medially and had spared the abducens nucleus, uncoordinated or dissociated eye movements might have been observed when attempts were made to gaze laterally to the opposite side. This intranuclear ophthalmoplegia would result from involvement of the

(A) corticobulbar fibers
(B) medial longitudinal fasciculus
(C) nucleus of Edinger-Westphal
(D) oculomotor nucleus
(E) trochlear nucleus

(End of question set)

452. In the section of cerebellum shown below, the structure indicated by the arrow is the

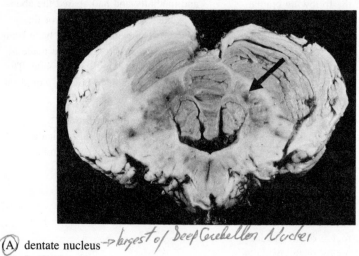

(A) dentate nucleus → *largest of Deep Cerebellar Nuclei*
(B) fastigial nucleus
(C) molecular layer
(D) superior medullary velum
(E) vermis

---

453. The inferior cerebellar peduncle contains only crossed afferent pathways to the cerebellum. All the following afferent pathways reach the cerebellum by way of the inferior cerebellar peduncle (restiform body) EXCEPT the

(A) anterior spinocerebellar
(B) cuneocerebellar
(C) olivocerebellar
(D) posterior spinocerebellar
(E) vestibulocerebellar

In Cerebellar Pe

454. The anterior spinocerebellar tract enters the cerebellum by way of the

(A) inferior cerebellar peduncle
(B) middle cerebellar peduncle
(C) olivary nuclei
(D) pontine nuclei
(E) superior cerebellar peduncle

455. The molecular layer of the cerebellar cortex contains cell bodies of which of the following neuron types?

(A) Basket cells
(B) Golgi cells
(C) Granule cells
(D) Outer stellate cells
(E) Purkinje cells

456. A 40-year-old woman complains of headaches and drowsiness. Physical examination of the patient reveals bilateral papilledema as well as ataxia, dysmetria, dysarthria, intention tremor, and general hypotonia—all on the right side. The bilateral papilledema is suggestive of an intracranial mass. The most likely location of the tumor is the

(A) left cerebellar hemisphere
(B) left internal capsule
(C) left precentral gyrus
(D) right cerebellar hemisphere
(E) right internal capsule

Questions 457-459

A patient complains of numbness on the left side of the face. On examination a corneal blink reflex cannot be elicited from the left side, but a normal consensual blink of the left eye is elicited from stimulation of the right cornea. In addition, the patient exhibits deviation of the jaw toward the left during protraction, and loss of pain and temperature senses from the contralateral side of the body and ipsilateral side of the face, as well as coarse intention tremor and a tendency to fall toward the left. There is no contralateral hemiplegia.

457. All the following signs are associated with the trigeminal nerve EXCEPT

(A) anesthesia of the left side of the face
(B) decreased jaw-jerk reflex
(C) deviation of the jaw toward the left during protrusion
(D) loss of the corneal blink reflex on the left
(E) paralysis of the orbicularis oculi muscle on the left

458. This patient's coarse intention tremor and tendency to fall toward the left are due to involvement of the

(A) left pontocerebellar fibers
(B) left pyramidal tract above the decussation
(C) left spinothalamic tract
(D) right lateral lemniscus
(E) right pontocerebellar fibers

459. The most likely location of a brain lesion capable of producing the signs observed in this patient would be the

(A) basal region of the midbrain
(B) lateral region of the midpons
(C) medial region of the midpons
(D) medial region of the upper medulla
(E) posterolateral region of the caudal medulla

(End of question set)

Questions 460-463

An elderly patient exhibits oculo-motor paralysis of the left eye. External strabismus (lateral direction) of the left eye, ptosis (drooping) of the left eye-lid, and mydriasis (dilatation) of the left pupil are observed. In addition, there is pseudobulbar palsy with weak-ness of the muscles of mastication, of the tongue, and of the left upper half of the face, and paralysis of the muscles of the left lower half of the face. Alter-nating hemiplegia of the body on the right side also is present.

460. In the patient described, ptosis of the left eyelid results from involvement of the

(A) accessory oculomotor (Edinger-Westphal) nucleus
(B) motor division of the facial nerve
(C) parasympathetic fibers within the facial nerve
(D) somatic portion of the oculomotor nucleus
(E) sympathetic nerves arising from the superior cervical ganglion

461. Mydriasis of the left pupil in this patient results from involvement of the

(A) accessory oculomotor (Edinger-Westphal) nucleus
(B) motor division of the facial nerve
(C) parasympathetic fibers within the facial nerve
(D) somatic portion of the oculomotor nucleus
(E) sympathetic nerves arising from the superior cervical ganglion

462. The observed pattern of pseudo-bulbar palsy of the upper half of the face with complete paralysis of the lower half of the face can be explained by differences in innervation of the up-per and lower halves of the nucleus of the facial nerve. The pattern of corti-cobulbar innervation to the nucleus of the facial nerve is best described as

(A) both ipsilateral and contralateral input to the lower half
(B) both ipsilateral and contralateral input to the upper half
(C) contralateral input only to the up-per half
(D) ipsilateral input only to the lower half
(E) ipsilateral input only to the upper half

463. A lesion that produces alternating oculomotor paralysis of the left eye, as well as pseudobulbar palsy with weak-ness of muscles of mastication, of the tongue, and of the upper half of the face, paralysis of muscles of the lower half of the left side of the face, and al-ternating hemiplegia of the body on the right side, must be located in the

(A) basal region of the midbrain
(B) medial region of the caudal pons
(C) medial region of the upper medulla
(D) posterolateral region of the caudal medulla
(E) posterolateral region of the mid-pons

(End of question set)

Parasymp→Iridial Constrict.

Symp→ " Dilator

464. True statements about the ventral posterolateral nucleus of the thalamus include all the following EXCEPT

(A) it is important for tactile discrimination
(B) it receives fibers from the arm via the nucleus cuneatus
(C) it receives fibers from the head via the trigeminothalamic tracts
(D) it receives fibers from the leg via the nucleus gracilis
(E) it relays fibers to the postcentral gyrus of the parietal lobe

465. Fibers of the optic tract terminate in

(A) the inferior corpus quadrigeminus (colliculus)
(B) the lateral geniculate body
(C) the medial geniculate body
(D) the ventral posteromedial nucleus of the thalamus
(E) none of the above

466. An elderly man, persuaded to have his eyes examined after a series of minor automobile accidents, was found to have bitemporal heteronymous hemianopsia (tunnel vision). This condition may be caused by

(A) a cerebrovascular accident involving the lateral-most fibers of the optic radiations
(B) a lesion of the optic tract
(C) a tumor involving the uncrossed fibers of the optic chiasm
(D) compression of the decussating fibers of the optic chiasm
(E) devascularization of the optic nerve

467. The hypothalamus receives afferent input via all the following EXCEPT the

(A) amygdaloid nuclear complex
(B) anterior and medial thalamic nuclei
(C) brain stem reticular formation
(D) hippocampal formation
(E) septal nuclei

468. A stroke involving the amygdaloid body of the limbic system results in aberrations in all the following EXCEPT

(A) hypophyseal hormone secretion
(B) intelligence
(C) sex drive
(D) temperament
(E) visceral autonomic responses

469. Damage to the basal ganglia is associated with all the following manifestations EXCEPT

(A) ataxia
(B) ballism
(C) chorea
(D) Parkinson's disease
(E) tremor

470. A lesion involving the basal ganglia results in motor disorders because of which of the following factors?

(A) Inhibitory input onto motor pathways is reduced
(B) Loss of basal neurons prevents motor output
(C) The basal ganglia are responsible for originating movement
(D) The pyramidal tracts pass through in the lateral medullary lamina between the putamen and globus pallidus
(E) None of the above

471. The section of brain shown below demonstrates all the following structures EXCEPT the

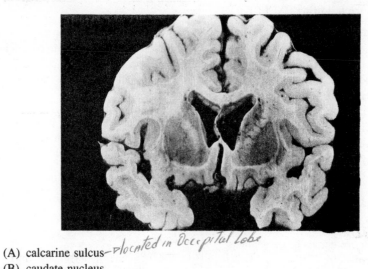

(A) calcarine sulcus—▷located in Occipital Lobe
(B) caudate nucleus
(C) internal capsule
(D) lateral ventricle
(E) putamen

---

472. The principal efferent pathway from the hippocampus is the

(A) alvear pathway
(B) fornix
(C) medial forebrain bundle
(D) perforant pathway
(E) stria terminalis

Questions 473-474

The corpus callosum of a 40-year-old man was sectioned several years previously to relieve the frequency of epileptic seizures.

473. When an object is placed in the patient's right hand and he is asked to name the object without looking, he is able to do so. However, when an object (even the same object) is placed in the left hand, he is unable to name it because

(A) fibers from the speech center have been severed
(B) he has a "split-brain personality"
(C) short-term memory ability has been destroyed
(D) tactile recognition centers are disconnected from the speech center
(E) tactile sensations do not reach the appropriate location of the cerebral cortex

474. In this patient, stereophonic localization is affected very little, if at all, because

(A) few, if any, association fibers connect the auditory areas through the corpus callosum
(B) input to the auditory areas is largely ipsilateral
(C) most auditory fibers cross in the trapezoid body
(D) stereophonic discrimination primarily occurs in the inferior colliculus
(E) the left auditory area is completely dominant in most persons

(End of question set)

475. Cerebrospinal fluid directly enters the cisterna magna

(A) at arachnoid granulations → Abs
(B) from the choroid plexus → Secretes
(C) through the foramina of Luschka and Magendie
(D) through the foramina of Monro
(E) via the iter of Sylvius (cerebral aqueduct)

Lateral
↓ Foramina of Monroe
3rd
— Sylvius
— Luschka (2)
4th
↓ Magendia
↓
Cist. Magna

DIRECTIONS: Each group of questions below consists of four lettered headings followed by a set of numbered items. For each numbered item select

A	if the item is associated with	(A) **only**
B	if the item is associated with	(B) **only**
C	if the item is associated with	**both** (A) and (B)
D	if the item is associated with	**neither** (A) nor (B)

Each lettered heading may be used **once, more than once, or not at all.**

Questions 476-480

(A) Upper motor neuron lesion
(B) Lower motor neuron lesion
(C) Both
(D) Neither

476. Flaccid muscular paralysis *B*

477. Muscular atrophy *C*

478. Spastic muscular paralysis *A*

479. Positive Babinski reflex *A*

480. Abolition of deep tendon reflexes *B*

Questions 481-484

(A) Basilar artery
(B) Internal carotid artery
(C) Both
(D) Neither

A 481. Supplier of the cerebellum

D 482. Supplier of the medulla → *Vertebral, Ant Spinal, Post Inf Cereb.*

C 483. Supplier of the pituitary gland

B 484. Supplier of the retina *by Ophthalmic branch*

Questions 485-487

(A) Cerebral vein rupture
(B) Meningeal artery rupture
(C) Both
(D) Neither

485. Will usually produce subarachnoid hemorrhage with blood in the cerebrospinal fluid *D (Aneurysm, Stroke)*

486. Will usually produce epidural hematoma *B (Mid Meningeal - Skull Fx)*

487. Will usually result in a subdural hematoma *B A (Bridging V.)*

DIRECTIONS: Each group of questions below consists of lettered headings followed by a set of numbered items. For each numbered item select the **one** lettered heading with which it is **most** closely associated. Each lettered heading may be used **once, more than once, or not at all.**

Questions 488-492

For each of the ascending pathways described, select from the diagram the most appropriate anatomic location.

488. A tract that conveys touch sensation from the arm E

489. A tract that transmits position sense to the cerebellum via the superior cerebellar peduncle D

490. An uncrossed tract for very fast transmission of impulses to the cerebellum via the inferior cerebellar peduncle B for coordination of postural movements

491. A tract that mediates vibratory sensation from the leg A

492. A crossed tract that mediates pain and temperature C

Lat Spinothala

Pain Ant
temp Post

Sacral + Region Most
Lumbar Later

thorac 3 most
Cervical 3 medial

Nuc Gracilis
- All Info from below
the t6

Nuc. Cuneatus Above
- All Info t6

Ant. Spinothala.
- Ligh touch -
to the VPL nuc

Ant Spinocerebellar
- Unconscious propioception
from Lower Body into
Cerebellum V- Sup Peduncle
- Crossed tract

Post Spinocerebellar
- originate Dorsal Nuc of Clarke
- chip from Upper + Lower Limb
Unsc
- Un - Crossed

Questions 493-497

For each functional area of the brain described in the following questions, select from the diagram the most appropriate region of the cerebral cortex as identified by Brodmann's numbers.

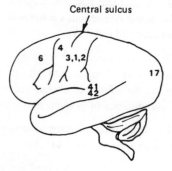

Central sulcus

(A) 3, 1, 2
(B) 4
(C) 6
(D) 17
(E) 41, 42

493. The area in which stimulation produces complex or global movements

494. The area in which a lesion may produce flaccid paralysis of the muscles that flex the elbow, wrist, and fingers on the right side

495. The area in which a lesion will produce sensory aphasia with regard to language comprehension

496. The area that receives input from the lateral geniculate body of the thalamus

497. The area that receives input primarily from the ventral posterior nuclei of the thalamus

Questions 498-500

For each of the following questions, identify the appropriate labeled structure on the accompanying cross section of the dorsomedian region of the cerebral hemisphere at the sagittal fissure.

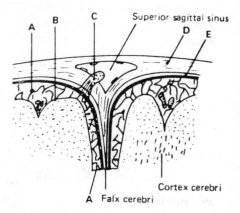

Superior sagittal sinus
Cortex cerebri
A Falx cerebri

498. Structure through which cerebrospinal fluid filters into the general venous circulation

499. The space that contains the major volume of cerebrospinal fluid

500. The structure in which the meningeal arteries course

Neuroanatomy

Answers

426. The answer is E. *(Carpenter, ed 3. pp 77-83. Noback, ed 3. pp 171-187.)* The posterior spinocerebellar tract does not carry axons from the opposite side of the body. Sensory signals from stretch receptors, muscle spindles, and Golgi tendon organs of the lower part of the body are conveyed centrally through the dorsal roots. These afferent fibers enter the spinal cord and synapse ipsilaterally on cells within the dorsal nucleus (of Clarke). This nucleus gives rise to the posterior spinocerebellar tract, which ascends in the lateral funiculus of the spinal cord to enter the cerebellum via the inferior cerebellar peduncle. The anterior spinocerebellar tract is an afferent pathway conveying impulses from the Golgi tendon organs of the contralateral lower extremity to the cerebellum. The anterior spinothalamic tract mediates light touch and pain, whereas the lateral spinothalamic tract mediates thermal sensation, both from the contralateral side of the body. The medial lemniscus of the brain stem consists of fibers arising from the neurons of the nuclei gracilis and cuneatus, which decussate in the medulla and ascend to the thalamus. It relays sensations of touch, pressure, position, and movement from the dorsal columns (fasciculi gracilis and cuneatus) to the thalamus.

427. The answer is A. *(Carpenter, ed 3. pp 72-73. Noback, ed 3. pp 190-192.)* Muscle spindles comprise several fibers of modified striated muscle referred to as *intrafusal muscle fibers*, a term derived from the fusiform-shaped spindle. The spindle is attached at each end to a larger extrafusal skeletal muscle fiber. There are two types of intrafusal fibers, named for the appearance of their clusters of cell nuclei: the nuclear bag fiber and the nuclear chain fiber. Both types of intrafusal fibers are innervated by gamma motor neurons and activate two types of sensory fibers—the primary afferents (annulospiral endings) and, to a lesser extent, group II afferents (flower-spray endings). The gamma motor neurons innervate the intrafusal fibers and cause them to contract sufficiently to maintain sensory activity within the two types of afferent fibers, regardless of the overall length of the whole muscle. The muscle spindle afferents affect the sensitivity of the alpha motor neurons that control the extrafusal fibers. Thus, a sudden stretch of the *intra*fusal fibers, such as occurs in eliciting tendon reflexes, prompts increased activity in the alpha motor neuron–*extra*fusal muscle fiber system. The Golgi tendon organs are primarily muscle tension monitors that serve to prevent excessive stretch. They respond to tension by inhibiting the agonist, and facilitating the antagonist, muscles.

428. The answer is A. *(Noback, ed 3. pp 86-87.)* Axonal transection is followed by wallerian degeneration whereby the axon fragments and loses its myelin sheath.

215

The soma exhibits the axon reaction wherein the cell body swells and the Nissl bodies undergo chromatolysis as the RNA redistributes in preparation for protein synthesis. Fibers of the brain and spinal cord do not regenerate effectively. Repair and regeneration of a severed peripheral nerve depends on proliferation of Schwann cells from the stump of the axon and the division and sprouting of axis cylinders from the central end of the cut nerve. Axonal growth rate is normally 1 to 4 mm per day.

429. The answer is B. *(Carpenter, ed 3. p 56. Noback, ed 3. p 160.)* The cervical segments of the spinal cord are characterized by their relatively large size and oval shape. In addition, the lower cervical segments have enlarged posterior horns and well-developed anterior horns. The white matter becomes more abundant at each succeeding higher level of the cord as spinal afferent fibers enter and efferent fibers leave the spinal cord. In the cervical region, the septum of the posterior funiculus divides the medial fasciculus gracilis from the lateral fasciculus cuneatus.

430. The answer is B. *(Carpenter, ed 3. pp 85-89. Noback, ed 3. pp 197-199, 509.)* The pyramidal tract begins in the large pyramidal cells (of Betz) in the motor cortex of the precentral gyrus. The axons pass through the internal capsule of the forebrain, the crus cerebri of the midbrain, and the pyramids of the upper medulla before decussating in the lower medulla. About 90 percent of the fibers cross to the lateral corticospinal tract while about 10 percent remain uncrossed in the anterior corticospinal tract. The crossed axons terminate directly on the lower motor neurons of the spinal cord.

431. The answer is E. *(Carpenter, ed 3. pp 99-101. Noback, ed 3. pp 210-212.)* *Upper* motor neuron lesions are characterized by spastic paralysis. Immediately following an upper motor neuron lesion, however, the stretch receptors are temporarily depressed and the paralyzed muscles are flaccid. After an interval that varies from weeks to months, stretch reflexes return and become more active than normal— increased tonus (spasticity) of arm flexors and leg extensors are characteristic. Tendon reflexes are hyperactive so that muscle resistance to passive movement is exaggerated and gives way in a clasp-knife fashion as force is applied. The Babinski sign (a remnant of the withdrawal reflex) becomes apparent. There is no immediate muscle atrophy because the innervation remains intact, but in time some disuse atrophy ensues. Characteristics of *lower* motor neuron paralysis include hypoactive tendon reflexes followed by muscle atrophy, fasciculations of specific muscle bundles, and fibrillation of specific muscle fibers.

432. The answer is E. *(Noback, ed 3. pp 207-208.)* Tabes dorsalis, an increasingly common manifestation of late syphilis, involves a primary lesion of the dorsal root ganglion cells and dorsolateral fasciculus with secondary involvement of the dorsal columns in the posterior funiculus. Consequently, there are root signs of radicular pain and paresthesia. Loss of position and vibratory sense and resulting ataxia are associated with posterior column degeneration.

433. The answer is C. *(Carpenter, ed 3. pp 98-101. Noback, ed 3. pp 211-212.)* The symptoms associated with the tumor described in the question point to a lesion in the lateral region of the spinal cord on the right side. Such a tumor first affects the anterolateral spinothalamic tracts on the right side, causing loss of the sense of pain and temperature inferior to the level of the tumor on the contralateral side. As it expands, the tumor affects the corticospinal tract, causing spastic paralysis below the lesion on the ipsilateral side.

434. The answer is E. *(Carpenter, ed 3. pp 99-101. Noback, ed 3. pp 211-212.)* Brown-Séquard's syndrome is a consequence of injury to the posterior funiculus (position sense and two-point discrimination), the anterolateral tracts (pain and temperature), and the pyramidal tracts (motor function)—all on one side. The pyramidal tracts have already crossed so that spastic (upper motor neuron) paralysis occurs below the lesion on the *ipsilateral* side; flaccid (lower motor neuron) paralysis occurs *ipsilaterally* at the level of the lesion. The posterior funiculus contains uncrossed proprioceptive and tactile fibers so that damage produces *ipsilateral* loss of position sense and two-point tactile discrimination at and below the level of injury. The anterolateral tract contains crossed pain and temperature fibers so that injury produces *contralateral* loss of these modalities at and below the level of the lesion. Multiple crossed and uncrossed tracts convey simple touch so there is little loss of this modality, except at the level of injury.

435. The answer is A. *(Carpenter, ed 3. p 101. Noback, ed 3. p 213.)* Bilateral dissociated sensory loss is associated with syringomyelia. This cavitating disease in the region of the central canal of the spinal cord frequently extends ventrally to involve the decussating tracts of the anterior white commissure. Such involvement produces bilateral loss of pain and thermal sense within the segments of the lesion. In the patient presented in the question, loss of tactile sense was slight because, although the sensory fibers for light touch cross in the anterior white commissure to the contralaterally anterior spinothalamic tract, touch-pressure and position senses remain intact inasmuch as these modalities travel in the ipsilateral posterior columns.

436. The answer is A. *(Carpenter, ed 3. p 101. Noback, ed 3. p 213.)* Anterolateral spread of the degenerative changes associated with syringomyelia will damage the motor neurons of the anterior gray horn. This results in a lower motor neuron paralysis with flaccidity, loss of tendon reflexes, and atrophy of the muscles.

437. The answer is C. *(Carpenter, ed 3. pp 67, 186. Noback, ed 3. p 213.)* Horner's syndrome results from interference with the sympathetic pathway to the head. In the patient presented in the question, the syndrome most likely is due to extension of the degenerative process into the lateral gray column of the spinal cord. This cell column contains the cell bodies of the preganglionic neurons of the two-neuron sympathetic pathway. Interruption of the sympathetic outflow in the lower cervical and upper thoracic region results in enophthalmia (paralysis of the orbitalis muscle of Müller across the inferior orbital fissure), pseudoptosis of the eyelid (paralysis of the superior palpebral muscle of Müller in the eyelid), and miosis (constricted pupil caused by unopposed action of the iridial constrictor). The trophic changes in the left hand are due to loss of sympathetic vasomotor control.

438. The answer is D. *(Carpenter, ed 3. pp 98-101. Noback, ed 3. p 213.)* The shawl-like distribution of the pain and temperature sensory deprivation, paralysis of the hand muscles, and involvement of the sympathetic outflow to the arm and head of the patient described in the question localize the lesion to the last two cervical levels and the uppermost thoracic level of the spinal cord.

439. The answer is A. *(Carpenter, ed 3. pp 127-128. Noback, ed 3. pp 261-265.)* General visceral afferent fibers from both glossopharyngeal and vagus nerves terminate in the nucleus of the solitary tract. Increased blood pressure stimulates baroreceptors in the wall of the carotid sinus, which is innervated by the glossopharyngeal nerve. Connections between the solitary nucleus and the parasympathetic dorsal motor nucleus of the vagus nerve will complete the reflex arc involved in slowing the heart rate. Information from the chemoreceptors of the carotid sinus also is mediated by the glossopharyngeal nerve. Connections between the solitary tract and the respiratory center influence respiration. Similar reflexes are mediated from the aortic bodies by the vagus nerves. The gag reflex is elicited on touching the posterior pharynx. This reflex is mediated by glossopharyngeal afferents entering the solitary tract. The reflex arc is completed when synaptic connections are made with the nucleus ambiguus, which sends efferent fibers to the striated muscles of the pharynx to cause constriction and elevation of the pharynx. Coughing is a reflex mediated by afferent impulses reaching the solitary nucleus via the vagus nerve in response to irritation of the larynx, trachea, bronchial tree, external auditory canal, or tympanic membrane. The efferent limb of this reflex is mediated by neurons of the nucleus ambiguus to the muscles of the larynx and pharynx as well as by neurons that control somatic musculature. The afferent limb of the blink reflex is conveyed by the trigeminal nerve, which projects to the trigeminal sensory nucleus (spinal nucleus of CN V); the efferent limb is via the facial nerve, which arises from the facial nucleus.

440. The answer is E. *(Carpenter, ed 3. pp 127-130.)* General visceral efferent fibers, which originate in the inferior salivatory nucleus, are conveyed via the lesser petrosal nerve to the otic ganglion, from which postganglionic parasympathetic secretory impulses pass to the parotid gland. Special visceral efferent fibers of CN IX (glossopharyngeal nerve) arise from the nucleus ambiguus to innervate the styopharyngeus muscle. The lateral portion of the receives special visceral afferent (taste) fibers from the vagus nerves. The caudal and medial portions of the so... visceral afferent fibers from the vagus nerve as well as some yngeal fibers. The spinal nucleus of CN V receives somatic sens... the external auditory meatus. All the afferent nerves have cell bodies petrosal or jugular ganglia.

441. The answer is E. (*Noback, ed 3. pp 317-318.*) Lower motor neuron paralysis of the vagus nerve or motor nucleus produces a number of symptoms in the pharynx and larynx. Inasmuch as the vagus nerve innervates the muscles of the soft palate through the pharyngeal plexus, ipsilateral paralysis of the muscles responsible for the nasopharyngeal seal will result in difficulty with phonation and deviation of the uvula of the soft palate toward the normal side. Because the vagus also innervates the muscles of the larynx, ipsilateral paralysis of the posterior cricothyroid muscle will produce adduction of the vocal cords with hoarseness. Moreover, the vagus innervates several muscles instrumental in deglutition; consequently, swallowing also may be impaired.

442. The answer is A. (*Noback, ed 3. pp 317-318.*) In the patient who is the subject of the question, loss of pain and temperature modalities on the left side of the body may best be explained by involvement of the crossed spinothalamic tract on the right side. Involvement of the nucleus of the trigeminal tract on the right explains the loss of sensation of pain and temperature on the right side of the face.

443. The answer is D. (*Noback, ed 3. pp 317-318.*) Pain and temperature fibers from the face travel in the spinal trigeminal nucleus and tract, whereas touch modality travels in the principal sensory nucleus and tract of the trigeminal nerve. The dissociation of pain and temperature from touch in the patient described in the question indicates that the principal sensory nucleus of the trigeminal nerve is above the level of the lesion.

444. The answer is D. (*Noback, ed 3. pp 317-318.*) Lower motor neuron paralysis involving the vagus nerve is due to a lesion in the vicinity of the nucleus ambiguus on the right side in the posterolateral region of the upper medulla. Such a lesion also involves the crossed spinothalamic tract, mediating the sensation of pain and temperature from the contralateral side of the body, as well as the spinal trigeminal nucleus and tract, mediating pain and temperature from the same side of the face. However, touch from the face, traveling in the principal sensory nucleus of the trigeminal nerve, is above the level of the lesion. Such a lesion may result from occlusion of a branch of the posterior inferior cerebellar artery on the right side.

445. The answer is C. (*Noback, ed 3. pp 316-317.*) Atrophy of the intrinsic musculature of the tongue on one side is due to a lesion of the ipsilateral hypoglossal

...lt on protrusion results from the unopposed ...e, innervated by the left hypoglossal nerve. The ...ates numerous other tongue muscles involved in de-

...wer is E. (Noback, ed 3. pp 316-317.) A lesion of the right pyramidal ...d to the decussation will produce hemiplegia on the left side of the body. ...contralateral paralysis thus produced is the spastic variety usually characteristic of an upper motor neuron lesion. The medial lemniscus conveys the crossed afferent tracts from the nuclei cuneatus and gracilis. Injury to the medial lemniscus above its decussation as the internal arcuate fibers in the caudal medulla results in loss of tactile, proprioceptive, and kinesthetic senses on the contralateral side of the body. The lateral lemniscus conveys afferent auditory fibers. Corticobulbar fibers project to the cranial nerve nuclei.

447. **The answer is C.** (Noback, ed 3. pp 316-317.) Three distinct, symmetrically paired nuclear columns are situated in the upper (rostral) medulla: the nucleus of the hypoglossal nerve near the midline, the dorsal motor nucleus of the vagus nerve beside the hypoglossal nerve nucleus, and the medial and inferior vestibular nuclei located laterally. A lesion that involves the hypoglossal nerve (CN XII) must be located in the medial portion of the upper medulla. Inasmuch as the patient described in the question displays a tongue that is atrophied on the right side and deviates to the right, the lesion must be on the right side. The decussation of the pyramidal tract is located at the extreme caudal end of the medulla. Thus, the lesion must be located in the medial region of the upper medulla. Such a lesion could result from occlusion of a paramedian branch of the anterior spinal artery.

448. **The answer is D.** (Noback, ed 3. pp 259-260, 318.) A lesion of the facial nerve results in the following ipsilateral deficits: (1) paralysis of the muscles of facial expression, (2) loss of taste from the anterior two-thirds of the tongue, (3) marked diminution of secretion from the lacrimal, nasal, submandibular, and sublingual glands, and (4) loss of the blink reflex in response to both contralateral and ipsilateral stimulation caused by paralysis of the left orbicularis muscle, a muscle of facial expression innervated by the facial nerve. In addition, there is hyperacusis caused by paralysis of the stapedius muscle. The parotid gland, which is innervated by the glossopharyngeal nerve (CN IX), would be unaffected.

449. **The answer is E.** (Carpenter, ed 3. pp 153-154. Noback, ed 3. pp 253-254.) The abducens nerve (CN VI) innervates the lateral rectus muscle. Loss of innervation to the lateral rectus results in unopposed tension by the medial rectus, producing internal strabismus. The oculomotor nerve (CN III) innervates the medial, superior, and inferior recti, the inferior oblique, and the levator palpebrae superioris muscles. Paralysis of this nerve would result in lateral deviation of the eye (external strabis-

450. **The answer is B.** (*Noback, ed 3, p 318.*) Alternating ophthalmoplegia involving the abducens nerve (CN VI) is characteristic of the Millard-Gubler syndrome. A lesion in the basal medial region of the caudal pons involves the abducens nucleus, paralyzing the lateral rectus muscle and resulting in a medially directed eye. Lesions in this region also will involve the facial nucleus or nerve, producing Bell's palsy. Moreover, lesions in this region usually will involve the pyramidal tract before it decussates, producing a contralateral hemiplegia in the body with spastic paralysis usually associated with upper motor neuron damage. Such lesions usually result from occlusion of a paramedial branch of the basilar artery.

451. **The answer is B.** (*Carpenter, ed 3, pp 147-149, 153-154.*) The medial longitudinal fasciculus (MLF) lies close to the midline and connects the nuclei of the extraocular muscles. This tract also has a strong vestibular input. The MLF plays an important role in conjugate eye movements. Lesions of the MLF produce intranuclear ophthalmoplegia, wherein direction of the eye medially on attempted lateral gaze to the opposite side is not possible, but the eye may be directed medially in convergence.

452. **The answer is A.** (*Carpenter, ed 3, p 209. Noback, ed 3, pp 330-334, 336-337.*) In the cerebellar section appearing in the question, the structure indicated by the arrow is the dentate nucleus, the largest of the deep cerebellar nuclei. This serpentine nucleus is composed of large multipolar neurons. Axons of these cells pass through the white matter to enter the superior cerebellar peduncle. Inhibitory signals from the Purkinje cells of the cerebellar cortex are relayed via this nucleus to the contralateral ventral lateral nucleus as well as to the rostral intralaminar (reticular) nucleus of the thalamus. This inhibitory pathway thence extends to the motor cortex of the cerebrum, where modulation of the pyramidal cells occurs. Loss of this pathway results in release phenomena, exemplified by intention tremor and dysmetria (past pointing).

453. **The answer is A.** (*Carpenter, ed 3, pp 210-214. Noback, ed 3, pp 330-333.*) The anterior spinocerebellar tract is an uncrossed afferent pathway that enters the cerebellum through the superior cerebellar peduncle. The superior cerebellar peduncle, which connects the cerebellum with the midbrain, is the main outflow pathway from the cerebellum, sending nerve fibers from the dentate, emboliform, and globose nuclei to the red nucleus and thalamic nuclei. Inhibitory efferent projections from the cerebellum to the motor cortex of the cerebrum are relayed through the thalamus. The middle cerebellar peduncle connects the pons with the cerebellum and consists pontine *nuclei*. The inferior cerebellar ... om cell *groups* in the spinal cord and medulla.

...*penter, ed 3. pp 211-214. Noback, ed 3. pp 330-334.*) ... to the *superior* cerebellar peduncle are from the anterior ... Fibers from the vestibular nerve, inferior olivary nucleus, and ...erebellar and cuneocerebellar tracts enter the cerebellum through the ...bellar peduncle. The middle cerebellar peduncle consists almost entirely ...ssed fibers from the pontine nuclei.

455. The answer is D. (*Carpenter, ed 3. pp 349-352. Noback, ed 3. pp 327-328.*) The cells found in the molecular layer of the cerebellar cortex are outer stellate cells. Axons of outer stellate cells synapse with dendrites of the Purkinje cells. The axons and dendrites of the outer stellate cell are confined to the molecular level. Basket cells, which are found near Purkinje cell bodies in the underlying Purkinje layer, produce dendrites that ascend into the molecular layer. One basket cell may synapse with the cell bodies of as many as 10 Purkinje cells. In addition to the two neuronal cells, the molecular layer also contains dendrites of Purkinje and Golgi cells, as well as the parallel fibers (axons) of granule cells. The granule cells and Golgi type II cells are located in the granular cell layer of the cerebellar cortex.

456. The answer is D. (*Carpenter, ed 3. pp 217-219. Noback, ed 3. pp 330-337.*) Ataxia (asynergic activity during walking), dysmetria (inability to stop a movement at the desired location with past pointing), and dysarthria (uncoordinated speech) are all characteristics of cerebellar dysfunction. In addition, diminished deep tendon reflexes result in general hypotonia. The tremor of cerebellar dysfunction is an intention tremor from a lesion that involves the cerebellar nuclei or the efferent pathways of the superior cerebellar peduncle. In contrast to cortical signs, cerebellar signs occur on the same side as that of the lesion because the fibers entering and exiting the cerebellum are uncrossed. Involvement of the precentral gyrus or the internal capsule produces upper motor neuron signs such as spastic paralysis.

457. The answer is E. (*Noback, ed 3. p 318.*) An elicited consensual blink reflex on the left side indicates that the facial nerve, which innervates the orbicularis oculi, is normal. The trigeminal nerve provides the motor supply to the muscles of mastication. Paralysis of this nerve will result in deviation of the jaw toward the side of the lesion because of the unopposed action of the right lateral pterygoid muscle. Paralysis of the sensory pathway of the trigeminal nerve results in facial anesthesia and inability to initiate the corneal reflexes from the affected side. If the lesion occurs at the level of the spinothalamic tract, there will be loss of pain and temperature sensation from the same side of the face and the opposite side of the body.

458. The answer is A. (*Noback, ed 3. p 318.*) Interruption of the pontocerebellar fibers produces ipsilateral cerebellar signs such as coarse intention tremor, hypotonia,

nd a tendency to fall toward the side of
ment produces loss of pain and temperature
body. Involvement of the lateral lemniscus may re...
the contralateral side. Had the pyramidal tracts been i...
plegia would have been evident.

459. The answer is B. (*Noback, ed 3, p 318.*) The patient discussed ...
demonstrates Wallenberg's syndrome. Involvement of the motor and sens...
sions of the left trigeminal nerve with left cerebellar signs places the lesion in ...
left lateral portion of the midpons. The spinothalamic tract is involved, producing
loss of pain and temperature sensation from the same side of the face and the opposite
side of the body. Wallenberg's syndrome is frequently the result of occlusion of the
circumferential branch of the basal artery.

460. The answer is D. (*Noback, ed 3, pp 318-319.*) Paralysis of the superior,
medial, and inferior recti muscles produces lateral strabismus in which the left eye
is directed to the left side. Because the oculomotor nerve also innervates the levator
palpebrae superioris, there is ptosis of the left eyelid.

461. The answer is A. (*Noback, ed 3, pp 318-319.*) The iridial muscles are controlled by the autonomic nervous system. The parasympathetic neurons of the accessory oculomotor nucleus (of Edinger-Westphal), the visceral portion of the oculomotor nucleus, control the iridial constrictor muscle via a second neuron that lies in
the ciliary ganglion. Loss of the parasympathetic component of CN III results in a
dilated pupil because there is no counterbalance to the sympathetic control of the
iridial dilator. The sympathetic supply to the iridial dilator muscle is from neurons
in the superior cervical ganglion that course along the blood vessels of the head to
reach the eye.

462. The answer is B. (*Noback, ed 3, pp 318-319.*) Pseudobulbar palsy results
from involvement of the corticobulbar tracts. Because most cranial nerve nuclei
receive crossed as well as uncrossed innervation from both sides of the cerebral
cortex, in pseudobulbar palsy there is only weakness—not paralysis—of the muscles
of mastication (CN V₃), of the upper face (CN VII), and of the tongue (CN XII) on
the ipsilateral side. However, inasmuch as the lower half of the facial nucleus is
innervated only by the contralateral side of the cerebrum, there is complete paralysis
of the muscles of facial expression (CN VII) of the lower side of the face.

463. The answer is A. (*Noback, ed 3, pp 318-319.*) Weber's syndrome, the symptoms and signs of which are described in this question, is due to a lesion in the basal
region of the left midbrain. The precise location of the lesion is diagnosed by the
involvement of the oculomotor nerve or nucleus. The attendant pseudobulbar palsy
is ascribed to involvement of the corticobulbar tracts. Involvement of the pyramidal

...duces an *alternating upper motor neuron*...

...enter, ed 3. pp 241-242. Noback, ed 3. p 433.) Nerve ...d the *cord* to form the fasciculus gracilis, whereas fibers ...d lateral *to the* leg fibers as the fasciculus cuneatus. When they ...d medulla, these fasciculi terminate in their respective nuclei. Fibers ...cells of *these* nuclei promptly decussate in the medial lemniscus, which ...ascends to the thalamus and terminates in the ventral posterolateral nucleus. Pain, temperature, and touch fibers also cross through the anterior commissure to ascend in the anterior and lateral spinothalamic tracts. Having already synapsed in the intermediate gray area of the spinal cord, they project directly to the ventral posterolateral nucleus of the thalamus. Thalamocortical fibers from this relay center continue to the postcentral gyrus of the parietal lobe, a somesthetic area. This pathway is necessary for proprioception, as well as for tactile discrimination and vibratory sensation. The trigeminothalamic tracts, conveying sensory information from the head, project to the ventral posteromedial (VPM) nucleus of the thalamus.

465. The answer is B. *(Carpenter, ed 3. pp 246-247. Noback, ed 3. pp 408-412, 417.)* Most of the fibers of the optic tract (optic nerve) terminate in the lateral geniculate body of the thalamus, the remainder terminating in the superior colliculus. Uncrossed nerve axons from the temporal side of the retina of the ipsilateral eye and crossed nerve axons from the nasal side of the retina of the contralateral eye project the same portion of the visual field (contralateral half) to the ipsilateral lateral geniculate body. The lateral geniculate bodies are organized in a specific cytoarchitectonic manner. From these nuclei the visual impulses relating the opposite half of the visual field are projected to the vicinity of the calcarine fissure of the occipital lobe. The medial geniculate body and the inferior colliculus receive neural influence from the cochlear nerve. The only special sense associated with the ventral posteromedial nucleus is taste.

466. The answer is D. *(Carpenter, ed 3. pp 259-260. Noback, ed 3. pp 408-412, 417.)* At the optic chiasm the visual pathways are sorted such that the nasal portions of each retina, upon which the inverted lateral visual fields are focused by the lens, cross and project to the opposite side of the brain. The pathways from the temporal portions of each retina remain uncrossed. Thus, the right visual fields, falling on the left sides of both retinas, project to the left side of the brain. A tumor of the pituitary gland that compresses the decussating fibers of the optic chiasm will produce blindness of both temporal fields—heteronymous hemianopsia (tunnel vision). A lesion involving the uncrossed fibers of the optic chiasm would affect the nasal visual field of the appropriate eye. A lesion of the optic tract or optic radiations produces loss of the same half of the visual field in both eyes, while loss of the optic nerve produces total blindness in one eye.

467. The answer is B. (*Carpenter,* ... Hippocampal-hypothalamic fibers from the ... primarily to the mamillary bodies. However, so... the fornix project to the preoptic and septal nuclei. A... run in the stria terminalis to the preoptic and anterior hy... amygdalofugal fibers pass ventral to the lentiform nucleus to rea... thalamic nuclei. The median forebrain bundle carries fibers from the ... as well as from the basal olfactory region to the lateral parts of the hyp... The hypothalamus also receives olfactory input as well as sensory input from... genous zones via the brain stem reticular formation. The anterior thalamic nucleu... projects to the cingulate gyrus; the dorsal medial nuclei project to the prefrontal cortex and neotemporal cortex as well as to the amygdaloid complex.

468. The answer is B. (*Carpenter, ed 3. Noback, ed 3. pp 477-478.*) Lesions in the amygdala of the brain consistently alter aggressive behavior and usually have some effect on sexual behavior as well. Reports of stereotactic lesions produced in the amygdaloid complex in humans suggest that such lesions produce a marked reduction in emotional excitability. Bilateral lesions that are fairly well confined to the amygdaloid complex in monkeys and cats produced hypersexuality as a prominent feature, according to some, but not all, studies. Visceral autonomic responses include changes in respiratory rate, cardiovascular functions, and gastrointestinal secretion and motility. The hypothalamic projections from the amygdala regulate hypophyseal function. Intelligence is not affected by amygdaloid lesions.

469. The answer is A. (*Carpenter, ed 3. pp 317-319. Noback, ed 3. pp 458-459.*) Chorea is one of the dyskinesias resulting from lesions in the basal ganglia. Tremor, athetosis, and ballism (ballismus) are other motor abnormalities seen with lesions of the basal ganglia. Parkinson's disease is the most common of these illnesses and is associated with degeneration of various portions of the basal ganglia and substantia nigra. Unlike the sudden involuntary muscle movements of chorea, the chief manifestations of Parkinson's disease are generalized muscle rigidity and a resting tremor. Ataxia is usually associated with loss of proprioceptive input to the cerebellum, cerebellar lesions, or the temporary effects of alcohol on the cerebellum.

470. The answer is A. (*Carpenter, ed 3. pp 317-319. Noback, ed 3. p 457.*) The basal ganglia are the principal components of the extrapyramidal system and exert inhibitory influence upon the pyramidal pathways. The primary input to the basal ganglia is from the ipsilateral cerebral cortex and the thalamic intralaminar nuclei. The principal output is to the ventral rostral thalamic nuclei, which in turn project to the ipsilateral motor cortex. Lesions involving the basal ganglia remove inhibitory control with resultant dyskinesias such as tremor, athetosis, chorea, and ballism.

...Penter, ed 3. pp 339, 345.) The brain section shown ...on the midportion of the cerebrum. Included are the lateral ...te nucleus, globus pallidus, and putamen of the basal ganglia, ...intervening internal capsule. The calcarine sulcus is located in the ...bes.

472. **The answer is B.** (Carpenter, ed 3. pp 337-338. Noback, ed 3. pp 474-475.) The fornix constitutes the principal efferent pathway from the hippocampal formation. It begins in the large pyramidal cells of the hippocampal cortex, the axons of which converge to form fimbria that coalesce into the fornices. Each fornix arches superiorly then posteriorly and terminates in a mamillary body. The mamillothalamic tract continues the pathway to the anterior nuclear group of the thalamus. The alvear and perforant pathways provide afferents to the hippocampal cortex from, respectively, the medial and lateral entorhinal cortex, which in turn receives afferents from the prepiriform cortex (lateral olfactory gyrus). The hippocampal system is involved in short-term memory. The medial forebrain bundle runs from the basal olfactory regions primarily to the amygdaloid region, the septal nuclei, and the midbrain tegmentum. The stria terminalis is the most prominent efferent pathway from the amygdaloid nuclear complex.

473-474. **The answers are: 473-D, 474-C.** (Carpenter, ed 3. pp 141, 387-390. Noback, ed 3. pp 520-524.) Section of the corpus callosum cuts the association fibers between the left and right sides of the brain so that contralateral associations are not possible. The speech area (supramarginal gyrus, Broca's area) is located in the left cerebral cortex in most persons. Because the left hand projects to the postcentral gyrus of the right cortex, even though the patient recognizes the object he cannot articulate the name because tactile recognition centers on the right cortex are disconnected from the speech center on the left side. However, because the right hand projects to the left cortex, the association fibers between the right hand area and the speech area (both on the same side) are unaffected.

Even though audition is bilaterally represented in the cortex, section of the corpus callosum does not affect stereophonic localization because most auditory fibers arising from the ventral cochlear nucleus cross in the trapezoid body of the pons to form the lateral lemniscus. This crossed tract terminates primarily in the medial geniculate body with relay to the auditory area of the cortex. However, some auditory fibers terminate in the inferior colliculus of the midbrain tectum, which is responsible for such auditory reflexes as blinking and starting to loud sounds.

475. **The answer is C.** (Carpenter, ed 3. p 13. Noback, ed 3. p 21.) Cerebrospinal fluid (CSF) is secreted by choroid plexuses located in the lateral, third, and fourth ventricles. From the lateral ventricles, ... of Monro; from the third ventricle to th... aqueduct). CSF leaves the ventricular system th... and two lateral foramina of Luschka in the roof of... cisterna magna, a dilatation of the subarachnoid space. C... space to enter the venous blood via arachnoid villi.

476-480. The answers are: 476-B, 477-C, 478-A, 479-A, 480-B. (Ca... 3. *pp 95-98. Noback, ed 3. pp 209-210.*) A *lower* motor neuron lesion, s... destruction of anterior (ventral) horn cells or motor fibers of peripheral nerve... abolishes the voluntary reflex responses of skeletal muscle. This form of motor denervation results in flaccid paralysis with loss of muscle tonus and abolition of deep tendon reflexes. Within a few weeks, the muscle fibers begin to atrophy, displaying fibrillations and fasciculations characteristic of lower motor neuron paralysis.

Upper motor neuron lesions remove voluntary control, and the deep tendon reflexes become hyperactive as indicated by a positive Babinski reflex and spastic paralysis. In due course, the involved muscles will undergo atrophy through disuse.

481-484. The answers are: 481-A, 482-D, 483-C, 484-B. (*Carpenter, ed 3. pp 398-403. Noback, ed 3. p 33.*) The cerebellum receives its blood supply from the vertebral arteries. The posterior inferior cerebellar arteries arise directly from the vertebral arteries, while both the anterior inferior and superior cerebellar arteries arise as branches of the basilar artery.

The mesencephalon receives most of its blood supply from branches of the basilar artery. However, the medulla and pons are supplied by the vertebral artery by way of the anterior and posterior spinal arteries as well as the posterior inferior cerebellar arteries.

The pituitary gland is located in the center of the circle of Willis, which results from the anastomosis between the internal carotid and basilar arteries. The pituitary gland therefore receives its blood supply from both sources.

The retina is supplied by the ophthalmic branch of the internal carotid artery. The central artery of the retina enters the optic nerve and diverges over the retina from the blind spot. Examination of the retinal arteries for signs of systemic disease is an important part of the physical examination.

Most of the telencephalon and diencephalon are supplied by branches of the internal carotid arteries. The basilar artery, which is formed by the united vertebral arteries, supplies the brain stem and cerebellum as well as portions of the occipital and temporal lobes of the cerebral cortex.

485-487. The answers are: 485-D, 486-B, 487-A. (*Carpenter, ed 3. pp 1-8. Noback, ed 3. pp 43-44.*) Subarachnoid hemorrhage (stroke, cerebrovascular accident) is generally the result of rupture of a cerebral artery, often one weakened by atheroma

...subarachnoid space, a lumbar t...

...only the result of fracture of the parietal or
...the underlying, embedded middle meningeal
...re a large hematoma rapidly forms between the bone
and lethally displacing the brain. The cerebral
...matoma may result from sudden jarring of the head. The cerebral
...rough the arachnoid and dural layers to reach the major venous sinuses.
...relatively fragile veins cross the potential subdural space, they are subject to
...earing forces that may result in a tear. Under the very low venous pressure, blood
slowly oozes into the subdural space and forms a hematoma external to the arachnoid
layer, so that blood generally will not be evident in a spinal tap. A subdural bleed
may not produce lethal brain compression because the slow space-filling hematoma
may be compensated for by reduced CSF production.

488-492.   The answers are: 488-E, 489-D, 490-B, 491-A, 492-C. *(Carpenter, ed
3. pp 74-83. Noback, ed 3. pp 169-177, 180-186.)* The anterior spinothalamic tract
(E in the diagram accompanying the question) conveys light touch sensation to the
posterior ventral lateral nucleus of the thalamus. This tract originates in the contralateral posterior horn, and the fibers reach the tract via the anterior white commissure.

The anterior spinocerebellar tract (D) conveys information from the lower portion of the body to the cerebellum *via* the superior cerebellar peduncle. This predominantly crossed tract, which originates in the spinal border cells of the anterior
horn and reaches the contralateral side via the anterior white commissure, conveys
unconscious proprioception from the muscles and joints of the lower limb to the
cerebellum and thus functions in the coordination of postural and voluntry muscle
movement in the lower limb.

The posterior spinocerebellar tract (B) conveys information from the lower portion of the body to the cerebellum via the inferior cerebellar peduncle. This predominantly uncrossed tract, which originates in the dorsal nucleus (of Clarke), also
receives upper extremity fibers from the accessory cuneate nucleus. This tract conveys unconscious proprioception from the muscles and joints of the upper and lower
limbs and thus also functions in coordination of postural and voluntary movements
of the limbs.

The fasciculus gracilis (A) contains long, uncrossed ascending branches of
nerves that enter the sacral, lumbar, and lower six thoracic dorsal roots and terminate
by synapsing in the nucleus gracilis in the medulla. Above the sixth thoracic level,
the fibers ascend in the fasciculus cuneatus and synapse in the cuneate nucleus. The
fasciculus gracilis conveys touch-pressure, kinesthetic information, and vibratory
sense to the thalamus via the medial lemniscus.

The area labeled C represents the lateral spinothalamic tract. Fibers of this tract
cross to the opposite side, usually in the same spinal segment, and the fibers related
to pain tend to be anterior to those related to temperature sensation. Fibers within

this tract are somatotopically arranged, with those arising from sacral and lumbar segments most lateral and those from the thoracic and cervical segments most medial.

493-497. The answers are: 493-C, 494-B, 495-E, 496-D, 497-A. *(Carpenter, ed 3. pp 356-362, 373-376, 378-384. Noback, ed 3. pp 485-487.)* The premotor area (Brodmann's area 6) is located immediately rostral to the primary motor area (4) on the lateral side of the cerebral hemisphere. The main input is from the ventral anterior nucleus of the thalamus and the output is through area 4. Electrical stimulation of the premotor area produces more global or complex movements than does stimulation of the primary motor area.

The primary motor area of the cerebral cortex (Brodmann's area 4) lies on the anterior wall of the central sulcus of the frontal lobe and adjacent portions of the precentral gyrus. The unusually thick cortex of this region is a result of the increased number of pyramidal cells (of Betz), located in layer V, which give rise to the lateral corticospinal (pyramidal) tract. Some fibers are distributed to the nuclei of voluntary cranial nerves after decussating in the lower medulla; other fibers continue to the spinal cord and terminate on the motor cells of the anterior horn. On electrical stimulation of discrete sections of the primary motor area, a discrete set of muscles on the side of the body contralateral to the site of stimulation exhibits isolated, discontinuous contractions. A lesion here produces flaccid paralysis of a corresponding portion of the body on the contralateral side.

The primary auditory cortex (Brodmann's area 41) is located in the transverse gyrus (of Heschl), which projects medially into the lateral fissure from the superior temporal gyrus. The association auditory cortex (42) is located in the adjacent superior temporal gyrus. However, the two regions are frequently grouped together functionally. Auditory input is from the medial geniculate body of the thalamus. A lesion here can produce a variety of signs from contralateral deafness and inability to stereophonically locate sounds to sensory aphasia (inability or difficulty in recognizing sounds).

The primary visual cortex of the occipital lobe (Brodmann's area 17) receives visual input from the lateral geniculate body of the thalamus via the optic radiations. A lesion here results in blindness of the same half of a visual field in both eyes. Most of the fibers of this area project to the visual association areas.

The primary general somatic sensory cortex (Brodmann's areas 3, 1, and 2) lies in the postcentral gyrus of the parietal lobe. This region receives proprioceptive and tactile input relayed from the ventroposterior nucleus of the thalamus. As in the primary motor area, the input from each region is highly localized and proportional to the amount of sensory innervation. Most of the fibers from this area project to association areas and to the thalamus.

498-500. The answers are: 498-C, 499-A, 500-D. *(Carpenter, ed 3. pp 9-13. Noback, ed 3. p 46.)* The arachnoid villus (labeled C in the diagram accompanying the question) is a projection of the subarachnoid space into the venous blood-filled superior sagittal sinus. It is completely lined by arachnoid membrane, and the dura over the tip of the villus is considerably thinned. The pressure of the cerebrospinal fluid within the subarachnoid space is greater than that of the blood in the dural sinuses, resulting in filtration and even bulk flow of cerebrospinal fluid into the superior sagittal sinus.

The subarachnoid space (labeled A on the diagram accompanying the question) is located between the arachnoid membrane externally and the pia mater internally. This space is traversed by numerous trabeculae and varies in size from one region of the cerebral hemispheres to another. Where it is quite large, the space is designated a "cistern." The major volume of cerebrospinal fluid is within the subarachnoid space. Because the spinal subarachnoid space is continuous with the cranial subarachnoid space, cerebrospinal fluid is readily obtained by puncture in the lower lumbar region.

The outermost and densest of the meninges—the dura mater (labeled D in the diagram accompanying the question)—is primarily composed of fibrous connective tissue with some sensory nerves and blood vessels. A flat sheet of mesenchymal epithelium forms its inner surface. This inner surface is separated from the arachnoid membrane by a fluid-filled, thin space called the subdural space (shown as E on the diagram accompanying the question).

The pia mater (labeled B in the diagram) is a vascular layer of delicate connective tissue that is intimately attached to the brain and spinal cord.

Bibliography

Alberts B, Bray D, Lewis J, et al: *Molecular Biology of the Cell,* 2nd ed. New York, Garland, 1989.

April EW: *Anatomy,* 2nd ed. New York, John Wiley & Sons, 1990.

Carpenter MB: *Core Text of Neuroanatomy,* 3rd ed. Baltimore, Williams & Wilkins, 1985.

Cormack DH: *Ham's Histology,* 9th ed. Philadelphia, JB Lippincott, 1987.

Hollinshead WH, Rosse C: *Textbook of Anatomy,* 4th ed. New York, Harper & Row, 1985.

Junqueira LC, Carneiro J: *Basic Histology,* 6th ed. East Norwalk, CT, Appleton & Lange, 1989.

Kelly DE, Wood RL, Enders AC: *Bailey's Textbook of Microscopic Anatomy,* 18th ed. Baltimore, Williams & Wilkins, 1984.

Moore KL: *The Developing Human,* 4th ed. Philadelphia, WB Saunders, 1988.

Noback CR, Demarest RJ: *The Human Nervous System: Basic Principles of Neurobiology,* 3rd ed. New York, McGraw-Hill, 1981.

Sadler TW: *Langman's Medical Embryology,* 6th ed. Baltimore, Williams & Wilkins, 1990.